# IONIZATION PHENOMENA
# IN GASES

To
Margaret

# IONIZATION PHENOMENA IN GASES

GORDON FRANCIS

B.Sc., M.A., D.Phil., A.Inst.P.

*Clarendon Laboratory, Oxford,*
*now at*
*Atomic Energy Research Establishment,*
*Harwell*

LONDON
BUTTERWORTHS SCIENTIFIC PUBLICATIONS
1960

BUTTERWORTHS PUBLICATIONS LTD
88 KINGSWAY, LONDON, W.C.2

AFRICA: BUTTERWORTH & CO. (AFRICA) LTD
 DURBAN: 33/35 Beach Grove

AUSTRALIA: BUTTERWORTH & CO. (AUSTRALIA) LTD
 SYDNEY: 8 O'Connell Street
 MELBOURNE: 430 Bourke Street
 BRISBANE: 240 Queen Street

CANADA: BUTTERWORTH & CO. (CANADA) LTD
 TORONTO: 1367 Danforth Avenue

NEW ZEALAND: BUTTERWORTH & CO. (AUSTRALIA) LTD
 WELLINGTON: 49/51 Ballance Street
 AUCKLAND: 35 High Street

*U.S.A. Edition published by*
ACADEMIC PRESS INC., PUBLISHERS
111 FIFTH AVENUE
NEW YORK 3, NEW YORK

*Printed in Great Britain at the Pitman Press, Bath*

# PREFACE

THIS book is intended to be complementary to the several excellent textbooks on ionized gases published in recent years. For this reason I have avoided repeating accounts of the more well-known discharges—the arc, spark and glow, for example—and have treated, instead, those branches of the subject which are closely linked with other branches of physics, and which cannot, as far as I am aware, be studied except by intensive searching through the literature. Thus in atmospheric phenomena one finds links with astrophysics, high-frequency discharges and radio wave propagation, and in high-current discharges with nuclear physics and electrodynamics. A chapter on fundamental processes is included for the sake of completeness, and to provide a general background for the reader who is not very familiar with the subject, but it has been kept as brief as possible, consistent with clarity.

The book is written mainly for those finishing their degrees at university, or about to begin research, in the hope that they may see a broader picture than is often revealed by specialized and sharply-divided curricula. I have laid stress on the physical principles of the behaviour of ionized media, sometimes at the expense of mathematical rigour, and have also tried to include up-to-date discoveries and ideas, where these have some notable physical importance. It has been necessary to select carefully from the current thermonuclear research, amongst which are many ingenious pieces of apparatus, all designated with names derived from Greek mythology or the music-hall, and processes described by a weird and growing jargon (few, except the initiated, could conceive a plasma crowbarred into a torus). Here again, an understanding of physical principles has been the aim.

The equations are presented, unrepentantly, in the usual mixture of units. Even devotees of better systems nearly always quote densities in electrons per cubic centimetre, which is understandable, since a cubic metre of suitably hot plasma (at ground level) would be looked on with wonder and envy.

The writing of this book has come at the end of a very happy ten years' association with Dr A. von Engel at the Clarendon Laboratory, Oxford, first as pupil and then as colleague and friend. I want especially to thank him for his teaching and encouragement, and to pay tribute to the way in which he has always stimulated and helped younger physicists. I am grateful to my wife for checking the manuscript and drawings, and to my colleagues Dr P. F. Little, Dr S. J. B. Corrigan, K. Arnold, R. N. Franklin, C. C. Goodyear and, more recently, to friends at A.E.R.E., Harwell for helpful discussion. I wish to thank the Research Council of the Central Electricity Authority for supporting much of my work at Oxford, and for their permission to publish some of the results quoted in Chapter 4; I wish also to thank Messrs Springer for permission to include, in my treatment of the similarity laws (Chapter 3), some work previously published in the article on 'glow discharge' in *Handbuch der Physik*. Finally, my warmest thanks go to Miss Pamela Carter for her excellent typing of unfamiliar manuscript, and to the publishers for their patient co-operation.

Oxford,                                                         GORDON FRANCIS
*March*, 1959

# CONTENTS

# INTRODUCTION

### THE NUCLEAR ATOM

DIRECT experimental evidence from the scattering of particles and electrons by thin foils, and from the diffraction of X-rays, and indirect evidence from the spectra of the elements, leads to the conclusion that an atom consists of a central positive charge, the nucleus, surrounded by a cloud of revolving electrons, the whole structure being electrically neutral. Almost the entire mass of the atom is concentrated in the nucleus, the mass of the electrons being negligible by comparison. The chemical properties of the atom, and hence its position in the periodic table, depend on the number and arrangement of the electrons, since it is the electrical forces between these electrons and the electrons of another atom which constitute a chemical bond. The number of electrons revolving around the nucleus is $Z$, where $Z$ is the atomic number of the element, and the nucleus therefore has a positive charge, $+ Ze$, where $e$ is the charge on the electron ($e = 4.803 \times 10^{-10}$ e.s.u.).

The simplest atom, hydrogen, consists of a nucleus with one electron revolving around it. The nucleus of the hydrogen atom is called the proton and is one of the fundamental particles of physics: it has a mass of $1.673 \times 10^{-24}$ g which, following chemical practice, is taken as one atomic mass unit (actually $1.008$, the atomic weight of oxygen being 16); it is 1,837 times greater than the mass of the electron.

Nuclei are composed of two fundamental particles, namely: (*a*) the proton, of mass 1 atomic unit, charge $+ e$; (*b*) the neutron, of mass 1 atomic unit, charge zero. If the atomic weight of an atom is $A$ and its atomic number is $Z$ it follows that there are $Z$ protons and $A - Z$ neutrons in the nucleus. These are bound together in a very small space by short-range attractive forces whose nature is not properly understood, but which are much stronger than the electrostatic repulsion between the protons. The radius of a nucleus is of the same order as that of an electron, namely about $10^{-13}$ cm.

The cloud of revolving electrons extends over a sphere of radius about $10^{-8}$ cm, centred about the nucleus. It is clear that this sphere consists mostly of empty space, within which are constantly varying electric fields; whereas from some distance away the atom appears to be an electrically neutral sphere. This structure is not rigid, of course, and in a sufficiently strong electric field the cloud of electrons becomes displaced, and the atom is polarized.

### SPECTRA: ELECTRON ORBITS AND ENERGY LEVELS

The spectra of many elements consists of series of lines of definite wavelength, and a mass of experimental evidence compiled in the nineteenth century led to empirical formulae for the wavenumber $\tilde{\nu}$ $(= 1/\lambda)$ of the line of wavelength $\lambda$ as the difference between two terms of the form $C/(n + a)^2$ where $C$ and $a$ are constants and $n$ is a chosen integer. The simplest of these is the formula giving the frequency, $\nu$, of the series of atomic hydrogen:

$$\nu = R\left(\frac{1}{n_2^2} - \frac{1}{n_1^2}\right) \qquad \dots (1.1)$$

where $R$ is the Rydberg constant and $n_1$, $n_2$ are integers $(n_1 > n_2)$.

In the nuclear model of the atom, an electron revolves around the nucleus by virtue of the electrostatic attraction between them, this force providing the necessary inward acceleration for orbital motion. Classical theory can explain neither the stability of such a system nor the observed spectra, for an accelerated electron should radiate energy of changing wavelength and spiral in towards the nucleus. In order to describe the actual conditions, Bohr postulated that in the simplest atom, H, an electron can revolve only in certain circular orbits, those for which the angular momentum about the nucleus is an integral multiple, $n$, of a constant $h/2\pi$. $h$ is Planck's constant $(= 6.55 \times 10^{-27}$ erg sec), and $n$ is called the principal quantum number; such an orbit in which the electron does not radiate is termed a stationary orbit. It is then easily shown that the total energy $\varepsilon_n$ (kinetic + potential) of an electron in an orbit of quantum number $n$ is:

$$\varepsilon_n = -\frac{2\pi^2 m e^4}{n^2 h^2} \qquad \dots (1.2)$$

Bohr further postulated that radiation is emitted only when an electron jumps from an orbit of quantum number $n_1$ to one of number $n_2$ $(n_1 > n_2)$, the frequency, $\nu$, of this radiation being determined by the equation

$$h\nu = \varepsilon_1 - \varepsilon_2 \qquad \dots (1.3)$$

whence

$$\nu = \frac{2\pi^2 m e^4}{h^3}\left(\frac{1}{n_2^2} - \frac{1}{n_1^2}\right) \qquad \dots (1.4)$$

which is of the same form as the equation found empirically by Balmer for certain spectral series of hydrogen, and the expression $2\pi^2 me^4/h^3$ agrees closely with the Rydberg constant. When the motion of the electron and nucleus is treated more rigorously, remembering that both revolve about a point which lies between them but close to the nucleus, the mass, $m$, of the electron in the above equations is replaced by the expression

$$\mu = \frac{m}{1 + \dfrac{m}{M}} \qquad \ldots\ldots(1.5)$$

The mass, $M$, of the nucleus thus affects very slightly the wavelength of the spectrum lines.

More generally, considering a single electron revolving around a central mass $M$, which has a charge $+ Ze$, the total energy of the electron plus the nucleus associated with an orbit of quantum number $n$, is:

$$\varepsilon_n = - \frac{2\pi^2 Z^2 e^4}{n^2 h^2} \cdot \frac{m}{1 + \dfrac{m}{M}} \qquad \ldots\ldots(1.6)$$

The radius, $r$, of a simple Bohr orbit of quantum number, $n$ (assuming a stationary nucleus) is:

$$r = n^2 \cdot \frac{h^2}{4\pi^2 me^2 Z} \qquad \ldots\ldots(1.7)$$

For hydrogen, $r \approx 0.5 \times 10^{-8}$ cm for the smallest orbit ($n = 1$), which is of the same order as that derived from experiments based on the kinetic theory of gases.

Bohr's theory was generalized by Sommerfeld to apply to simple elliptic orbits in the hydrogen atom by imposing the restrictions

$$\oint p_r \mathrm{d}r = n_r h, \qquad \oint p_\theta \mathrm{d}\theta = n_\theta h \qquad \ldots\ldots(1.8)$$

(see *Figure 1.1*) where $p_r$ is the momentum resolved along the radius, $r$, $p_\theta$ the momentum perpendicular to it and $n_r$, $n_\theta$ are integers called the radial and azimuthal quantum numbers. Although two quantum numbers are now introduced, no new energy levels result, because both radial and azimuthal motion have the same periodicity*; the expression for the energy contains only

---

* A system in which two separate quantum conditions reduce to a single quantum condition is said to be degenerate.

$n = n_r + n_\theta$, where $n$ is called the principal quantum number, but $n_\theta$ determines the angular momentum. However, in an elliptic orbit the speed of the electron varies and, when passing close to the nucleus, can be so large that its mass changes significantly; the greater the eccentricity of the orbit, the greater the relativity correction, with the result that the energy of the electron depends on both $n_r$ and $n_\theta$, i.e. on both quantum numbers, in a way which

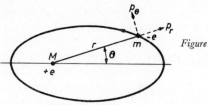

Figure 1.1. *Elliptic orbit of an electron in the hydrogen atom*

can describe certain doublet spectral lines. When the value of $n$ is chosen, $n_\theta$ can be given any integral value from 1 to $n$; later it was empirically found better to use as the azimuthal number, $l = n_\theta - 1$; $l$ can thus be given values $0, 1, \ldots n - 1$.

This quantum picture was further extended by assuming that an electron spins about its axis, having an angular momentum restricted to $s\dfrac{h}{2\pi}$, where $s$, the spin quantum number, can have only the value $\frac{1}{2}$. The total angular momentum of an electron is now composed of two parts, one due to its orbital motion and one due to its spin; these are added vectorially and the sum is given by $j\dfrac{h}{2\pi}$ where

$$\vec{j} = \vec{l} + \vec{s} \qquad \qquad \ldots (1.9)$$

$j$ is called the total or inner quantum number and is itself restricted to odd multiples of $\frac{1}{2}$ (i.e. $\frac{1}{2}, \frac{3}{2}, \frac{5}{2} \ldots$). It must be emphasized that although the picture presented is based on the physical idea of an electron spinning in its orbit, the quantum restrictions are introduced arbitrarily in order to describe, in a self-consistent manner, the observed spectra.

The use of the four quantum numbers $n$, $l$, $s$ and $j$ leads to a large number of energy levels, and if transitions between all these levels could occur there would be more spectral lines than are actually seen. It is necessary, therefore, to impose further restrictions called selection rules, namely that only transitions between levels such that the change $\Delta l$ in $l$ is $\pm 1$, and $\Delta j$ in $j$ is $\pm 1$ or $0$ are permitted: there are no restrictions on changes of $n$.

It should be noted that $l$, $s$ and $j$ define the numerical value of the angular momentum (orbital, spin or total, respectively) but not its direction in space—as would be expected since the atom itself has no preferred direction. A fixed direction can be imposed on the system by applying an external magnetic field $H$. An electron moving in an orbit or spinning has a magnetic moment, and in the presence of this magnetic field the atomic magnet must precess about the imposed direction, with consequent change in energy. Thus there results a further splitting of energy levels, and a greater multiplicity of spectral lines. In order to account for the observed lines it must be assumed that the projection $m_l$ of the vector $l$ along $H$ is quantized to integral values ($m_l$ has $2l + 1$ values from $- l$ through $0$ to $+ l$), and also that the projection $m_s$ of $s$ is either $+ \frac{1}{2}$ or $- \frac{1}{2}$, i.e. that the electron spin is parallel or opposite to the applied field. $m_l$ and $m_s$ are called magnetic quantum numbers, and this process is called spatial quantization. (It follows, of course, that the projection $m_j$ of $j$ is also quantized to odd multiples of $\frac{1}{2}$; $m_j$ is sometimes used as another, although not independent, quantum number.)

### WAVE MECHANICAL TREATMENT

Many of the results mentioned above follow more naturally, without the imposition of arbitrary conditions, from wave mechanics. de Broglie postulated that an electron of momentum $p$ ($= mv$) has associated with it a wavelength $\lambda$, given by

$$\lambda = \frac{h}{p} \qquad \ldots . (1.10)$$

A stationary orbit is one in which the waves do not cancel by interference, and hence it must contain a whole number, $n$, of wavelengths; mathematically putting $2\pi r = n\lambda$ leads at once, with de Broglie's hypothesis, to the angular momentum $pr = nh/2\pi$, which is Bohr's original quantum condition.

Schrödinger incorporated de Broglie's postulate of waves, associated with material particles, into the general wave equation

$$\frac{\partial^2 \Phi}{\partial x^2} + \frac{\partial^2 \Phi}{\partial y^2} + \frac{\partial^2 \Phi}{\partial z^2} = \frac{1}{w^2} \cdot \frac{\partial^2 \Phi}{\partial t^2} \qquad \ldots . (1.11)$$

where $\Phi$ is a wave function varying both in space and time, and assumed to be of the form

$$\Phi = u e^{i \cdot 2\pi \nu t} \qquad \ldots . (1.12)$$

The equation then reduces to

$$\nabla^2 u = -\frac{8\pi^2 m}{h^2} \cdot (\varepsilon - V) \cdot u \qquad \ldots (1.13)$$

where $\varepsilon$ is the total, $V$ the potential energy of the electron, and $u$ is said to be the wave function, which is a function of position only. If $u^2$ is multiplied by the surface area of a sphere, $4\pi r^2$, then the term $u^2 \cdot 4\pi r^2 dr$ represents the probability of finding the electron within a spherical shell of radii $r$, $r + dr$. Finite, single valued and continuous solutions for $u$ can be found for negative values of the total energy only when

$$\varepsilon = -\frac{2\pi^2 m e^4 \mathcal{Z}^2}{n^2 h^2} \qquad \ldots (1.14)$$

where $n$ is an integer which is Bohr's quantum condition, but solutions can be found for all positive $\varepsilon$, corresponding to a free electron. The solution of Schrödinger's equation also introduces two other numbers, $l$, $m_l$, which can take only integral values; $l$ can have the values 0, 1, 2 . . . $(n - 1)$, and corresponds nearly to the azimuthal quantum number $n_\theta$ (actually $l = n_\theta - 1$), and $m_l$ can have any of the $2l + 1$ integral values between $- l$ and $+ l$. The value of the wave function, $u$, depends on the values given to the integers $n$, $l$, $m_l$, which are called quantum numbers.

As in Sommerfeld's theory, different values of $l$ do not give rise to different energy levels, unless a relativity factor is introduced into equation (1.14), i.e. mass dependent on the energy of the electron; further spatial quantization (the quantum number $m_l$, exactly analogous with the magnetic quantum number previously introduced) also arises from the solution of the equation, which has itself been formulated with reference to a fixed direction, i.e. the reference frame of the observer. The wave mechanical treatment can be extended to include electron spin, and the quantum numbers, $s$, $m_s$, having respectively the values $\frac{1}{2}$ and $\pm \frac{1}{2}$ are derived.

Thus in both the Bohr–Sommerfeld and the wave mechanical theories, the energy and angular momentum of a single electron are described by $n$, $l$, $j$, and additionally by $m_l$, $m_s$ (or $m_j$) when a magnetic field is present. Wave mechanics enables the energy levels to be calculated more rigorously and shows also that although the integers, or half integers, $l$, $s$, $j$, may be formally used for description, they must be replaced in numerical calculation by

$\sqrt{l(l+1)}$, $\sqrt{s(s+1)}$, $\sqrt{j(j+1)}$ respectively; $m_j$, however, remains half integral.

## ATOMS WITH MANY ELECTRONS: SPECTROSCOPIC NOTATION

When a number of electrons revolve around a nucleus, each electron can be described by a set of quantum numbers. However, the calculations of electron energy are more complicated because the electron moves in a field determined not only by the central positive charge but by the other electrons also. Optical spectra arise from transitions which occur when the outermost electrons move from one energy level to another; X-ray spectra arise when inner and more closely bound electrons change their energy. It is more proper to speak of the energy states of the atom than that of each individual electron, and for this purpose quantum numbers bearing the capital letters $L$, $S$, and $J$ are used. It is found that in most circumstances the orbital angular momenta of the separate electrons combine together, and the spin angular momenta separately combine together (so-called Russell–Saunders coupling), so that

$$\left.\begin{array}{l} L = \Sigma l \\ S = \Sigma s \end{array}\right\} \qquad \ldots (1.15)$$

may be written, whence the total angular momentum of the atom is designated by

$$\vec{J} = \vec{L} + \vec{S} \text{ (vector sum)} \qquad \ldots (1.16)$$

Quantum theory shows that the orbital angular momenta, $l$, can only be orientated in discrete directions, whilst spin vectors, $s$, can only be parallel or opposite to each other. Thus $L$ can only be integral; $S$, and consequently $J$, are integral if the number of electrons is even, and an odd multiple of $\frac{1}{2}$ if the number of electrons is odd.

Following a spectroscopic convention which is derived from early empirical results of the terms necessary to describe the sharp, principal, diffuse and fundamental series ($S$, $P$, $D$, $F$), a state in which $L = 0$ is termed an $S$ state, $L = 1$ a $P$ state, $L = 2$ a $D$ state, $L = 3$ an $F$ state, etc. The multiplicity of a state of given $L$ (i.e. the number of closely spaced energy levels) is determined by the number of values of $J$ resulting from the combination of $L$ and $S$. If $L > S$ there result $2S + 1$ states: if $L < S$ there are $2L + 1$. Notably for $S$ terms ($L = 0$) there is only one value of $J$, ($J = S$). However, although it may occasionally seem inconsistent, the multiplicity is generally quoted as $2S + 1$. An energy state is then described in the following notation:

Multiplicity

$S, P, D, F, \ldots$ state $\qquad$ i.e. $\qquad L_J$

value of $J$

$\qquad$ $2S + 1$

For example, consider the term $^1D_2$ of helium which has two electrons; $S = 0$, giving $2S + 1 = 1$, i.e. a singlet state. It is a $D$ state, implying $L = 2$, hence $J = L + S = 2$.

Since, in optical spectra, only the outermost electrons are important, the principal quantum number, $n$, of these electrons is frequently quoted, and the energy state of the atom described in the following notation:

Multiplicity $\qquad\qquad\qquad\qquad\qquad 2S + 1$

$n \qquad S, P, D, F \ldots$ state $\qquad$ i.e. $n \qquad L_J$

angular momentum

For example, in sodium the familiar doublet $D$ lines are due to transitions from one of the upper levels $3^2P_{1/2}$ or $3^2P_{3/2}$, i.e. $n = 3$, $L = 1$ (there is one outermost electron, $s = \frac{1}{2}$, hence $S = \frac{1}{2}$, $J = L + S = \frac{1}{2}$ or $\frac{3}{2}$) to the lower level $3^2S_{1/2}$.

Transitions that can occur are again limited by the selection rules

$$\Delta L = \pm 1, \qquad \Delta J = \pm 1 \text{ or } 0 \qquad \ldots.(1.17)$$

Quantum jumps which do not conform to these rules are called forbidden transitions, and the radiation emitted forbidden lines. Rigorous wave mechanical treatment shows that the probability of such a transition is not, in fact, zero but extremely small compared with other possible changes. If an atom is left undisturbed for sufficiently long, forbidden lines are observed, for example, from excited atoms in the upper atmosphere.

### ELECTRON CONFIGURATION: PAULI'S EXCLUSION PRINCIPLE

It is found that the details of spectra, chemical properties and the building up of the periodic table can be described by the quantum numbers already derived, if it is assumed that no two electrons can have the same set of quantum numbers $n, l, m_l, m_s$. This assumption is known as Pauli's exclusion principle, and is purely arbitrary, but Lindemann has shown that it is consistent with Heisenberg's uncertainty principle; it implies that of all possible energy levels of the atom (including those created by the application of a magnetic field) only one electron can occupy each energy level.

8

The electron configuration in an atom is then deduced as follows: those having the same value of $n$ form a shell, or main energy level. Among this group the electrons have values of $l$ from 0 to $(n - 1)$, and for each value of $l$ there are $2l + 1$ values of $m_l$; furthermore, for each combination of $n$, $l$, and $m_l$ there are the two values $\pm \frac{1}{2}$ for $m_s$. Thus in helium, both electrons have $n = 1$, $l = 0$ ($s$ electrons), $m_s = \pm \frac{1}{2}$; in the next shell (Li, Be, B. . .) electrons having $l = 1$ ($p$ electrons) are added, until all possible combinations of the quantum numbers have been satisfied when 6 $p$ electrons are added, and the shell is then full (or closed). In a closed shell it can be shown that $S = 0$, $L = 0$, $\mathcal{J} = 0$, and hence only the outermost electrons contribute anything to the angular momentum of the atom. To conform with X-ray notation, the shells are designated by letters as follows:

$$n = 1 \qquad 2 \qquad 3 \qquad 4 \qquad 5$$

$$K \qquad L \qquad M \qquad \mathcal{N} \qquad O$$

$$\dots.(1.18)$$

The electron configuration of the elements is given in Appendix I.

### IONIZATION AND EXCITATION

An atom is said to be excited when an electron is lifted from a lower to a higher energy level, and if this occurs it may be due to a mechanical collision, when an electron, ion or even a fast neutral particle hits the atom*, or when a quantum of radiation of the correct energy is absorbed. The electron in the higher level will, in most circumstances, remain in that state for about $10^{-8}$ sec, before falling to a lower state with the emission of radiation of frequency given by equation (1.3), but it may return to its original state in one or several jumps. However, the electron may be excited into a state from which it cannot fall spontaneously, or at least the probability of such a transition is extremely small. This is a metastable state, and a transition to a lower state would break the selection rules given on p. 8. It follows that the reverse process, excitation into this state by absorption of radiation, also has a very small probability. Metastable states can last for about $10^{-2}$ sec, but in most discharge conditions they are destroyed within this time by the atom hitting another object. Metastable states are usually found among the lower energy levels, since there are few even lower levels into which the electron can fall.

---

* We speak loosely of a 'mechanical collision'. Actually, of course, it is the electric field of the impinging particle which causes the change.

The electron may be excited into a state from which it can fall to a lower level (usually the ground state), with a very high probability of its emitting radiation; excitation into this state by the absorption of the correct frequency radiation is also a very probable process. Such states are called resonance states, and the radiation called resonance radiation; a gas illuminated with this light causes it to diffuse through slowly by a process of absorption and re-emission.

Ionization can in some ways be regarded as an extreme case of excitation, when the electron is given energy which is greater than the highest excited level of the atom $(n = \infty)$. The electron escapes from the attraction of its parent nucleus with some kinetic energy, and the atom becomes an ion, having one positive charge.

The energy which an electron must be given, expressed in volts, to be raised into an excited state is termed the excitation potential of that state, and similarly the energy necessary just to remove the electron from the atom is the ionization potential of the atom.

## SPECTRA OF IONS

An atom which has lost one electron and become an ion has an electronic configuration the same as the atom one place below it in the periodic table. Hence, the spectrum of the ion will be very similar (except for the difference in nuclear charge) to the spectrum of the next atom, the spectral terms being identical apart from the factor $Z^2$ in the lighter elements, or $(Z - a)^2$ when the screening effect of many inner electrons around the nucleus has to be taken into consideration. Thus $He^+$, $Li^{++}$, $Be^{+++}$ all have hydrogen-like spectra. Atoms from which successive outer electrons are removed by multiple ionization are sometimes called 'stripped atoms'.

## CONDUCTION OF ELECTRICITY IN A GAS

It is common experience that in regions of low electric field a gas is an extremely good insulator. It can only become a conductor if it is ionized by some agency, giving electrons and positive ions to act as charge carriers. The ionization will be enhanced in a sufficiently strong electric field, because the free electrons accelerated by the field will hit other gas molecules and ionize them, thus producing yet more ions and electrons. The properties of ionized gases therefore depend largely on collisions between electrons and gas molecules, and these must be studied in detail.

An electron which approaches close to an atom is repelled by the cloud of atomic electrons, but in turn disturbs the arrangement of the cloud itself, and so the final result depends on the speed of the electron and the direction in which it is moving. A slow electron will be easily repelled, and move off in another direction with almost undiminished speed, whilst the atomic electron cloud will suffer only a small transient disturbance; this is an elastic collision. Classically it would be represented as a collision between two perfectly elastic spheres, but this picture does not correctly predict electron scattering from atoms. A faster electron, if it has an energy greater than a particular excitation energy of the atom, and if it moves so as to penetrate deeply into the atom, may excite it, but it may not approach so closely and only be elastically deflected. Similarly a still faster electron, having greater energy than the ionization potential of the atom, may ionize it, or excite it to some lower level, or be elastically deflected. Encounters in which excitation or ionization of the atom result are inelastic, since some kinetic energy of the striking electron has been transformed into potential energy of the atom. However, in most conditions met in discharges, elastic collisions predominate.

## BIBLIOGRAPHY

RICHTMEYER, F. K. KENNARD, E. H. and LAURITSEN, T., *Introduction to Modern Physics*, 5th edn; New York: McGraw-Hill, 1955

BORN, M., *Atomic Physics*; London: Blackie, 1947

HERZBERG, G., *Atomic Spectra and Atomic Structure*; New York: Dover Publications, 1944

HERZBERG, G., *Molecular Spectra and Molecular Structure*, Vols. I and II; New York: van Nostrand, 1946, 1950

# FUNDAMENTAL PROCESSES

## I: ATOMIC EVENTS

### MOTION OF PARTICLES IN A GAS: BASIC CONCEPTS

IN THIS chapter, consideration is mainly given to particles, both charged and uncharged, which move about at random in the gas, making frequent collisions with gas molecules; many concepts derived from the kinetic theory of gases can be applied. The mean free path, $\lambda$, of a given kind of particle is the average distance which a particle travels in free flight between any two collisions with gas molecules. According to classical kinetic theory, the mean free path of a particle, type I, diameter $d_1$ (radius $a_1$) and mean energy $\varepsilon_1 = \frac{1}{2}mv_1^2$ which is present in small concentration in a gas consisting of $n$ particles per cm³, type II of diameter $d_2$ (radius $a_2$) and mean energy $\varepsilon_2 = \frac{1}{2}mv_2^2$ is:

$$\lambda = \frac{1}{n\pi(a_1 + a_2)^2\sqrt{1 + v_2^2/v_1^2}} \qquad \dots(2.1)$$

(Note that $\lambda$ depends, though only slightly, on the velocity $v_1$, of the particles.) This is based on the assumption that the mean energies are maintained by some agency and of course that the particles behave as an ideal gas, i.e. occupy negligible volume and exert no influence on the gas molecules. This applies strictly to the neutral gas molecules themselves; the mean free path, $\lambda_{\text{atom}}$, of atoms in their own gas is found by putting $\varepsilon_1 = \varepsilon_2$, $d_1 = d_2 = d$, the atomic diameter giving

$$\lambda_{\text{atom}} = \frac{1}{\sqrt{2}n\pi d^2} \qquad \dots(2.2)$$

An ion is sometimes regarded simply as an atom which is negligibly lighter by the mass of one electron, and hence has the same mean free path. In fact, a charged ion polarizes neutral molecules, and the resulting attractive force shortens the mean free path. The effect, naturally depending on the type of gas, is greatest in gases which are easily polarized, but the result is usually that $\lambda_{\text{ion}}$ is less than $\lambda_{\text{atom}}$ by a small numerical factor.

Classically an electron is considered as a small sphere of negligible size and mass ($d_1 \ll d_2$) so that even if the electrons have a mean energy comparable with the gas atoms, $v_1 \gg v_2$, and this leads to

$$\lambda_{\text{electron}} = 4\sqrt{2}\lambda_{\text{atom}} \approx 4\sqrt{2}\lambda_{\text{ion}} \qquad \ldots(2.3)$$

Although this is a useful guide to orders of magnitude, the classical theory breaks down completely here, because the scattering of an electron by an atom must be described by its wave properties, which leads (in accordance with experimental observation) to a mean free path depending on the speed of the electron. This is discussed more fully on pp. 18 and 19.

The mean free path defined here refers to all types of collisions. Mean free paths for ionization, excitation, etc., may be similarly defined as the average total distance travelled by a particle between two ionizing, or exciting, collisions; they will of course be longer than the normal mean free path since not every collision results in ionization or excitation. This idea is more usefully applied to cross sections.

### Distribution of Free Paths

Consider a group, initially of $N_0$ particles moving in the $x$ direction through a gas with a velocity $c$. If the mean free path is $\lambda$, then in a distance $dx$ there will be $N \cdot \dfrac{dx}{\lambda}$ collisions. Assume that each collision removes a particle from the group, then the number lost $(- dN)$ in moving $dx$ is:

$$dN = - N\frac{dx}{\lambda} \qquad \ldots(2.4)$$

Hence

$$N = N_0 e^{-x/\lambda} = N_0 e^{-\mu x} \qquad \ldots(2.5)$$

$N/N_0$ is the fraction of particles which have free paths exceeding $x$ and the fraction having free paths between $x$ and $x + dx$ is:

$$\frac{dN_{x \to x+dx}}{N_0} = \frac{1}{\lambda} \cdot e^{-x/\lambda} \cdot dx \qquad \ldots(2.6)$$

$\mu = \dfrac{1}{\lambda}$ is an absorption coefficient, describing the attenuation of a beam of particles. This shows that mean free paths many times $\lambda$ are rare, e.g. only one particle in about 150 has a path equal to $5\lambda$. The expression is exact only for particles of a particular velocity;

13

if the particles have a Maxwellian distribution of velocities and behave as solid spheres the law is $e^{-\frac{1\cdot04x}{\lambda}}$ . However, greater deviations are to be expected if $\lambda$ varies appreciably with velocity, other than as described by equation (2.1).

## Cross Sections

Suppose that the gas molecules behave as solid spheres of cross section $\sigma$, and that there are $n$ of them per cm³. Consider the same group of particles as above (initially $N_0$) moving through a section of the gas 1 cm square: the probability of a collision in a distance $dx$ is simply the ratio of obstructed area to free space, i.e. $\dfrac{n\sigma\,dx}{1}$ (since $n\sigma\,dx \ll 1$), and the number of collisions is $Nn\sigma\,dx$. Hence

$$Q = n\sigma = \frac{1}{\lambda} = \mu \qquad \qquad \dots(2.7)$$

$\sigma$ is called the atomic cross section of the gas atom or molecule measured in cm², and is of the order of $10^{-16}$ cm²; $Q$ is called the total effective cross section of all the molecules in 1 cm³ of gas, and is in cm²/cm³. Since this value must depend on $n$, it is usually quoted for gas at $p = 1$ mm Hg and temperature 0°C, when $n$ is a universal constant, $3\cdot56 \times 10^{16}$ mol./cm³.

$Q$ represents the effective area presented by the molecules in 1 cm³ for all types of collisions. Other cross sections are introduced to describe particular kinds of collisions; for example, only a fraction, $p_i$, of collisions between the incoming particles and gas molecules may lead to ionization, where $p_i$ is the probability of ionization. Thus if only ionizing collisions are counted, the molecules present an effective area of only $p_iQ$: this is called $Q_i$, the cross section for ionization, and similarly for other processes, like excitation or attachment. Cross sections are convenient to use because, clearly, the total cross section, $Q$, for all collisions is the sum of the particular cross sections for particular types of collisions.

$$Q_{\text{total}} = p_{\text{elastic}}Q + p_{\text{ionization}}Q + p_{\text{excitation}}Q + p_{\text{attachment}}Q$$
$$= Q_{\text{elastic}} + Q_{\text{ionization}} + Q_{\text{excitation}} + Q_{\text{attachment}} \qquad \dots(2.8)$$

where the $p$'s are the probabilities that collisions will result in particular processes. This is true only if $n$ remains constant, substantially unaltered by the processes taking place, and if the processes are independent of each other. Atomic cross sections for different processes vary enormously: for ionization they can rise to $2 \times 10^{-16}$

14

cm$^2$; for collisions resulting in a nuclear reaction they are $10^{-24}$ cm$^2$ and less. A unit of $10^{-24}$ cm$^2$ is called a 'barn'.

*Efficiency*

The efficiency, $s$, of a particle in producing, say, ionization is defined as the number of ionizing collisions suffered by each particle in moving 1 cm through the gas (1 cm total random path). Hence

$$s = \text{probability} \times \text{number of collisions}$$
$$= p_i \cdot \frac{1}{\lambda}$$
$$= p_i Q \qquad\qquad \dots\dots(2.9)$$
$$= Q_i$$

Thus the efficiency for a process is numerically equal to the cross section (in cm$^2$/cm$^3$) for that process.

*Collision Frequency*

If particles having a random velocity, $v_r$, have a mean free path, $\lambda$, the number of collisions each particle makes with gas molecules per second is:

$$v = \frac{v_r}{\lambda} = v_r Q \qquad\qquad \dots\dots(2.10)$$

The mean time, $\tau$, between collisions is the inverse of $v$. Referring also to the frequency, $v_n$, of collisions which result in a particular process, $n$, e.g. $v_i$ the collision frequency for ionization, these frequencies are, of course, always lower than $v$ since not every collision results in that process. Thus

$$v_i = \frac{v_r}{\lambda_i} = v_r Q_i \qquad\qquad \dots\dots(2.11)$$

illustrates a general relationship.

TYPES OF COLLISION

*Elastic Collisions—Kinetic Energy Conserved*

The electron is represented by a small sphere of mass, $m$, moving with a velocity, $u$, about to hit an atom represented by a larger stationary sphere of mass, $M$. After collision the atom moves with velocity, $V$, along the line of centres, and the electron moves with velocity, $v$, at some angle, $\theta$, to its original direction (*Figure 2.1*). By applying the equations conserving energy and momentum it is

15

found that the fraction of energy transferred from the electron to the atom is:

$$\frac{MV^2}{mu^2} = \frac{4mM}{(M+m)^2}\cos^2\theta \qquad \dots(2.12)$$

The probability, $P(\theta)\mathrm{d}\theta$, of a collision occurring between $\theta$ and

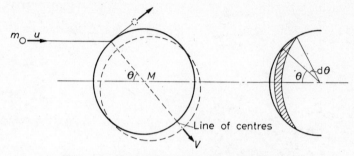

*Figure 2.1. Classical picture of an electron hitting an atom*

$\theta + \mathrm{d}\theta$ is given by the ratio of the projected area of the shaded ring (*Figure 2.1*) to the total area presented by the atom and is:

$$P(\theta)\mathrm{d}\theta = \sin 2\theta\ \mathrm{d}\theta \qquad \dots(2.13)$$

Hence combining equations (2.12) and (2.13) and averaging over all angles, the average transference of energy in collisions is:

$$\kappa = \frac{\overline{MV^2}}{mu^2} = \frac{2mM}{(M+m)^2} \approx \frac{2m}{M} \text{ when } m \ll M \quad \dots(2.14)$$

$\kappa$ is the average fraction of energy lost by an electron in an elastic collision.

Even for the lightest atoms $M \gg m$, and $\kappa$ is very small (e.g. in helium $\kappa = 2\cdot7 \times 10^{-4}$, in argon $2\cdot7 \times 10^{-5}$). For electrons moving with a Maxwellian energy distribution corresponding to a temperature $T_e$ ($\frac{1}{2}mv^2_{\text{random}} = \frac{3}{2}kT_e$) in a gas at temperature $T_{\text{gas}}$, proper averaging leads to the result

$$\kappa = \frac{8}{3}\frac{mM}{(M+m)^2} \cdot \left\{1 - \frac{T_{\text{gas}}}{T_e}\right\} \approx 2\cdot66\frac{m}{M} \quad \dots(2.15)$$

since the fractional loss of energy in collisions is so small that, in discharges, electrons attain average energies greatly exceeding that of the gas molecules. When heavy ions hit gas molecules however $m \approx M$ and $\kappa = \frac{1}{2}$, so that their mean energies are nearly equal. Ions and gas molecules have about 0·04 eV at room temperature, electrons have several eV.

16

*Elastic Scattering: Angular Distribution*

If $I_\phi$ is the fraction of electrons scattered per unit solid angle at an angle, $\phi$, it can easily be shown that $I = \dfrac{1}{4\pi} = \text{constant}$,

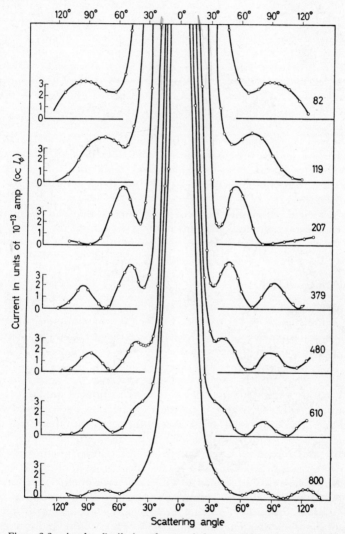

Figure 2.2. *Angular distribution of scattered electrons. Curves for 800, 610, 480, 379, 207, 119, and 82 volt electrons (the horizontal lines are zero levels of the various curves).* (By courtesy of the Royal Society)

17

provided $m \ll M$, i.e. that electrons are scattered isotropically, and after a collision all directions are equally probable. The fraction of electrons scattered in between the angles $\phi$, $\phi + d\phi$ is thus:

$$\frac{dn_{\phi \to \phi + d\phi}}{n} = I_\phi \,.\, 2\pi \sin \phi, \, d\phi = \tfrac{1}{2} \sin \phi \, d\phi \quad \ldots (2.16)$$

Experiments on the scattering of electron beams having a single well-defined energy, show that this expression, applicable to collisions between solid spheres, is very much at variance with the facts, except at low electron energies ($\gtrsim 1$ eV) where it is approximately true. At higher energies the curves of $I_\phi$ against $\phi$ show maxima and minima, with pronounced forward scattering. In light gases the maxima and minima are most noticeable in a relatively small range of electron energies (up to 6 eV in $H_2$, 15 eV in He) but in heavier gases, e.g. mercury, they have been observed at energies up to 800 eV. The total number scattered ($I_\phi = 2\pi \sin \phi \,.\, d\phi$) is large between $2°$ and $10°$, and is zero when $\phi = 0$ (see *Figure 2.2*).

It is clear, from the shape of these curves, that this is a wave phenomenon; the maxima and minima arise from the diffraction of the electron waves by the electric field of the atom. In its simplest form the effect should be pronounced when the wavelength of the electron waves $\left( \lambda = \dfrac{h}{mv} = \sqrt{\dfrac{154}{V}} \,.\, 10^{-8} \text{ cm} \right)$ is comparable with the 'radius' of an atom, and it is clear that this is true, for example, in helium for $V \sim 1$–15 volts. Further the maxima and minima move in to smaller angles as the energy of the electrons is increased, and their wavelength decreased.

*Elastic Cross Sections*

On the solid sphere model the cross section of an atom is a constant, $\sigma = \pi a_0^2$, where $a_0$ is the radius. It is known, however, that an atom is not solid, but a system of charges with their resultant electric fields. An electron passing by the atom is deflected by these fields and is said to have suffered a collision. But an electron, however far away, will suffer some effect from the atomic field, and thus on this simple picture the elastic cross section of an atom should theoretically be infinite, and its measured value would depend only on the resolving power of the apparatus to detect sufficiently small angles of scattering. This would imply a zero mean free path which is quite contrary to experience. TOWNSEND and his school[1], from the lateral diffusion of electron swarms, and

18

RAMSAUER and KOLLATH[2] from the scattering of electron beams, have found that the cross section for elastic collisions varies with the energy of the electrons, and exhibits maximum and minimum values in the energy range 1–20 eV. This, clearly, is also associated with the diffraction of the electron waves by the electric field of the atom, and proper application of the quantum theory leads to

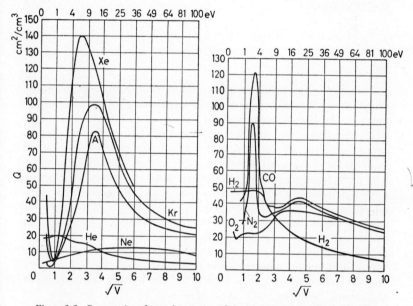

*Figure 2.3. Cross sections for total scattering of electrons with energy, V electron volts in various gases.* (By courtesy of Massachussetts Institute of Technology and John Wiley and Sons, Inc.)

the result that, if the potential at a distance, $r$, from the nucleus is $V = \dfrac{A}{r^n}$, the cross section is finite, provided $n < 2$ for small $r$, and $n > 2$ for $r \rightarrow \infty$, a condition which is satisfied by all atoms. Measured values of $Q$ are given in *Figure 2.3*; microwave techniques have recently made possible measurements at very low energies ($\sim 4 \times 10^{-2}$ eV—see Chapter 4).

The elastic cross section can be calculated from the scattering curves, though not with great accuracy. If a beam of $N$ electrons passes through a gas the fraction of electrons scattered into all angles by each atom is given by integrating equation (2.16). If there are $n$ atoms per cm³, the total fraction of the beam removed

19

by scattering as it penetrates a slice 1 cm² in area and thickness $dx$ is:

$$\text{Fraction scattered} = \frac{d\mathcal{N}}{\mathcal{N}} = n \int_0^\pi I_\phi \cdot 2\pi \sin \phi \cdot d\phi \cdot dx \quad \ldots (2.17)$$

Hence by comparison with equations (2.4) and (2.7) the elastic cross section is:

$$Q_{\text{elastic}} = 2\pi \int_0^\pi I_\phi \cdot \sin \phi \cdot d\phi \qquad \ldots (2.18)$$

*Momentum Transfer*

Transport phenomena in gases (diffusion, mobility) are based on the property of colliding particles in transferring momentum to one another. In the elementary theory of the drift motion of electrons in electric fields, for example, it is assumed that at the end of each mean free path all the momentum which the electron has gained from the field in its last free flight is lost in the collision. The mean free path thus quoted is the average distance which an electron moves between two collisions in which all its momentum (in a particular direction) is destroyed $(\lambda_m)$, and this is clearly not the same as the average distance between any two elastic collisions $(\lambda_e)$ except when the scattering is spherically symmetrical. If there is pronounced forward scattering, an electron suffers several collisions before its directed momentum is destroyed—thus $\lambda_m > \lambda_e$. There arose the concept of a cross section for momentum transfer, $\sigma_m$ or $Q_m$, being the imaginary area presented by an atom such that electrons suffering elastic collisions are deflected on the average perpendicular to some fixed direction, and thus have all their directed momentum destroyed; similarly $\nu_m$, the 'collision frequency for momentum transfer', is the number of times per second an electron loses all its momentum in elastic collisions. When electrons are mainly scattered forward $Q_m < Q_{\text{elastic}}$; if they are scattered backward $Q_m > Q_{\text{elastic}}$ since, in collisions, electrons would lose more than their entire momentum by gaining a negative momentum (i.e. a component in the opposite direction).

An electron of velocity, $v$, scattered at an angle, $\phi$, loses momentum

$$d(mv) = mv(1 - \cos \phi) \qquad \ldots (2.19)$$

(neglecting the small change in $v$ due to the recoil of the atom). Since the fraction of electrons scattered into the angle $\phi$ is given by equation (2.17), the fraction of momentum removed from the beam, on average, is:

$$\frac{\mathrm{d}(mv)}{mv} = n \int_0^\pi I_\phi \cdot 2\pi \sin\phi \cdot \mathrm{d}\phi \cdot (1 - \cos\phi) \cdot \mathrm{d}x \quad \ldots (2.20)$$

hence

$$Q_m = 2\pi \int_0^\pi I_\phi \sin\phi (1 - \cos\phi) \mathrm{d}\phi = Q_{\text{elastic}} \overline{(1 - \cos\phi)} \quad \ldots (2.21)$$

The average value $\overline{(1 - \cos\phi)}$ is 1, if all values of $\phi$ are equally probable; then $Q_m = Q_{\text{elastic}}$.

A similar result can be obtained from energy considerations, the average fractional loss of energy $\kappa = \frac{2m}{M}\left(\frac{Q_m}{Q_{\text{elastic}}}\right)$; in general, when considering the transport of momentum, these results can be included by using the cross section $Q_m$, mean free path $\lambda = \frac{1}{Q_m}$ (at $p = 1$ mm Hg), and assuming that $\kappa$ remains $\frac{2m}{M}$.

$Q_m$ is sometimes called the diffusion cross section on account of its application to transport phenomena. *Figure 2.3* shows measured values of the total scattering cross section. For energies less than a few volts there is no difference between $Q_{\text{elastic}}$, $Q_m$ and the curves drawn.

## Cross Sections at Higher Energies

*Figure 2.3* shows that many cross sections have a maximum value at some energy ($\varepsilon_{\text{max.}}$) below 20 eV, and then fall steadily to low values at higher energies. Thus in an electron swarm subjected to an electric field it is difficult for many electrons to attain energies greater than $\varepsilon_{\text{max.}}$, but those few which do achieve this are presented with a steadily decreasing cross section, and an increasing mean free path so that they can gain even more energy. Furthermore, as their energy increases, forward scattering becomes more prominent (which is another way of saying that the graph of $Q_m$ falls more steeply than that of $Q_{\text{elastic}}$), thus further improving their chances of acquiring yet more energy. Electrons which have gained great energies due to this effect have been observed in discharges excited by large fields and are called runaway electrons[17-23].

## Scattering of Ions

At low energies the scattering of positive ions by gas molecules can best be described by the classical solid sphere theory. There

21

are two disturbing influences due to the charge on the ion. First, charges are induced on nearby molecules which thus become polarized; this results only in small deflections due to the large masses of the particles. Secondly, charge transfer—exchange of an electron but not of kinetic energy—between the colliding particles is important especially at energies between 5 and 20 eV, and among ions moving in their own gas. Diffraction effects, analogous to those in electron scattering, set in when the particle waves have a length $\lambda = h/Mv$ comparable with, but rather smaller than, the radius of the atoms (e.g. $He^+$ in He, the effect is pronounced at energies of the order of 1,000 eV); then intense forward scattering is observed.

Experimentally, it is difficult at large energies to distinguish between elastic and inelastic scattering of ions because in both types of collision large amounts of energy are transferred.

### Inelastic Collisions

In an inelastic collision some of the kinetic energy of the impinging particle is converted into the potential energy necessary to lift an atomic electron into a higher energy level (excitation) or to remove it from the atom completely (ionization).

### Excitation by Electron Collisions

Excitation can occur when the energy of the electrons exceeds the excitation potential of the atom for the particular state under consideration; in the collision, however, linear momentum and angular momentum about the common centre of mass must be conserved. The change in angular momentum, $\Delta p$, during the collision must therefore balance the difference in the angular momentum of the atom in its initial and final state. Hence

$$\Delta p = \frac{h}{2\pi} \cdot \Delta J \qquad \qquad \dots (2.22)$$

where $\Delta J$ is the change in the inner quantum number. It follows that if electrons have exactly the energy necessary to excite, they would be stationary after a collision and must therefore hit at precisely the angle necessary to satisfy the above condition. The probability of this is extremely small and so the excitation probability is zero when $\varepsilon = eV_{\text{exc}}$ and increases at higher energies when the electron itself can carry away the excess energy in a direction which helps to satisfy the angular momentum condition.

The probability, or cross section for excitation, varies considerably with electron energy [this curve $Q_{\text{exc.}}$ as $f(\varepsilon)$ is called the excitation

22

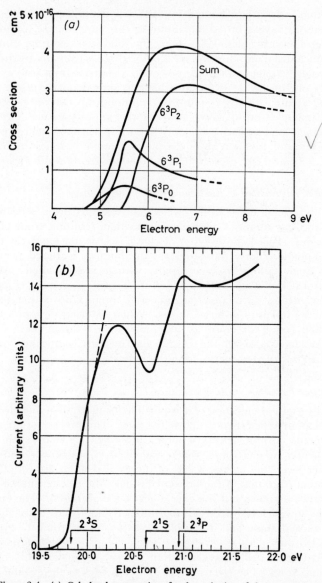

*Figure 2.4.* (a) *Calculated cross sections for the excitation of the mercury atom from an initial state* $7^3S_1$ *into the* $6^3P_{0,1,2}$ *states, by electrons of different energies;* (b) *probability (in arbitrary units) of excitation of helium from the ground state into the metastable levels indicated.* (By courtesy of Massachusetts Institute of Technology and John Wiley and Sons, Inc.)

function]. In atoms having two valency electrons, singlet–singlet transitions have a broad maximum in this function, $Q_{max.}$ lying at energies several times $eV_{exc.}$; here, the total spin quantum number $S$ is unchanged and thus the spins of the two electrons are unaltered. In singlet–triplet transitions, however, $S$ changes from 0 to 1, and hence one of the electrons must have its spin vector reversed. For many atoms with weak spin-orbit coupling, this can only occur if one atomic electron is replaced by the impinging one (electron exchange) and since this can only happen in a narrow energy range the excitation function has a sharp maximum at energies just above $eV_{exc.}$. Typical curves of excitation functions are shown in *Figure 2.4*.

### Angular Distribution of Electrons after Exciting Collisions

The angular distribution of electrons scattered from a beam by exciting gas atoms is very similar to that resulting from elastic collisions. When the fraction of energy lost is not too great there is pronounced forward scattering, the number scattered per unit solid angle falling off very rapidly with increasing angle. When electrons lose a small fraction of their energy in exciting heavy atoms, strong diffraction maxima and minima are found in the scattered intensity at large angles. When an electron loses a large fraction (say $\frac{1}{3}$ or more) of its energy in a collision there is less resemblance between the elastic and inelastic scattering curves; this is also true for energy losses by ionization.

### Multiple Excitation: 'Auto-ionization'

In certain circumstances it is possible for more than one electron in an atom to be raised to an excited level. This process is important when the current density is large, and when an atom is hit very frequently by electrons. When one electron has been raised to a higher level, the energy levels of the excited atom are, of course, different from that of the unexcited atom; the new term scheme is not always known but the energy levels are all raised. The energy of the lowest level of the excited atom is more than twice that of the normal atom, and if another electron is raised from the ground state to one of these levels, the total energy $eV^{\star\star}$ of the doubly excited atom can be greater than the ionization potential of the normal atom. The electrons can both fall back to the ground state with the emission of a single quantum of radiation of energy $h\nu = eV^{\star\star} > eV_i$ (anomalous radiation), or one electron falls to the ground state and the other leaves the atom carrying away the excess $e(V^{\star\star} - V_i)$ as kinetic energy; this process is called

24

auto-ionization and there is great probability of this happening when $(V^{\star\star} - V_i)$ is small.

## Ionization by Single Electron Impact

The collision can be treated approximately by the usual classical equations conserving energy and linear momentum, with the addition of a potential energy term equal to $eV_i$. No quantum conditions need to be satisfied for angular momentum since a third body, the free electron, emerges. Ionization can occur when the

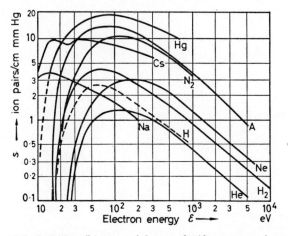

*Figure 2.5. Ionization efficiency, s, of electrons of uniform energy, ε, in various gases. (From A. VON ENGEL[10], by courtesy of Springer)*

energy of the electrons exceed $eV_i$; when $\varepsilon = eV_i$ the probability of ionization is zero, but it rises rapidly as the energy increases. The initial rise is linear and recent refined experiments, using retarding potentials to limit the energy spread of the electron beams to $\frac{1}{10}$ volt or less, have shown the curve to be accurately linear right down to the threshold energy $eV_i$; at higher energies the curve rises more slowly reaching a broad maximum at about 100 eV and afterwards decreases; for alkali vapours, however, the maximum lies at about 20 eV. These properties are usually expressed in curves of ionization efficiency, $s_e$, against energy ($s_e$, the number of ion pairs produced by one electron moving 1 cm, through the gas, is numerically equal to $Q_i$, the ionization cross section). These are given reduced to $p = 1$ mm Hg for common gases in *Figure 2.5*.

25

Useful analytical approximations for certain ranges of electron energy, $eV$, are:

$$s_e = \frac{dN}{dx} = ap(V - V_i) \quad \text{for} \quad V \leqslant 2V_i \quad \ldots \text{(2.23)}$$

Here $N$ is the number (not density) of ion pairs produced in an actual electron path of total length $dx$

$$s_e = p \cdot (s_{\text{max. at 1 mm Hg}}) \cdot [1 - e^{-b(V - Vi)}] \quad \text{for} \quad V \leqslant V_{\text{max.}} \quad \ldots \text{(2.24)}$$

$V_{\text{max.}}$ being the energy at which $s_e$ is maximum.

Clearly for small values of $(V - V_i)$ equation (2.24) reduces to equation (2.23) with $a = bp(s_{\text{max. at 1 mm Hg}})$

$$s_e = p \cdot \frac{C_1}{VV_i} \log \frac{C_2 V}{V_i} \quad \text{for} \quad V > \text{several hundred eV} \quad \ldots \text{(2.25)}$$

where $C_1$ and $C_2$ are constants. This equation is derived from wave mechanical calculations and although it shows a maximum at low energies it is accurate only at large energies. Values of $a$ and $b$ are given in *Table 2.1*.

*Table 2.1.* Values of $a$ and $b$ for various gases [equations (2.23) and (2.24)]

|  | He | Ne | A | H₂ | N₂ | O₂ | Air | Hg | Na | K | Cs |  |
|---|---|---|---|---|---|---|---|---|---|---|---|---|
| $a$ | 4·6 | 5·6 | 71 | 21 | 26 | 24 | 26 | 83 | 45 |  | 280 | all $\times$ 10⁻² |
| $b$ | 3·54 | 1·86 | 54·5 | 5·83 | 2·55 | 2·29 |  | 4·88 | * | * | * | all $\times$ 10⁻² |
| $s_{\text{max}}$ | 1·3 | 3 | 13 | 3·6 | 10·2 | 10·5 |  | 17 | 3·7 | 4·8 | 9·8 | ion pairs/cm for $p = 1$ mm Hg |

\* Equation (2.24) not applicable.

### Multiple Ionization

The removal of one electron leaves an ion with a net positive charge of $+ e$; the removal of another electron consequently requires greater energy. Furthermore, since the nuclear charge, $Z$, is now less effectively screened by the surrounding electrons, the radius of the electron orbits decreases and hence the cross section for ionization. On Bohr's simple theory an atom with a single electron has an orbit of area $\propto \frac{1}{Z^2}$, and therefore it might be expected that the threshold energy for double and triple ionization would increase, and $s_{max.}$ for these processes would decrease roughly as $\frac{1}{2^m}$, $\frac{1}{3^m}$, where $m$ is about 2. Very fast electrons $(\varepsilon > 10^4 \text{ eV})$ can eject electrons from the inner shells with consequent emission of X-rays.

## Ionization of Excited Atoms

An outer valency electron, which has been raised to a higher energy level, revolves in an orbit of greater radius than its normal one. The atom thus presents a larger target to oncoming electrons especially in the light atoms having only one valency electron, for then $r \propto n^2/Z$ where $n$ is the principal quantum number. The ionization function of an excited atom begins at a low energy (since only $eV_i - eV_{exc.}$ is required to remove the electron) and can be an order of magnitude greater than the normal curve.

## Angular and Energy Distribution of Electrons after Ionization

The analysis of these distributions is complicated because after

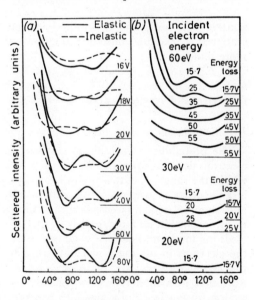

*Figure 2.6. Observed angular distribution of electrons scattered in argon: (a) the horizontal lines mark the abscissae of the curves for electrons of incident energies of 16, 18, 20, 30, 40, 60, and 80 eV. (———) Elastic scattering; (- - - - -) electrons scattered after exciting argon to $^3P_1$ level in which the energy loss is 11·6 eV; (b) ionizing collisions by electrons of initial energies of 20, 30, and 60 eV, with energy losses from 15·7 to 55 eV. (From H. S. W. MASSEY and E. H. S. BURHOP[3], by courtesy of Clarendon Press)*

an ionizing collision, two electrons are present. The energy remaining after the impinging electron has given up the energy $eV_i$ to ionize, is not distributed equally between the two electrons; one of them carries away most of the energy and the other is slow.

Although it is experimentally impossible to distinguish the origin of either electron, the fast electron is usually referred to as the scattered one and the slow electron as the ejected one. The angular distribution is illustrated in *Figure 2.6*; the fast electrons are largely

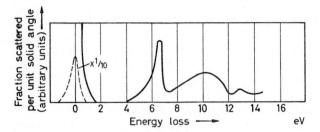

*Figure 2.7. Energy loss of electrons having incident energy of 42 eV after scattering through 90° in Hg vapour. The very large peak at almost zero energy loss is due to elastic collisions, and that at 6·7 eV to excitation of the 6³P₁ level.* (From H. S. W. MASSEY and E. H. S. BURHOP³, by courtesy of Clarendon Press)

scattered forward, and distributed in angle very much as those scattered by exciting collisions; the slow ones are distributed much more uniformly.

In *Figure 2.7* a typical energy distribution curve for electrons scattered at a fixed angle (90°) in mercury shows the preponderance of electrons of very low energy ($\sim 1$ eV).

### Inelastic Collisions between Atoms

The probability of a collision resulting in a transition of atomic electrons depends upon the time during which the two particles are within the range, $a$, of their atomic fields ($a \sim 10^{-8}$ cm). This time is of the order $a/v$, where $v$ is the relative velocity of the two particles, and should be compared with the time taken by an electronic transition within an atom, which by quantum theory is $h/\Delta\varepsilon$, where $\Delta\varepsilon$ is the total internal energy change in the system. If $a/v \gg h/\Delta\varepsilon$, the electrons in the atom will have time to adjust their motion to the changes caused by the slowly approaching particle, and a transition to a higher level is unlikely to occur. Thus the cross section (or efficiency of ionization) will theoretically be small when

$$\frac{a|\Delta\varepsilon|}{hv} \gg 1,$$ rising rapidly to a maximum when this expression

becomes of the order unity, and more detailed analysis shows that it should fall more slowly at higher energies. Heavy ions or atoms

28

are thus much less effective in exciting and ionizing than electrons of the same energy because their speed is so much smaller. Experimental results largely confirm these predictions for simple atomic systems for the processes set out below; collisions between molecules, however, show wide discrepancies from theory.

*Charge transfer*—In this process an electron leaves an atom and neutralizes an impinging ion, giving, for example:

$$A^+_{fast} + A_{slow} \rightarrow A_{fast} + A^+_{slow} \qquad \ldots (2.26)$$

Here, $\Delta\varepsilon = 0$ (ion moving in its own gas). The cross section is a maximum, approximately the same as the gas kinetic cross section, for slow ions ($v \sim 0$) and decreases slowly as their energy increases. For ions moving not in their own gas

$$A^+ + B \rightarrow A + B^+ \qquad \ldots (2.27)$$

Here $\Delta\varepsilon$ is not zero, and the cross section is less. Protons ($H^+$) moving in $H_2$ have a maximum cross section (at about 7 keV) very much larger than in any other gas. These large cross sections make charge transfer an important process; it affects the mobility of ions in their own gas, and the ionization of gases by ion beams. Intermediate metastable states are often significant[15].

*Ionization by ions and atoms*—The equations of energy and momentum applied to the impact of two spheres of equal mass show that potential energy, $eV_i$, can be transferred to one sphere (i.e. atom) only if the energy of the incident particle exceeds $2eV_i$. There is some rather scanty experimental evidence that $2eV_i$ is the critical energy for ionization by positive ions and neutral atoms moving in their own gas (notably in helium). The curves of ionization efficiency (or cross section) against the energy of the ions have been measured, though not with great accuracy, for: A and $A^+$ in A, Ne and $Ne^+$ in Ne, He and $He^+$ in He, $H^+$ and $H_2$ in $H_2$, $N_2$ in $N_2$ and $K^+$ in A, Ne and recently Hg. The initial slope of the curves lies between $10^{-4}$ and $5 \times 10^{-4}$ cm²/cm³ eV for the lightest atoms, the curves becoming steeper as the mass of the impinging particle increases. Argon ions or atoms are especially effective as ionizing agents, a fact which is not understood. The probability of these processes is very much smaller than that of ionization by electrons of the same energy, and smaller than that of charge transfer.

It should be remembered that measured values of ionization by fast heavy particles may be considerably greater than would be expected from the simple considerations set out above, due to the contribution of the electrons which can be ejected with energies up to 100 eV or so and themselves produce appreciable ionization. Thus α particles in air would be expected to produce their maximum ionization at between $10^4$ and $5 \times 10^4$ eV; actually it is found at 1·5 MeV.

*Collisions of the second kind. Penning effect*—Collisions between excited atoms, or between an excited atom and one in the ground state, can result in the potential energy of the excited atom being released as kinetic energy of the resultant particles; if ionization of one of the atoms occurs, much of the surplus energy (if any) is carried away by the electron. Such collisions are termed 'of the second kind' or superelastic. There are many examples of these, generally following the rule that the cross section is small when $\Delta\varepsilon$ is large and $v$ is small. They have been fully summarized by MASSEY and BURHOP[3]. One process of special interest in discharges is the ionization of one kind of atom by an impact with the metastable state of another kind, when $eV_{metastable} \geqslant eV_i$ (the Penning effect). It is well known in a mixture of neon ($V_{metastable} = 16\cdot53$ volts, $3P_2$) state with a small proportion of argon ($V_i = 15\cdot76$ volts); the probability here is large—almost unity per collision—because $\Delta\varepsilon$ ($\sim 0\cdot8$ eV) is small and the effect is enhanced by the long lifetime of the metastable state. Common molecular gases, having $V_i \sim 15$ volts, are easily ionized by metastable atoms of the rare gases ($V_{metastable} \sim 16$–20 volts).

*Absorption of Photons: Photo-excitation and Photo-ionization*

A photon of energy $h\nu$ can be absorbed by an atom or molecule, exciting it to a higher state, provided $eV^\star = h\nu$. The probability of this process depends, by the principle of detailed balancing, on the selection rules governing the reverse process. For example, a metastable state, from which an electron cannot revert to the ground state by emission of radiation, cannot be excited from the ground state by the absorption of the appropriate quantum of radiation. On the other hand, resonance lines, corresponding to the transition from resonance to ground states, are heavily absorbed.

Photo-ionization occurs when $h\nu \geqslant eV_i$, an electron being ejected with kinetic energy equal to the difference between the energy of the photon and the ionization energy of the gas. The wavelength (in Å) of light necessary is given by $\lambda_i \leqslant 12,400/V_i$ where $V_i$ is in volts. Thus 2,000–3,000 Å (ultra-violet) will ionize alkali metals and 500 Å will ionize rare and molecular gases. The probability of a photon ionizing an atom or molecule is a maximum when $(h\nu - eV_i)$ is small ($\sim 0\cdot1$–1 eV), and decreases with

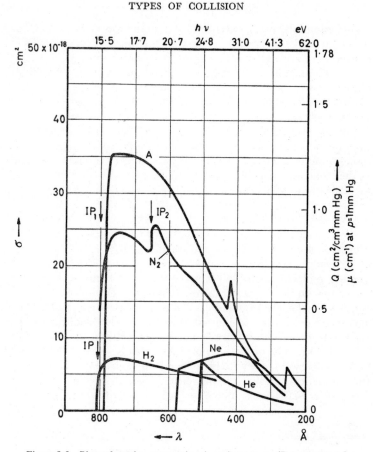

*Figure 2.8. Photo-absorption cross sections in various gases.* (By courtesy of Massachusetts Institute of Technology and John Wiley and Sons, Inc.)

decreasing wavelength, the cross section or absorption coefficient* (at $p = 1$ mm Hg) being given by

$$\mu = Q = C \cdot \frac{\lambda^4}{\lambda_i - \lambda} \qquad \dots (2.28)$$

The reverse process to this is radiative recombination and the

---

\* The measured absorption coefficient must, of course, be corrected to separate the true absorption from scattering. In the literature, $\mu$ is most frequently quoted for atmospheric pressure, and one must be careful in deducing the cross section for photo-ionization for comparison with other processes, whose cross sections usually refer to $p = 1$ mm Hg.

above equation corresponds to a recombination cross section proportional to $1/(eV)^2$ where $eV$ is the electron energy. This law is obeyed over a range of several hundred Ångström units.

Photo-ionization can occur in steps, although the probability of this process is small; it becomes important only in regions of high photon density. Photons of very large energy ($\lambda \sim 1$ Å, $\varepsilon \sim 10^4$ eV) i.e. X-rays, eject electrons from the inner shells of atoms. These electrons often have large energy and produce far more ionization than the original photons. At the X-ray absorption edges there are discontinuous changes of $\mu$. The cross sections for photo-ionization at their maxima are about 100 or 1,000 times less than the maxima for ionization by electron or ion collision (see *Figure 2.8*).

*Electron Attachment*

Electrons colliding with certain atoms or molecules can become attached, forming heavy negative ions. In particular, atomic oxygen and hydrogen, molecular oxygen, the halogens and large organic molecules readily form negative ions; nitrogen and the rare gases do not. The electron is bound to the molecule with an energy $\varepsilon_a$ (the electron affinity) and a quantum of radiation of energy $h\nu = \varepsilon_a + eV$ is emitted where $eV$ is the kinetic energy of the electron. $\varepsilon_a$ varies from 3 to 4 eV for halogen atoms to about 0·5 eV for Li. The probability of attachment is greatest for electrons of low energy ($\sim 1$ eV) which spend an appreciable time within the influence of the atomic field. Cross sections are small ($Q_{\text{attachment}} \sim 0·4$ for $I_2$, down to $10^{-5}$ cm$^2$/cm$^3$ for H atoms).

*Thermionic Emission*

The electrons in a metal are distributed in the energy bands according to the Fermi–Dirac law, up to the limit $\mu$ ($\sim 10$ eV) at zero temperature. As the temperature increases, a few achieve larger energies, and at high temperatures some achieve sufficient energy to overcome the potential barrier (work function $e\phi$) at the surface of the metal and also the attraction of the image charges as they leave the solid. The current density, $j$, of electrons emitted at an absolute temperature, $T$, is given by:

$$j = AT^2e^{-\frac{e\phi}{kT}} = AT^2e^{-\frac{11,600}{T}\phi} \qquad \ldots\ldots(2.29)$$

where $\phi$ is in volts, $T$ in °K.

A similar equation describes the emission of positive ions from heated metals; ion currents are very much smaller, except from specially compounded substances, e.g. Kunsman sources, and require much higher temperatures (very near to the melting point of the metals) when the ions are mixed with a preponderance of evaporating neutral atoms.

*Field Emission*

The application of an external field changes the shape of the potential barrier from a rectangle to a triangle; the larger the field the steeper the slope of the decreasing potential barrier. Wave mechanical calculations show that an electron in the potential well, i.e. the metal, has a finite probability of escaping through this barrier to a free state of the same potential energy: the probability increases as the barrier becomes thinner, i.e. as the applied field increases. The current density in A/cm$^2$ is given by

$$j = 6 \times 10^{-6} \times \frac{\sqrt{\mu/\phi}}{\mu + \phi} \times X^2 e^{-\frac{2 \cdot 1 \times 10^8 \times \phi^{3/2}}{X}} \qquad \ldots (2.30)$$

Here, $X$ is the field in volts/cm, $\mu$ the Fermi limit of the energy distribution, and $\phi$ the normal work function, both in volts. Current densities of several A/cm$^2$ are achieved with fields of $10^7$–$10^8$ volts/cm; it is, of course, extremely difficult to maintain such fields over an appreciable area, and in practice a current density of this magnitude would be emitted from a thin wire or small point, yielding a total current of a few microamperes. The state of the surface is of the greatest importance, and the results quoted above apply only to pure clean surfaces.

When the surface is contaminated with oxide or gas films, an emission dependent on the applied field is found with fields of $10^5$–$10^6$ volts/cm. There is also reason to believe that charges (electrons) residing on insulators, or on metal surfaces covered with gas films, can be pulled off by fields as low as $10^3$ volts/cm, but it is not thought that this has any resemblance to the mechanism of field emission (see Chapter 4).

The application of a strong field can also assist thermionic emission; the effective work function is reduced by the field, which helps to overcome the image force as the electron leaves the surface. $\phi$ decreases to $\phi'$ where

$$\phi' = \phi - \sqrt{eX} \qquad \ldots (2.31)$$

Normal thermionic emission (without external field) is thus increased by the factor $e^{e\sqrt{eX}/kT}$. This has been experimentally confirmed for fields up to $10^6$ V/cm.

33

Thermionic and field emission are distinguished by two properties: (a) source of energy—thermionic electrons take energy from the metal and cool it while field electrons obtain theirs solely from the applied field; and (b) energy distribution—thermionic electrons have a Maxwellian distribution while field electrons are emitted predominantly with almost zero energy.

They are both largely independent of gas processes unless intense space charges create the necessary fields, or bombardment by heavy energetic particles (e.g. ions or excited atoms) heats the solid.

## Secondary Electron Emission

When electrons strike a solid surface a fraction of them are reflected with hardly any loss of energy, but the majority penetrate the structure of the solid (metal or insulator) causing the emission of true secondary electrons. The ratio between the total number of ejected electrons and the number of incident primary electrons is called the secondary emission coefficient, or yield $\delta$; of course no electrons can be ejected unless the energy of the incident electrons exceeds $e\phi$, but there is no simple relation between $\delta$ and $\phi$. The main features of secondary emission are:

(a) $\delta$ rises with the energy of the primary electrons, has a maximum, $\delta_{max.}$, at several hundred electron volts for most substances, and then falls slowly. $\delta_{max.}$ is between 1 and 2 for commonly used metals, a little larger for glass, and much larger ($\sim 10$) for alkaline oxides (BaO, SrO). $\delta_{max.}$ is less than 1 for rough surfaces such as soot (see *Figure 2.9*).

(b) The values of $\delta$ quoted are for primary electrons at normal incidence; if they fall at an angle they penetrate less deeply and the secondary electrons have a greater chance of escape, hence $\delta$ increases.

(c) The energy of the secondary electrons is distributed, a large proportion having energies of a few eV; this mean energy is independent of the energy of the incident electrons.

(d) The angular distribution of the secondary electrons is given approximately by a cosine law, most being emitted normal to the surface, thus

$$\mathrm{d}n_{\theta\to\theta+\mathrm{d}\theta} \propto \cos\theta \qquad \dots\,.(2.32)$$

where $\mathrm{d}n$ is the total number emitted in the angle $\theta$ to $\theta + \mathrm{d}\theta$, measured from the normal. This refers to true secondaries (i.e. relatively slow electrons $\varepsilon \leqslant \frac{1}{2}\varepsilon_{primary}$) and is independent of the angle of the primary electrons. For reflected primaries the

34

distribution is different, although the angle of reflection is not equal to the angle of incidence.

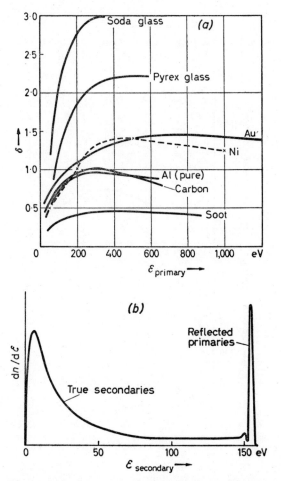

Figure 2.9. (a) Yield, δ, of secondary electrons from targets bombarded with a beam of primary electrons; (b) energy distribution of secondary electrons emitted when a primary beam of energy 160 eV hits a silver surface. (From H. BRUINING[12], by courtesy of Pergamon Press)

*Photo-electric Emission*

Electrons are ejected when photons of sufficient energy fall on the surface, their maximum kinetic energy depending on the frequency, $\nu$, of the incident light according to the well-known relation

$$\tfrac{1}{2}mv_{\text{max.}}^2 = h\nu - e\phi = h\nu - h\nu_0 \qquad \ldots\ldots(2.33)$$

where $\nu_0$ is the threshold frequency.

The yield $\gamma_p$, i.e. the number of electrons ejected by each incident photon depends markedly on the state and purity of the surface,

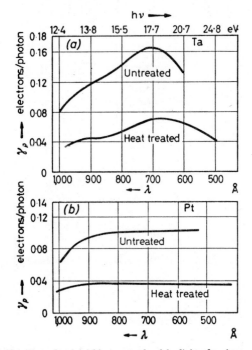

Figure 2.10. Photo-electric yields, $\gamma_p$, produced by light of various wavelengths falling on the surfaces of: (a) tantalum; (b) platinum (vacuum spectrometer measurements). (From P. F. LITTLE[4], by courtesy of Springer)

and on the angle of incidence and state of polarization of the light. Generally $\gamma_p$ is larger (by a factor 2–10) on rough surfaces than on smooth, and is increased by surface films.

At frequencies near the threshold ($h\nu \leqslant$ about $2h\nu_0$), $\gamma_p$ increases with $h\nu$ approximately in an exponential manner; in this range, electrons are ejected from the surface layers, and $\gamma_p$ rises to values of the order $10^{-4}$–$10^{-3}$. At shorter wavelengths ($h\nu >$ about 10 eV, short ultra-violet region) electrons are set free deeper in the volume of the solid and, being more energetic, produce secondary electrons in the surface layers. The total electron emission, and hence $\gamma_p$, rises to a maximum value about 100 times larger (up to $10^{-1}$ or even slightly more on gas-covered surfaces) at wavelengths about 500–700 Å ($h\nu \sim 20$ eV). At still shorter wavelengths electrons are produced at greater depths, fewer escape and $\gamma_p$ falls (see *Figure 2.10*).

*Emission of Electrons by Bombardment with Ions, Excited and Neutral Atoms*

*Ions*—A slow ion, approaching a solid surface with thermal velocity, distorts the potential barrier by reason of its electric field and gives electrons in the upper Fermi levels an opportunity to tunnel through the barrier. In order that electron emission shall be observed, two electrons must leave the metal, one of which neutralizes the ion. The total energy required to extract the electron is $2e\phi$, and the energy available is the potential energy of the ion $eV_i$. The process is thus only possible when

$$V_i > 2\phi \qquad \qquad \dots\,.(2.34)$$

If the ions are fast, i.e. having kinetic as well as potential energy, their effectiveness in releasing electrons is only slightly increased on clean surfaces\* indicating that the chief mechanism is due to the distortion of the surface potential barrier. Doubly charged ions cause many more electrons to be ejected, confirming this reasoning. The total electron yield per incident ion $\gamma_i$ depends on the kind of ion, the material of the surface and whether or not it has a surface film on it; there is an extremely wide variation in the measured values, depending on these factors. For example $He^{++}$ ions on clean molybdenum give $\gamma_i = 0\cdot7$, $N^+$ or $N_2^+$ on gas-covered tantalum give $\gamma_i \sim 10^{-4}$ electrons per ion. Typical values are shown in *Figure 2.11* and further details can be obtained from data compiled by LITTLE[4].

Ions striking a metal surface may also be reflected with appreciable loss of energy without being neutralized. The reflection coefficient, $R$, increases with the kinetic energy of the ions (linearly for gas-covered surfaces): in the rare gases the lighter ions suffer more reflection (see *Figure 2.12*).

---

\* On gas-covered surfaces, bombardment by ions of increasing energy may remove the gas film, changing the effective $\phi$. Here we have a mixture of effects which are difficult to separate.

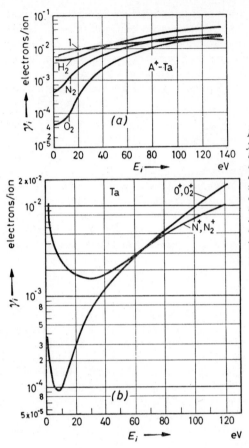

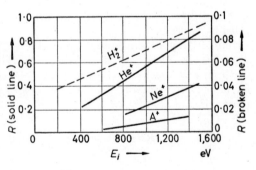

Figure 2.11. The electron yield, $\gamma_i$, from gas-covered tantalum surfaces when bombarded with positive ions of energy $E_i$: (a) $A^+$ ions bombarding surfaces covered with layers of $H_2$, $N_2$, $O_2$: curve 1 is the result for a clean gas-free surface; (b) mixtures of molecular gas ions bombarding surfaces covered with films of the same gas. (From P. F. LITTLE[4], by courtesy of Springer)

Figure 2.12. Reflection of hydrogen and rare gas ions falling perpendicularly on a nickel surface ($R$ = reflection coefficient). (From P. F. LITTLE[4], by courtesy of Springer)

An ion may also be reflected as an excited atom, especially if, when the ion is close to the metal, an unoccupied energy level in the atomic structure is at the same potential energy as an electron in one of the energy bands in the metal. There is then a resonance effect and a large probability that the electron will tunnel through the surface potential barrier (see *Figure 2.13*). If the electron is in

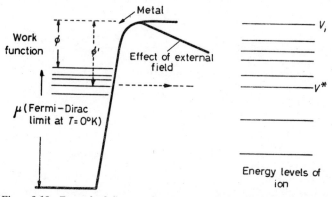

*Figure 2.13. Energy level diagram of a positive ion close to the surface of a metal. Here the external field is due to the charge on the ion*

an energy level which is $\phi'$ below the barrier, and the energy level in the ion is of potential $V^\star$ the condition for this effect to occur is that

$$e\phi' = eV_i - eV^\star \qquad \ldots . (2.35)$$

Reflection as a metastable atom, or an unexcited atom (i.e. without causing the ejection of another electron from the metal) are special cases of this, when $V^\star$ is $V_{\mathrm{metastable}}$ or the ground state.

*Atoms*—Emission of electrons by the impact of excited atoms occurs by the transfer of potential energy, provided $eV^\star \geqslant e\phi$; here, of course, only one electron has to be extracted from the metal. Metastable states are especially effective in most discharge phenomena because of their long lifetime. The yield ($\gamma_m$—number of electrons emitted per incident metastable atom) can be very large ($\sim 1$) especially when ($eV^\star - e\phi$) is large (see *Table 2.2*).

Neutral atoms in the ground state cause appreciable electron emission only when they have large kinetic energy ($\sim 1,000$ eV); at low energy their yield ($\gamma_n$) is much less than $\gamma_i$. For both fast ions and atoms, interaction with the lattice of the metal is an important process, and it leads not only to emission of electrons but

39

also to sputtering, i.e. ejection of atoms of the solid material. It has been suggested that local heating causes evaporation and thermionic emission but there are objections to this concept in small

Table 2.2. Emission due to metastable atoms.
(From P. F. LITTLE[4], by courtesy of Springer)

| Atom | State | Surface | Condition | $\gamma_m$ |
|------|-------|---------|-----------|-----------|
| Hg | $6^3P_0$ | W | Film of Hg + $O_2$ | $10^{-2}$ normally $1 - 10^{-5}$ extreme values |
| He | — | Mo, Ni, Mg | Clean | 1 |
| He | $2^3S$ | Pt | Gas film | 0·24 |
| He | $2^1S$ | Pt | Gas film | 0·40 |
| Ne | — | Pt | Gas film | 0·12 |

volumes containing few molecules only, and the proper explanation of many of these surface phenomena is still lacking.

## II: STATISTICAL PROCESSES

In the preceding subsections single atomic events, between particles of clearly defined energy, have been considered. In discharges these are usually not of immediate significance, because electrons, ions and atoms are widely distributed in energy about their respective mean values, and the various processes of production and loss determine their concentrations. Except in very intense fields the ions, by reason of their large mass and consequent rapid loss of energy in elastic collisions, have nearly the same mean energy as the gas molecules and both have a Maxwellian distribution of velocities. The most important statistical factor is the energy distribution of the electrons; their mean energy is considerably greater than that of the gas molecules and the distribution varies appreciably between one gas and another and at different values of applied field.

### ELECTRON ENERGY DISTRIBUTION

The calculation of electron energy distribution is a matter of some complexity, and is treated rigorously by the application of the Boltzmann transfer equation[5] (see Appendix V).

Basically, a calculation must be made of the rate at which the number of electrons in a particular energy interval is increased, by slower electrons gaining energy from the field in free flight and by faster electrons having lost different amounts of energy in elastic and inelastic collisions, and decreased by the electrons in this group themselves suffering these collisions. In the steady state, of course, the gain and loss are equal, and a constant energy distribution, written formally, is:

$$\frac{\mathrm{d}n}{n} = f(\varepsilon)\,\mathrm{d}\varepsilon \qquad \ldots\,(2.36)$$

where $\mathrm{d}n/n$ is the fraction of electrons having energies in the range $\varepsilon$ to $\varepsilon + \mathrm{d}\varepsilon$.

Two special examples are of interest: one is the energy distribution resulting when the only energy losses are by elastic collision, $\kappa$ and $\lambda_e$ being constants. This is the Druyvesteyn distribution:

$$\frac{\mathrm{d}n}{n} = C \cdot \sqrt{\varepsilon} \cdot \mathrm{e}^{-0\cdot55(\varepsilon/\bar{\varepsilon})^2} \cdot \mathrm{d}\varepsilon = 1\cdot04 \sqrt{\frac{\varepsilon}{\bar{\varepsilon}}} \cdot \mathrm{e}^{-0\cdot55(\varepsilon/\bar{\varepsilon})^2} \cdot \mathrm{d}\left(\frac{\varepsilon}{\bar{\varepsilon}}\right)$$
$$\ldots\,(2.37)$$

where $\bar{\varepsilon}$ is the mean energy, and $C$ is a number found by integrating over all energies from 0 to $\infty$ and equating to unity.

The other distribution is Maxwell's which applies when collisions between electrons themselves—i.e. interaction by their mutual repulsion—are responsible for the rearrangement of their energies, giving

$$\frac{\mathrm{d}n}{n} = C'\sqrt{\varepsilon}\,\mathrm{e}^{-\varepsilon/\bar{\varepsilon}} \cdot \mathrm{d}\varepsilon = \frac{2}{\sqrt{\pi}} \sqrt{\frac{\varepsilon}{\bar{\varepsilon}}} \cdot \mathrm{e}^{-\varepsilon/\bar{\varepsilon}} \cdot \mathrm{d}\left(\frac{\varepsilon}{\bar{\varepsilon}}\right) \qquad \ldots\,(2.38)$$

This occurs strictly at large current densities only, but many close approximations to it are found at small currents.

For the Maxwellian distribution an electron temperature, $T_e$, may be defined as:

$$\bar{\varepsilon} = \tfrac{3}{2}kT_e = \tfrac{1}{2}m\overline{v_r^2} \qquad \ldots\,(2.39)$$

Where $k$ is the Boltzmann constant, and $v_r$ the random velocity. The proper conversion factor is:

$$1 \text{ eV (mean energy)} = 7,733°\text{K} \qquad \ldots\,(2.40)$$

The 'electron temperature' is often loosely used to describe the mean energy of other energy distributions.

For the same mean energy the Maxwellian distribution contains an appreciably larger fraction of electrons at higher energies than the Druyvesteyn, and hence causes more ionization. It should be noted that while transport phenomena, i.e. diffusion and drift, depend on the mean energy, ionization and excitation depend upon the number of electrons in the high energy tail.

It has been found that the Maxwellian distribution is often a good approximation in molecular gases: this is because these gases have excitation levels (including vibrational levels) widely spread out up to ionization potential. Hence inelastic losses set in at relatively low energies; the average electron energy is low but the losses are so distributed as to produce an approximately Maxwellian distribution. In rare gases, however, the excitation levels are much closer to ionization potential, thus at low values of $X/p$ only elastic losses are important; the average energy is much higher than in molecular gases at the same value of $X/p$ and the Druyvesteyn distribution applies approximately. Due to the Townsend–Ramsauer effect ($\lambda_e$ not constant, but varying with electron energy) the distribution is even more deficient in high energy electrons than equation (2.37) would suggest.

### PROCESSES LEADING TO IONIZATION

*Ionization and Excitation by Electron Collision*

The number of ion pairs, $dn$, produced by a cloud of $n$ electrons moving with random velocities and drifting a distance $dx$ in the direction of a uniform field, $X$, is described by Townsend's coefficient, $\alpha$, where

$$dn = n\alpha\,dx \qquad \ldots.(2.41)$$

If $n_0$ electrons cross the plane, $x = 0$ and, due to multiplication in the gas, $n$ electrons cross a plane at $x = d$, integration gives

$$\frac{n}{n_0} = \left(\frac{i}{i_0}\right) = e^{\alpha d} \qquad \ldots.(2.42)$$

If parallel plates are placed at $x = 0$ and $x = d$, $i_0$ represents the electron current due to the steady emission of $n_0$ electrons per second and $i$ the total current flowing between the plates when a uniform field, $X$, is applied. It must be emphasized that this is a steady-state equation, and applies only for low currents, where space charges do not distort the applied field.

Experimentally, an externally produced current $i_0$, e.g. photo-electric current, is released from the cathode plate. The current, $i$, flowing between these plates is found to vary with distance in accordance with equation (2.42), and provided secondary effects at the cathode are avoided, $\alpha$ can be derived. $\alpha$ depends on the energy, $eXx$, which an electron picks up in an actual free path, $x$: assuming that all electrons having long enough free paths ($eXx > eV_i$) ionize, the number of ionizations follows from the distribution of free paths [equation (2.6)]. Hence

$$\frac{\alpha}{p} = Ae^{-B/(X/p)} = f\left(\frac{X}{p}\right) \qquad \ldots.(2.43)$$

The constants $A$, $B$, and the range over which the formula applies are given in *Table 2.3*, and measured values of $\alpha/p$ in *Figure 2.14*.

If the atomic ionization cross section, energy distribution function and drift velocity are accurately known, $\alpha$ can be calculated, since

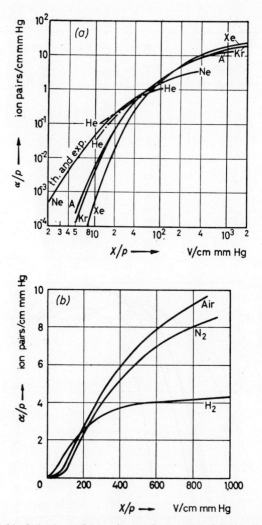

*Figure 2.14. Ionization coefficient, $\alpha/p$, as a function of the field per unit pressure $X/p$: (a) rare gases. In the helium curve the upper branch is experimental, the lower is theoretical (theory and experiment agree in neon); (b) molecular gases.*
(From A. von ENGEL[10], by courtesy of Springer)

43

the number of ionizing collisions made per second by the group $n \cdot f(\varepsilon)\mathrm{d}\varepsilon$ of electrons in the energy range $\varepsilon$, $\varepsilon + \mathrm{d}\varepsilon$ is

$$n \cdot f(\varepsilon)\mathrm{d}\varepsilon \cdot Q_i(\varepsilon) \cdot v_r \qquad \dots(2.44)$$

*Table 2.3.* Constants $A$ and $B$ in equation (2.43).
(From A. VON ENGEL[10], by courtesy of Springer)

| Gas | $A$ | $B$ | Range of validity | $V_i$ |
|---|---|---|---|---|
| | ion pairs | V | $X/p$ | V |
| | $\overline{\text{cm} \times \text{mm Hg}}$ | $\overline{\text{cm} \times \text{mm Hg}}$ | $\overline{\text{cm} \times \text{mm Hg}}$ | |
| $H_2$ | 5 | 139 | 22–1,000 | 15·4 |
| $N_2$ | 12 | 342 | 100– 600 | 15·5 |
| $O_2$ | — | — | — | 12·2 |
| $CO_2$ | 20 | 466 | 500–1,000 | 13·7 |
| Air | 15 | 365 | 100– 800 | — |
| $H_2O$ | 13 | 290 | 150–1,000 | 12·6 |
| HCl | 25 | 380 | 200–1,000 | — |
| He | 3 | 34 (25) | 20– 150 (3–10) | 24·5 |
| Ne | 4 | 100 | 100– 400 | 21·5 |
| A | 14 | 180 | 100– 600 | 15·7 |
| Kr | 17 | 240 | 100–1,000 | 14 |
| Xe | 26 | 350 | 200– 800 | 12·1 |
| Hg | 20 | 370 | 200– 600 | 10·4 |

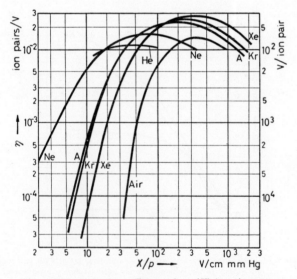

*Figure 2.15. Ionization coefficient $\eta$ ($= \alpha/X$) in various gases.*
(From A. VON ENGEL[10], by courtesy of Springer)

44

Hence

$$n\alpha\,\mathrm{d}x = \int_{\varepsilon_i}^{\infty} n\,.f(\varepsilon)\,.\,\mathrm{d}\varepsilon\,.\,Q_i(\varepsilon)v_r\,.\,\frac{\mathrm{d}x}{v_{\mathrm{drift}}} \qquad \ldots\,(2.45)$$

Many calculations of this kind have been made, with only partial

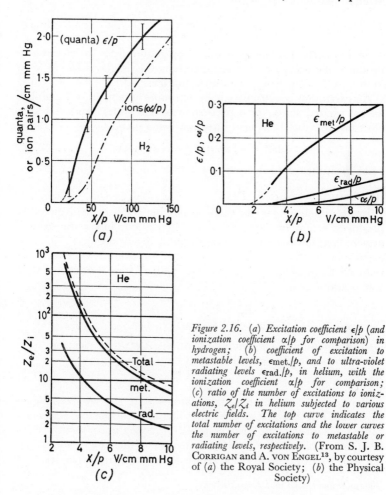

Figure 2.16. (a) Excitation coefficient $\epsilon/p$ (and ionization coefficient $\alpha/p$ for comparison) in hydrogen; (b) coefficient of excitation to metastable levels, $\epsilon_{\mathrm{met.}}/p$, and to ultra-violet radiating levels $\epsilon_{\mathrm{rad.}}/p$, in helium, with the ionization coefficient $\alpha/p$ for comparison; (c) ratio of the number of excitations to ionizations, $Z_e/Z_i$ in helium subjected to various electric fields. The top curve indicates the total number of excitations and the lower curves the number of excitations to metastable or radiating levels, respectively. (From S. J. B. CORRIGAN and A. VON ENGEL[13], by courtesy of (a) the Royal Society; (b) the Physical Society)

success, since an accurate result depends critically on the choice of the proper energy distribution.

Sometimes it is convenient to describe ionization in an electric

45

field by the coefficient, $\eta$, the number of ion pairs produced by an electron moving through a potential difference of 1 volt. Then

$$\eta = \frac{\alpha}{X} = \frac{\alpha d}{V} \qquad \ldots\ldots(2.46)$$

So that

$$\frac{n}{n_0} = e^{\eta V} \qquad \ldots\ldots(2.47)$$

Thus $1/\eta$ is the average potential drop required for an electron to produce one ion pair; for fast electrons this is about 30–40 V in most gases. Values of $\eta$ are shown in *Figure 2.15*.

An excitation coefficient, $\epsilon$, can be similarly defined, the number $dn^\star$ of excited states (or a particular excited state) produced by $n$ electrons moving $dx$ in field direction being given by

$$dn^\star = \epsilon \,.\, n \,.\, dx = \epsilon \,.\, n_0 e^{\alpha x} \,.\, dx \qquad \ldots\ldots(2.48)$$

$\epsilon$ has been measured in hydrogen and helium (see *Figure 2.16*).

*Attachment\**

In an attaching gas, an electron moving 1 cm in field direction produces $\alpha$ new electrons by direct ionization, but a number, $a$, attach themselves to molecules, forming heavy negative ions and consequently do not contribute to further ionization. $\alpha$ is effectively reduced to $(\alpha - a)$; the $n$ electrons and $n^-$ ions formed between $x = 0$ and $d$ give:

$$\frac{i}{i_0} = \frac{n + n^-}{n_0} = \frac{1}{\alpha - a} \,.\, \{\alpha e^{(\alpha - a)\,.\,d} - a\} \qquad \ldots\ldots(2.49)$$

$a/p$ is a function of $X/p$, often large at low $X/p$ where electrons have small average energies, and small at large $X/p$.

*Penning Effect*

The production of metastable atoms is a special example of excitation but, because of their long lifetimes, metastable states can cause ionization in the gas if suitable impurities are present. It has been shown that this effect is equivalent to an increase in $\alpha$ and does not lead to an instability characteristic of secondary processes.

*Thermal Ionization and Excitation*

At high gas temperatures (several thousand degrees) many molecules in the tail of the Maxwellian energy distribution are fast

---

\* This is, of course, a process of redistribution of charge; it is considered here in order to illustrate its effect on the growth of current.

enough to excite and ionize other gas molecules. The number of ionizations and excitations per second could, in principle, be calculated from the collision frequency, cross section for the process and the energy distribution. It is simpler to regard the processes as chemical reactions and deduce the equilibrium concentrations.

1 mole neutral gas $+ eV_i \rightleftharpoons 1$ mole ions $+ 1$ mole electrons

or $\left.\rule{0pt}{40pt}\right\}$ (2.50)

1 mole neutral gas $+ eV^\star \rightleftharpoons 1$ mole excited molecules

Now if $p_{\text{gas, ions, electrons}} = kT \cdot n_{\text{gas, ions, electrons}}$ are the partial pressures of the components, application of the law of mass action and Nernst's heat theorem leads to the degree of ionization $\dfrac{n_e}{n_0} (= x)$, given by

$$\frac{x^2}{1-x^2} \cdot p = 2 \cdot 4 \times 10^{-4} T^{5/2} e^{-eV_i/kT} \qquad \ldots (2.51)$$

where $n_0$ is the concentration of gas molecules initially present, $p$ is the actual gas pressure in mm Hg at the temperature $T^\circ$K.

The degree of excitation is

$$\frac{n^\star}{n_0} = \frac{g^\star}{g_0} e^{-eV^\star/kT} \qquad \ldots (2.52)$$

where $g^\star$, $g_0$ are the statistical weights of the particular excited state and the ground state respectively ($g = 2J + 1$). It must be emphasized that these equations apply only in equilibrium conditions.

*Ionization due to Shock Waves*

In a shock tube, a region of gas at high pressure is separated from gas at low pressure by a thin diaphragm, which when punctured allows the compressed gas to rush, at high speed, into the rarer regions. A plane separating the low- and high-pressure regions (the shock front) advances with a speed considerably greater than the speed of sound; its velocity of propagation is usually described by the Mach number, i.e. the ratio of its velocity to that of sound in the undisturbed gas. There is a discontinuous change of pressure and density across the shock front; the zone of gas immediately behind the shock front is called the shock wave, and is a region of high gas density, pressure and temperature. Close to the shock front gas molecules have large directed velocities (in strong shocks

47

approximately equal to the random thermal velocity), but in the shock wave, some distance behind the front, thermal equilibrium is established at a high temperature: for example a shock front moving at Mach 18 in argon produces an equilibrium gas temperature of 14,000°K (argon initially at room temperature $p = 10$ mm Hg). A high degree of ionization is also present in the shock wave (in the above example the degree of ionization is about 25 per cent, i.e. $n_e = \frac{1}{4}n_{gas}$), and the gas is highly excited, the spectrum showing both excitation lines and a continuum due to recombination of ions and electrons.

The process of ionization is not completely understood, although a careful study has been made in argon by PETSCHEK and BYRON[6], and by KANTROWITZ and his colleagues[7-9] (argon was chosen as a suitable monatomic gas, so that dissociation is absent). About $\frac{1}{10}$ of the final equilibrium ionization is initially produced in the regions very close behind the shock front, and its subsequent growth is thought to occur in the following way: electrons produced with low energies by the initial ionization collide elastically with the hot gas atoms and gain sufficient average energy, so that the faster ones excite and ionize the atoms. The growth of ionization and emitted light are entirely consistent with the rates calculated for this process, but the initial ionization which produces the electrons cannot yet be satisfactorily accounted for. Collisions between neutral atoms, which one would naturally expect to produce ionization in these circumstances, appear to give an insufficiently fast initial rate of production. At high gas pressure, luminosity is first observed close to the walls, and it is possible that wall processes may be responsible for much initial ionization. Clearly, further study of this problem is needed.

### Secondary Effects

A secondary effect can arise if the ionization by electrons in the region $x$, $x + dx$ also creates some agency which produces more ionization nearer the cathode. This secondary ionization is further multiplied as the electrons move forward towards $x$, so that the total current is enhanced and grows faster than exponentially with distance. Examples of secondary processes are:

(*i*) Ionization of gas molecules by positive ions; it is supposed that each ion moving a distance, $dx$, in the direction of the field produces $\beta \cdot dx$ ion pairs. This process is of importance only at very low pressure (long free paths) and high fields, e.g. canal ray discharges.

(*ii*) Emission of electrons from the cathode by the incidence of ions $(\gamma_i)$ photons $(\gamma_p)$ or fast neutral atoms produced, say, by charge transfer $(\gamma_n)$. At low $X/p$ and low average electron energies the photo-electric effect is largely dominant, because there are many more exciting than ionizing collisions; at high $X/p$ and higher average electron energies, ionizing collisions and consequently $\gamma_i$ predominate (see *Figure 2.17*).

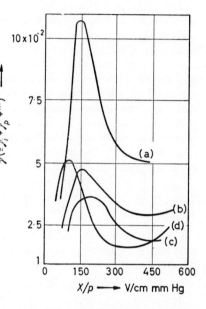

*Figure 2.17. The total secondary emission coefficient, $\gamma$, in pure $H_2$, from cathodes of: aluminium (curve a); nickel (curve b); thin film of nickel on aluminium (curve c); thicker film of nickel on aluminium (curve d). (From F. LLEWELLYN JONES and D. E. DAVIES[14], by courtesy of the Physical Society)*

If $\gamma$ represents, generally, the number of secondary electrons released from the cathode by one of these processes, then, for each ion pair produced in the gas, it can easily be shown that

$$\frac{i}{i_0} = \frac{e^{\alpha d}}{1 - \gamma(e^{\alpha d} - 1)} \qquad \ldots\ldots(2.53)$$

If several of these cathode mechanisms operate

$$\gamma = \gamma_i + \gamma_n + \bar{\gamma}_p + \ldots \qquad \ldots\ldots(2.54)$$

($\bar{\gamma}_p$, the effective value, $= f \cdot z \cdot \gamma_p$, where $z$ is the ratio of photons to ions produced in the gas, $f$ the fraction of those which strike the cathode and $\gamma_p$ the true photo-electric yield). Consideration of $\beta$ leads to an equation of exactly similar form.

Clearly if the values of the field, electrode distance and $\gamma$ are such that the denominator becomes zero, $i$ will be finite when $i_0$ is zero, i.e. when the externally produced current is removed. We then have a self-sustained current, and this is taken as the definition of 'breakdown'. Equation (2.53) does not, of course, describe what happens when the current grows to large values and space charges set in, but it has been found to predict correctly the onset of breakdown of gases in uniform electric fields over a wide range of values of $X/p$ up to the order of 1,000 V/cm mm Hg.

The Penning effect is, in this context, a secondary process but does not lead to an equation of the same form as equation (2.53) and hence cannot cause breakdown. Photo-ionization may, or may not, lead to breakdown; if photons are heavily absorbed in the gas, they produce ion pairs very close to the original ionization and the effect is merely an increase in $\alpha$, but if the absorption is too small the photons will either escape from the space or reach the cathode. Thus photo-ionization is an important secondary process only in certain gases, or mixtures, at certain values of field and pressure, particularly where the latter is high. Different secondary processes can be distinguished by measuring the rate of growth of current with time[12, 13].

PROCESS OF DE-IONIZATION

*Recombination*

Consider a region containing a density $n^+$ positive particles per cm³ and $n^-$ negative. The rate of disappearance of both types of particle per unit volume is described by

$$\frac{dn^+}{dt} = \frac{dn^-}{dt} = - Rn^+n^- \qquad \ldots (2.55)$$

where $R$ is the recombination coefficient. If, as is usual, $n^+ = n^-$, this reduces to $dn/dt = - Rn^2$. There are many complicated recombination processes, and detailed reviews must be referred to. The coefficient depends on the type of particles recombining, the age and size of the ions (whether they form clusters of gas molecules around them) and the proximity of other bodies (neutral atoms or walls). Distinguishing briefly between ion–ion recombination (coefficient $R_i$, both particles of molecular mass and size), and electron–ion recombination (coefficient $R_e$), the relative velocity of ions at low pressures is too large for recombination to be a probable event unless, by collision with a third body, one of them is sufficiently slowed down; the coefficient then increases as the density of gas molecules increases. At high pressure ($p > 1$ atmosphere), on the other hand, ions are mutually attracted by their electrostatic field and are brought together by their drift velocity in this field, which varies inversely with the pressure. Thus $R_i$ has a maximum, which for most gases lies at about atmospheric pressure, and has the value approximately $10^{-6}$ cm³/sec.

Electron–ion recombination coefficients are, in most circumstances, several orders of magnitude lower than ion–ion coefficients, as would be expected since the electrons, even at very low energy, are much faster than ions. Free electrons can fall into an atomic level with the emission of radiation (radiative recombination); theoretically $R_e$ is about $10^{-13}$ cm³/sec for this process. Electrons recombining with molecular ions (even in the rare gases, e.g. $He_2^+$) can lead to dissociation (dissociative recombination); this process has a much larger coefficient. Measured values of the general coefficient, including all the various processes, lie between $10^{-8}$ and $10^{-10}$ cm³/sec. (Recent microwave measurements giving appreciably larger values in $H_2$ have proved to be wrong—see Chapter 4.)

*Drift, Conductivity*

A cloud of electrons moving through a gas in random directions, with a wide distribution of velocities, and subjected to an electric field, $X$, has, superimposed upon this random motion, a slow drift of the centre of the cloud in the direction of the field. The average drift velocity can be derived to a first approximation by calculating the momentum, in field direction, gained by an electron moving along a free path, and assuming that the entire momentum is destroyed in a collision. Averaging over all lengths and directions of free paths gives

$$v_{\text{drift}} = C \cdot \frac{e\lambda_e \cdot X}{mv_r} \propto \frac{X}{p} \qquad \ldots\ldots(2.56)$$

or

$$b_e = C \frac{e\lambda_e}{mv_r} \qquad \ldots\ldots(2.57)$$

where $C$ is a numerical constant between $\frac{2}{3}$ and 1, depending on the method of averaging and whether the motion of the gas molecules is considered, $b_e$ is the electron mobility and is usually quoted for a gas at a pressure of 1 mm Hg. This applies only for moderate values of $X/p$; at higher values, $v_{\text{drift}} \propto \sqrt{X/p}$ is a better fit with the experimental values. Typical values of drift velocity are about $10^7$ cm/sec in $O_2$, $H_2$, $N_2$, for $X/p \sim 25\cdot4 \times 10^6$ cm/sec in He, Ne at $X/p \sim 4$ V/cm mm Hg (see *Figure 2.18*).

In an exact derivation of the drift velocity an accurate knowledge of the electron energy distribution, and also of any variation of $\lambda_e$ with energy, is required.

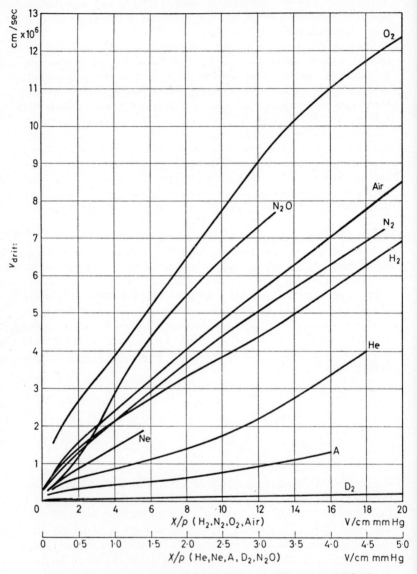

*Figure 2.18. The drift velocity of electrons in gases at different values of electric field. (Note that the curves for* $H_2$ *and* $D_2$ *refer to different ranges of* $X/p$*). (By courtesy of Massachusetts Institute of Technology and John Wiley and Sons, Inc.)*

Attempts to derive a simple expression for the mobility of ions by the same method gave results differing widely from experiment; the reason is that an ion, being relatively slow, stays in the vicinity of gas molecules long enough to polarize them. The resultant attractive force not only shortens the free path of the ion, but also causes a continuous exchange of momentum, and this appreciably reduces the drift velocity. Furthermore, the size of the ion (clustering) and charge transfer play important roles, the latter especially when ions move in their own gas. Here again the idea of an ion mobility, i.e.

$$v_{\text{drift}} = b^+ X \propto \frac{X}{p}$$

is valid only for small values of $X/p$; at larger values, in molecular gases $v^+_{\text{drift}} \propto \sqrt{X/p}$, but there is no general rule. The temperature of the gas also affects $b^+$, and data on the drift of ions in their own gases have been tabulated by VON ENGEL[10].

The drift of electrons in the field is responsible for the electrical conductivity ($\sigma$) of the gas, since it is the electrons which carry the current. The contribution of positive ions can generally be ignored because of their small drift speed. The current density, $j$, is given by

$$j = \sigma X \qquad \qquad \dots\,(2.58)$$

and also

$$j = nev_{\text{drift}} = C \cdot \frac{ne^2 \lambda_e}{mv_r} \cdot X \qquad \dots\,(2.59)$$

hence

$$\sigma = C \cdot \frac{ne^2 \lambda_e}{mv_r} = C \cdot \frac{ne^2}{mv} \qquad \dots\,(2.60)$$

where $v$ is the frequency with which electrons hit gas molecules. As would be expected intuitively, the conductivity increases with the concentration of electrons, and decreases with increase of gas pressure, i.e. with increase in the number of obstacles (since $\lambda_e = 1/\sigma \cdot n_{\text{gas}}$, $\sigma$ here being the cross section of a gas molecule).

This is true only provided that changes in $n$ do not change the gas density, i.e. provided the degree of ionization is small. In the limit of a fully ionized gas (no neutral gas molecules) the number of electrons is always equal to the number of obstacles (ions), and the conductivity is consequently independent of $n$. Furthermore, the collisions between ions and electrons are governed only by long-range electrostatic forces and obey the Rutherford scattering formula, i.e. cross section $\sigma_{\text{ion}} \propto 1/v_r^4$, hence $\lambda_e \propto \dfrac{v_r^4}{n}$. Consequently

$$\sigma_{\text{fully ionized}} \propto v_r^3, \text{ i.e. } \propto T_e^{3/2} \text{ (independent of } n) \quad \ldots (2.61)$$

The constant of proportionality cannot be extrapolated from this simple theory, but requires rigorous calculation. An experimental test of this variation of conductivity with degree of ionization has recently been made[17].

*Diffusion*

Particles in the gaseous form, moving about at random are continually colliding and exchanging momentum. If the density, $n$ (number of particles per unit volume) is not uniform, the larger number of particles in the regions of high concentration will transfer more momentum in the direction of regions of lower concentration than will be transferred in the reverse direction. There results a net force on the particles driving them towards the places of low concentration, and a consequent flow of $j$ particles per second across unit area, described by

$$j (= nv) = - D \text{ grad } n \qquad \ldots (2.62)$$

where $D$ is the diffusion coefficient. The particles flow as though they had a directed velocity $v$—the 'diffusion velocity'.

By well-known kinetic theory methods it may be derived that for ions moving in their own gas

$$D^+ = \tfrac{1}{3}\lambda_i v_r^+ \qquad \ldots (2.63)$$

and similarly for electrons

$$D_e = \tfrac{1}{3}\lambda_e v_r \qquad \ldots (2.64)$$

By virtue of their much smaller mass and consequent larger random velocity, electrons have diffusion coefficient orders of magnitude larger than ions. Equations (2.63) and (2.64) are, of course, only approximate; they show $D \propto \lambda$, and hence suggest $Dp$ should be constant. However, like the expressions for mobility they are sensitive to the energy distributions of the particles and variations of $\lambda$ with $v_r$.

It should be noted that equation (2.62) applies provided the density gradient is the only factor causing the flow of particles. If, in addition, the energy of the particles varies in space, the flow is given by $j = - \text{grad } (Dn)$ of which equation (2.62) is a special example.

Several well-known results of diffusion theory are:

(*a*) The mean square displacement, $\bar{x}^2$ or $\bar{r}^2$, of a particle from its original position in time, $t$ sec, is $2Dt$ cm² if diffusion is in one direction only (lateral), $4Dt$ if in two (cylindrical) and $6Dt$ if in three directions (spherical).

(b) If $\mathcal{N}$ particles start at $t = 0$ from an origin the density of particles ($n$ per cm³) at a distance, $r$, at time, $t$, is (for spherical diffusion)

$$n = \frac{\mathcal{N}}{(4\pi Dt)^{\frac{3}{2}}} \cdot e^{-r^2/4Dt} \qquad \dots (2.65)$$

(c) If, in addition to the concentration gradient, an electric field exerts a force on the particles, the drift and diffusive motions can be treated independently provided that the drift velocity is small compared with the random velocity, i.e. the electric field is not too large. Thus the distribution of particles in space corresponds to simple diffusion [equation (2.65)] with the centre of the cloud moving with the drift velocity.

(d) If the flow of charged particles of density $n$ per cm³ by diffusion is compared with an opposing drift velocity in an electric field, it may be shown that

$$\frac{b}{D} = \frac{en}{p} = \frac{e}{kT} \qquad \dots (2.66)$$

where $p$, $T$ are the pressure and temperature of the electron or ion gas ($p = nkT$ dynes/cm²). If $e$ is in e.s.u.'s the mobility, $b$, must be quoted in cm/sec e.s.u. of field. This formula applies only in the range where $v_{\text{drift}}$ is proportional to $X$, i.e. constant mobility, and, since a 'temperature' has been included, strictly applies only for Maxwellian distributions; it is more correctly applied to ions than electrons. Experimental values of $D$ are usually derived from equation (2.66) and measured values of mobility.

## Ambipolar Diffusion

In a mixture of nearly equal concentrations of electrons and ions the electrons diffuse rapidly away leaving a positive space charge. An electrostatic field, $X_s$, is set up which retards the electrons and accelerates the ions so that both diffuse at the same rate, described by the ambipolar diffusion coefficient $D_a$. The flow (particle current density) of both kinds of particles is the same, thus

$$j = - D_a \frac{dn}{dx} = - D^+ \frac{dn}{dx} + v_{\text{drift}}^+ = - D_e \frac{dn}{dx} - (v^e)_{\text{drift}} \qquad \dots (2.67)$$

Hence

$$D_a = \frac{D^+ v_{\text{drift}}^e + D_e v_{\text{drift}}^+}{v_{\text{drift}}^e + v_{\text{drift}}^+} \qquad \dots (2.68)$$

$$= \frac{D^+b_e + D_e b^+}{b_e + b^+} \qquad \text{for small } X \atop \text{(constant mobility)} \qquad \ldots\ldots (2.69)$$

$$\approx \frac{kT_e}{e} \cdot b^+ \qquad \text{provided } T_e \gg T_{\text{ions}} \atop \text{and } b_e \gg b^+ \qquad \ldots\ldots (2.70)$$

$$\text{or} \qquad \approx 2 \frac{kT}{e} \cdot b^+ = 2D^+ \qquad \text{when } T_e = T_{\text{ions}} \qquad \ldots\ldots (2.71)$$

These formulae apply only when the concentrations are so large that a sufficiently strong electric field can be created by small movements of charge at any point $(n^+ - n_e) \ll n^+$ or $n_e$; another way of expressing it is that the Debye length of the system, the range outside which the effect of a central charge is effectively annulled by surrounding opposite charges, shall be small compared with the extent of the ionized region. At low charge densities ambipolar diffusion slowly changes into free electron diffusion over several orders of magnitude of $n_a$.

Formulae similar to equations (2.67)–(2.71) can be derived for the ambipolar diffusion of more than two types of particle (e.g. positive and negative ions plus electrons, also ions of different masses and charges)[16]. For recent microwave measurements of $D_a$ see Chapter 4.

When charges of only one sign are present, an outward flow arises from mutual repulsion as well as from diffusion. Electrostatic repulsion is the controlling influence at high concentrations[11].

## A Plasma

Ionization results in separation of charge, not creation of new charges, and electrostatic attraction limits the amount of separation possible. Most regions of ionized gas are electrically nearly neutral; such a region in which $n^+ \approx n^- \gg | n^+ - n^- |$ is called a plasma, whether neutral gas is present or not.

### REFERENCES

[1] TOWNSEND, J. S., *Electricity in Gases*; Oxford: Clarendon Press, 1915

[2] RAMSAUER, C. and KOLLATH, R., *Ann. Phys.*, **3** (1929) 536 (and earlier papers); see also summary by KOLLATH, R., *Phys. Z.*, **31** (1930) 985

[3] MASSEY, H. S. W. and BURHOP, E. H. S., *Electronic and Ionic Impact Phenomena*; Oxford: Clarendon Press, 1952

[4] LITTLE, P. F. in *Handbuch der Physik*, Vol. 21; Heidelberg: Springer, 1956

[5] ALLIS, W. P. in *Handbuch der Physik*, Vol. 21; Heidelberg: Springer, 1956

[6] PETSCHEK, H. and BYRON, S., *Ann. Phys.*, **1** (1957) 270

[7] RESLER, E., LIN, S. C. and KANTROWITZ, A. R., *J. appl. Phys.*, **23** (1952) 1390

[8] PETSCHEK, H., ROSE, P. H., GLICK, H., KANE, A. and KANTROWITZ, A. R., *ibid.*, **26** (1955) 83

[9] LIN, S. C., RESLER, E. and KANTROWITZ, A. R., *ibid.*, **26** (1955) 95

[10] VON ENGEL, A. in *Handbuch der Physik*, Vol. 21; Heidelberg: Springer, 1956

[11] VON ENGEL, A., *Ionized Gases*; Oxford: Clarendon Press, 1956

[12] BRUINING, H., *Physics and Applications of Secondary Electron Emission*; London: Pergamon Press, 1954

[13] CORRIGAN, S. J. B. and VON ENGEL, A., *Proc. roy. Soc.*, **A245** (1958) 335; *Proc. phys. Soc. Lond.*, **72** (1958) 786 (excitation coefficients)

[14] LLEWELLYN JONES, F. and DAVIES, D. E., *ibid.*, **B64** (1951) 519

[15] LLEWELLYN JONES, F., *Ionization and Breakdown in Gases*; London: Methuen, 1957; see also *Handbuch der Physik*, Vol. 22; Heidelberg: Springer, 1956

[16] LOEB, L. B., *Phys. Rev.*, **113** (1959) 7

[17] SAKUNTALA, M., VON ENGEL, A. and FOWLER, R. G., *ibid.*, **114** (1959) in the press

[18] BARNETT, C. F. and STIER, P. M., *ibid.*, **109** (1958) 385

[19] OSKAM, H. J., *Thesis*, Utrecht, 1957; *Philips Res. Rep.*, **13** (1958) 335, 401; see also HOYAUX, M., *Rev. Gen. Elect.*, **60** (1951) 270, 317; ALLIS, W. P. and ROSE, D. J., *Phys. Rev.*, **93** (1954) 84 (general treatments)

[20] WILSON, C. T. R., *Proc. Camb. Phil. Soc.*, **42** (1925) 534

[21] GIOVANELLI, R. G., *Phil. Mag.*, **40** (1949) 206

[22] GIBSON, A., *Proceedings of the Third International Conference on Ionization Phenomena in Gases*, Venice, 1957

[23] DREICER, H., *ibid*; see also *Proceedings of the Second United Nations Conference on the Peaceful Uses of Atomic Energy*, Geneva, 1958, Vol. 31, p. 57

[24] HARRISON, E. H., *Phil. Mag.*, **3** (1958) 1318

[25] GIBSON, A., *Nature, Lond.*, **183** (1959) 101 (ion runaways)

[26] GEORGE, K. A., *ibid.*, **182** (1958) 745 (ion runaways)

Recent special references on fundamental processes are listed in Appendix VI. References before 1956 can be found in books and articles listed in the bibliography below.

## BIBLIOGRAPHY

The processes summarized briefly in this chapter are fully described in Volumes 21 and 22 of *Handbuch der Physik*; Heidelberg: Springer, 1956. See also special references 1, 3, 11 and 12.

THOMSON, J. J., *Conduction of Electricity through Gases*, 2nd edn.; London: Cambridge University Press, 1906

THOMSON, J. J. and THOMSON, G. P., *Conduction of Electricity through Gases*, 3rd edn., Vols. I and II; London: Cambridge University Press, 1936

LAPORTE, M., *Les Phénoménes Élémentaires de la Décharge Électrique dans les Gaz*; Paris, 1933

VON ENGEL, A. H. and STEENBECK, M., *Elektrische Gasentladungen*; Berlin: Springer, Vol. I, 1932, Vol. II, 1934

TYNDALL, A. M., *Mobility of Positive Ions*; London: Cambridge University Press, 1938

LOEB, L. B., *Fundamental Processes of Electrical Discharge in Gases*; New York: John Wiley, 1939

HEALEY, R. and REED, J. W., *Behaviour of Slow Electrons in Gases*; Sydney: Amalgamated Wireless, 1941

COBINE, J. D., *Gaseous Conductors*; New York: McGraw-Hill, 1941

TOWNSEND, J. S., *Electrons in Gases*; London: Hutchinson, 1947

COURANT, R. and FRIEDRICHS, K. O., *Supersonic Flow and Shock Waves*; New York: Interscience, 1948

MOTT, N. F. and MASSEY, H. S. W., *Theory of Atomic Collisions*; Oxford: Clarendon Press, 1949

MASSEY, H. S. W., *Negative Ions*; London: Cambridge University Press, 1950

MEEK, J. M. and J. D. CRAGGS, *Electrical Breakdown of Gases*; Oxford: Clarendon Press, 1953

LOEB, L. B., *Basic Processes of Gaseous Electronics*; California: The University Press, 1955

FIELD, F. H. and FRANKLIN, J. L., *Electron Impact Phenomena and the Properties of Gaseous Ions*; New York: Academic Press, 1957

DELCROIX, J. L., *Théorie des Gaz Ionisés*; Paris: Dunod, 1959

# 3

# THE SIMILARITY PRINCIPLE*

THE PURPOSE OF SIMILARITY RELATIONS

ANY chosen property of a discharge, for example the potential $V$, depends on a number of others, the current, gas pressure, size of the vessel and electrodes. The dependence is often complicated, and sometimes cannot be expressed analytically at all but only in the form of curves, whether theoretical or experimental, linking various parameters. Clearly, it would require an infinite number of such curves to describe all possible states of the discharge given by every combination of dimensions, $i$, $p$, etc., and therefore some simplification may be found by grouping together these parameters. For example, the starting potential $V_s$ of a gas between plane parallel electrodes depends both on their distance, $d$, apart, and on the pressure, $p$. It is found experimentally that $V_s$ does not change if the product $pd$ is kept constant (except at the highest pressure), i.e. $V_s = f(pd)$. $pd$ is thus one of the combinations sought, because for the purpose of discussing breakdown it describes completely the behaviour of the gas. Any particular $V_s = f(pd)$ refers, of course, only to one combination of gas and electrode material. The importance of such grouping was first realized by DE LA RUE and MÜLLER[1], and later by PASCHEN[2], TOWNSEND[3] and others who noted that $X\lambda$ represents the energy gained by an electron moving along a free path $\lambda$, and $pd$ is proportional to the total number of molecules between two electrodes of given size. If $X\lambda$ (or $X/p$) and $pd$ are kept constant the multiplication of electrons across the gap is thus fixed. These groups of parameters and others, can be deduced more generally as shown below, partly following the treatments of HOLM[4], VON ENGEL and STEENBECK[5], and DÄLLENBACH[6].

This is carried out by observing how the various parameters differ in two discharges in which the linear dimensions differ by a constant ratio, $a$. One obvious result is that a set of scaling laws can be derived, which enables a prediction to be made of the behaviour of a system which is inconveniently small or large for

* I am grateful to Messrs Springer (Heidelberg) for permitting me to use here much of the material published in a section of my article on the glow discharge, in *Handbuch der Physik*, Vol. 22 (1956).

experimental study, if the properties of a convenient, and geometrically similar, system are known. Such information is indispensable in the designing, for example, of large thermonuclear devices based on toroidal discharges. Of more physical significance is the fact that different atomic and statistical processes behave in different ways; in particular, those which depend upon the parameter $X/p$ preserve the similarity in every respect of geometrically similar discharges, whilst others destroy it. In this way, by measuring the properties of geometrically similar discharges it may often be inferred which fundamental processes occur in the discharge.

### DERIVATION OF THE RELATIONS

*General*

The object of the treatment is to define two discharges identical in only one or two chosen properties and different in others, and to derive groups of parameters which are invariant and can therefore be used to describe those properties identical in both discharges.

Consider two discharges in the same gas with the same electrode material, in which all the corresponding linear dimensions are different by a factor, $a$ (see *Figure 3.1*). This includes the vessel,

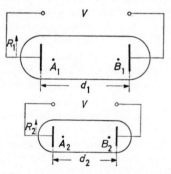

*Figure 3.1. Similar discharges*

electrodes and the properties of the gas, e.g. mean free path (but not the mean distance between molecules). Assume that the gas temperature is the same in both, and that corresponding points (e.g. $A_1$, $A_2$; $B_1$, $B_2$) have the same potential difference between them; the potential across the electrodes is $V$. Such discharges are called similar*.

---

* Sometimes it is defined that the currents also shall be the same at corresponding points in both discharges. This additional assumption can be partly avoided, and is discussed later. For this reason the presentation given here is somewhat different from the usual. Temperature changes can also be considered (p. 73).

Then the following relations hold for corresponding points in the two discharges:

For the linear dimensions of vessel and electrodes:

$$\left.\begin{array}{l} d_1 = ad_2 \\ r_1 = ar_2 \\ R_1 = aR_2 \end{array}\right\} \qquad \ldots\ldots(3.1)$$

where $r$ is any radially measured distance.

For elements of area:

$$dA_1 = a^2 dA_2 \qquad \ldots\ldots(3.1a)$$

For the mean free paths of electrons, ions or molecules in the gas:

$$\lambda_1 = a\lambda_2 \qquad \ldots\ldots(3.2)$$

Hence the gas density (number of molecules per cm³)

$$n_1 = \frac{n_2}{a} \qquad \ldots\ldots(3.3)$$

Since, by definition, the temperature* is the same in both, pressure $p$ is $\propto n$, hence for the pressure

$$p_1 = \frac{p_2}{a} \qquad \ldots\ldots(3.4)$$

The potential

$$V_1 = V_2, \qquad \text{by definition} \quad \ldots\ldots(3.5)$$

The electric field $X_x = -\dfrac{\partial V}{\partial x}$.

Hence

$$X_1 = \frac{X_2}{a} \qquad \ldots\ldots(3.6)$$

Surface and volume charge densities $\sigma$, $\rho_{\text{net}}$ can be derived from

$$\left.\begin{array}{l} X_{\text{surface}} = 4\pi\sigma \\ \dfrac{dX}{dx} = 4\pi(\rho^+ - \rho^-) \end{array}\right\} \qquad \ldots\ldots(3.7)$$

whence

$$\sigma_1 = \frac{\sigma_2}{a} \qquad \ldots\ldots(3.8)$$

---

* But see p. 73.

i.e.

$$(\rho_1^+ - \rho_1^-) = \frac{1}{a^2}(\rho_2^+ - \rho_2^-) \qquad \ldots(3.9)$$

from which

$$X_1\lambda_1 = X_2\lambda_2 \qquad \ldots(3.10)$$

$$\frac{X_1}{p_1} = \frac{X_2}{p_2} \qquad \ldots(3.11)$$

may be derived. Under certain circumstances the energy of the electrons and ions is determined by $X/p$ alone. Consider the average net gain in energy, $\delta\varepsilon$ of an electron in one free path: the electron gains energy from the electric field and loses a fraction, $\kappa$, of its total energy in collision, at the end of its path. Then

$$\delta\varepsilon = eX\lambda_e - \kappa\varepsilon \qquad \ldots(3.12)$$

In the steady state $\delta\varepsilon = 0$. If $\lambda_e$ and $\kappa$ are constants the solution is $\varepsilon = f(X\lambda_e)$, i.e. $= F(X/p)$. The same is true if $\kappa$ and $\lambda_e$ vary only with the energy corresponding respectively to inelastic collisions, and the Ramsauer effect. But suppose that electrons collide also with already excited atoms; the average energy lost in all collisions then depends both on $\varepsilon$ and on the relative concentration $N^*/n$ of excited atoms

$$\kappa = f\left(\varepsilon, \frac{N^*}{n}\right) \qquad \ldots(3.13)$$

To find $N^*/n$ equate the rates of production and loss of excited states. The production is due, supposedly, to direct collisions between electrons (concentration $N_e$) and gas molecules, giving

$$\left(\frac{dN^*}{dt}\right)_{\text{production}} \propto N_e \cdot n \qquad \ldots(3.14)$$

The rate of loss is given by

$$\left(\frac{dN^*}{dt}\right)_{\text{loss}} \propto N^* \qquad \ldots(3.15)$$

for molecules which simply radiate, or $\propto N^*n$ for metastable states destroyed by hitting gas molecules. This gives

$$\frac{N^*}{n} \propto N_e \quad \text{or} \quad \propto \frac{N_e}{n} \qquad \ldots(3.16)$$

Since $N_e$ is not normally dependent only upon $X/p$ but also upon the gas pressure it follows that when two-stage processes occur, the mean energy of the electrons is not defined simply by $X/p$.

This qualitative argument has been presented here firstly because it shows that the Ramsauer effect does not upset similarity relationships, and secondly because it shows that even if $X/p$ is the same in both discharges the velocities of the charged particles are equal only when two-stage processes are absent. This point is often ignored at this stage, although demonstrated later.

*Assuming Only Single-stage Processes*

Drift or random velocity is the same in both discharges:

$$v_1 = v_2 \qquad \qquad \text{....(3.17)}$$

and hence mean energy (which can be defined for any general energy distribution)

$$\varepsilon_1 = \varepsilon_2 \qquad \qquad \text{....(3.18)}$$

If the particles have Maxwellian distributions, the mean energy can be defined in terms of temperature, giving

$$(T_{e,\,+,\,-})_1 = (T_{e,\,+,\,-})_2 \qquad \qquad \text{....(3.19)}$$

for electron, positive and negative ion temperatures, respectively.

For processes involving time, the relation can be found from $v = \mathrm{d}x/\mathrm{d}t$, giving:

for time intervals

$$\mathrm{d}t_1 = a\,\mathrm{d}t_2 \qquad \qquad \text{....(3.20)}$$

for frequencies, e.g. any collision frequency

$$\nu_1 = \nu_2/a \qquad \qquad \text{....(3.21)}$$

Applied frequency of the field in a.c. discharges $f_1 = f_2/a$.

The relation between applied magnetic fields can be derived from the radius of curvature $(r')$ of the path of a moving charge. Since $Hev = \dfrac{mv^2}{r'}$, $H \propto v/r'$, hence for applied magnetic fields

$$H_1 = \frac{H_2}{a} \qquad \qquad \text{....(3.22)}$$

*Relations Involving Current*

Relations between the net space charge densities have already been found

$$(\rho^+ - \rho^-)_1 = \frac{1}{a^2}\,(\rho^+ - \rho^-)_2 \qquad \qquad \text{....(3.9)}$$

$\rho^-$ includes both electrons and negative ions.

It does not necessarily follow that $\rho^+$, $\rho^-$ are each separately $1/a^2$ times the corresponding densities in the second discharge, except in regions where there are charges of only one sign, i.e. either $\rho_1^+$, $\rho_2^+ = 0$ or $\rho_1^-$, $\rho_2^- = 0$. However, this proportionality cannot be assumed as a general law.

The general expression for the total current density is:

$$j = \rho^+ v^+ + \rho^- v^- = (\rho^+ - \rho^-)(v^+ - v^-) + \rho^- v^+ + \rho^+ v^- \ldots (3.23)$$

To find the relation between $j_1$ and $j_2$, use the second form of the above equation, adding the appropriate suffixes 1 and 2. Then, using equation (3.9) and assuming only single-stage processes so that $v_1 = v_2$ it can easily be seen that a simple proportionality between $j_1$ and $j_2$ can arise only when

$$\rho_1^- v_2^+ + \rho_1^+ v_2^- = \frac{1}{a^2}(\rho_2^- v_2^+ + \rho_2^+ v_2^-) \qquad \ldots (3.24)$$

which, together with equation (3.9), results in

$$\rho_1^+ = \frac{1}{a^2}\rho_2^+; \quad \rho_1^- = \frac{1}{a^2}\rho_2^- \qquad \ldots (3.25)$$

Particle and current densities are thus related by

$$\mathcal{N}_1^+ = \frac{1}{a^2}\mathcal{N}_2^+; \quad \mathcal{N}_1^- = \frac{1}{a^2}\mathcal{N}_2^- \qquad \ldots (3.26)$$

$$j_1 = \frac{1}{a^2}j_2 \qquad \ldots (3.27)$$

and, since areas transform by the factor $a^2$, total current is

$$i_1 = j_1\, dA_1 = \frac{1}{a^2} \cdot j_2 \cdot a^2 dA_2 = i_2 \qquad \ldots (3.28)$$

This equality of current in two discharges has been used by most writers as part of the definition of similar discharges, i.e. two discharges are defined as similar when the potential and current at corresponding points are equal, and all linear dimensions are different by a factor, $a$. The relations between current densities, charge densities and particle densities in the two systems follow very simply by using the above arguments in reverse order.

The first derivation, not assuming that the currents in the two discharges are equal, requires a little more complicated algebra, but it has the advantage of making fewer assumptions and proving that the only possible simple relation between $i_1$ and $i_2$ is their equality.

The relationship between the self-magnetic field generated by the flow of current in the two discharges can now be found. Consider a cylindrical element carrying a total current, $I$, in one discharge; a similar element (i.e. one differing in linear dimensions by a factor, $a$) in the second discharge also carries the same current, $I$. The magnetic field at similar distances, $r_1$, $r_2$, is:

$$(H_{\text{self}})_1 = \frac{2I_1}{r_1} = \frac{2I_2}{ar_2} = \frac{(H_{\text{self}})_2}{a} \qquad \ldots (3.29)$$

This is consistent with equation (3.22) for applied magnetic fields, and leads to curved paths whose radii of curvature are different in the two systems by a factor, $a$, which is, of course, consistent with the basic assumption of equation (3.1).

Now we assume that current and voltage are the same in both discharges and examine the processes which can occur. It is not possible to prove that certain processes will lead to concentrations of charged particles differing in the two discharges by the factor $1/a^2$, but it may be shown that some combinations of processes are consistent with the assumption of this $1/a^2$ relation, while other combinations are not. Such processes are distinguished as 'permitted' or 'forbidden'—terms purely of convenience, having nothing to do with what can happen physically.

### PERMITTED AND FORBIDDEN GAS PROCESSES

The concentration, $N$, of any type of charged particle at any point in a steady state discharge can be derived by equating the rates of production and loss at that point. Since $N_1$ must equal $(1/a^2)N_2$, and $dt_1 = a\, dt_2$ then

$$\left(\frac{dN}{dt}\right)_1 = \frac{1}{a^3}\left(\frac{dN}{dt}\right)_2 \qquad \ldots (3.30)$$

$dN/dt$ is the sum of the rates of production by a number of elementary processes, e.g.

$$\left(\frac{dN}{dt}\right)_{\text{total}} = \left(\frac{\partial N}{\partial t}\right)_{\text{electron collision}} + \left(\frac{\partial N}{\partial t}\right)_{\text{drift}} + \left(\frac{\partial N}{\partial t}\right)_{\text{diffusion}}$$

$$+ \left(\frac{\partial N}{\partial t}\right)_{\text{photo-ionization}} + \ldots \quad \ldots (3.31)$$

Each process, whether of gain or loss, must transform by the factor $1/a^3$ in order that equation (3.30) shall be satisfied. Considering the processes separately, we refer always to corresponding points or small volumes in the two discharges.

## Ionization by Single Collisions

The rate of ionization by single collisions of electrons with gas molecules depends on the concentration, $N_e$, of electrons and their energy, and on the concentration, $n$, of gas molecules. Assuming that the electron energy is the same in both discharges, the rate of production of ions and electrons is

$$\left(\frac{\partial N}{\partial t}\right)_1 = CN_{e_1}n_1 = C\frac{N_{e_2}}{a^2}\frac{n_2}{a} = \frac{1}{a^3}\left(\frac{\partial N}{\partial t}\right)_2 \quad \ldots(3.32)$$

The process is therefore permitted.

The constant $C$, and in the following equations $C_1$, $C_2$, ... merely indicate proportionality.

## Stepwise Ionization: Collisions of the Second Kind

Ionization by these processes can occur when the electron hits an already excited molecule, when two excited molecules collide, or when an excited (metastable) molecule of one gas hits and ionizes a neutral molecule of another (Penning effect). This last process can occur only when the excitation potential of the one gas exceeds the ionization potential of the other.

The equilibrium concentration $N^\star$ of excited molecules is given by equating rates of production and loss, assuming that electrons produce, by single collisions, excited states having an average life, $\tau$:

$$\left(\frac{\partial N^\star}{\partial t}\right)_{\text{production}} \propto N_e n \quad \ldots(3.33)$$

$$\left(\frac{\partial N^\star}{\partial t}\right)_{\text{loss}} \propto \frac{N^\star}{\tau} \quad \ldots(3.34)$$

Hence

$$\frac{N^\star}{\tau} \propto N_e n \quad \ldots(3.35)$$

For excited molecules which simply radiate within about $10^{-8}$ sec, and whose radiation is not absorbed in the gas, $\tau$ is much shorter than the time between collisions and is therefore a constant. This gives $N \propto N_e n$, i.e.

$$N_1^\star = \frac{1}{a^3}N_2^\star \quad \ldots(3.36)$$

For metastable atoms or molecules (concentration $N_m^\star$) destroyed by collision with gas molecules (their own gas or impurities) or on the walls $\tau \propto 1/n$ or $\tau \propto R$ hence

$$(N_m^\star)_1 = \frac{1}{a^2} (N_m^\star)_2 \qquad \ldots (3.37)$$

This is true provided that no metastables are produced by electrons falling from higher levels.

In conditions where resonance radiation is appreciably absorbed and re-emitted in travelling through the gas the rate of production of resonance states $(N_r^\star)$ in any given volume is determined by the net flow of resonance photons through this volume, as well as by equation (3.33). These photons come from other parts of the discharge, and the net flow in any one direction (e.g. $x$) is proportional to $\dfrac{\partial}{\partial x} \left( \dfrac{N_r^\star}{\tau} \right)$. Hence for resonance states:

$$\frac{N_r^\star}{\tau} \propto N_e n + \text{const.} \frac{\partial}{\partial x} \left( \frac{N_r^\star}{\tau} \right) \qquad \ldots (3.38)$$

and taking $\tau = \text{constant}$

$$N_r^\star \propto N_e n + \text{const.} \frac{\partial N_r^\star}{\partial x} \qquad \ldots (3.39)$$

From this, it follows that $N_r^\star$ does not transform with any simple factor of $a$, in particular

$$(N_r^\star)_1 \neq \frac{1}{a^2} (N_r^\star)_2 \qquad \ldots (3.40)$$

The rate of ionization caused by electrons hitting these excited molecules is proportional to the concentrations of both. Equations (3.36), (3.37) and (3.40) are used to derive the following. For ionization by:

Electrons—excited molecules
$$\left( \frac{\partial N}{\partial t} \right)_1 = C_1 N_e N_1^\star = \frac{1}{a^5} \left( \frac{\partial N}{\partial t} \right)_2$$

Electrons—metastable molecules
$$\left( \frac{\partial N}{\partial t} \right)_1 = C_2 N_e (N_m^\star)_1 = \frac{1}{a^4} \left( \frac{\partial N}{\partial t} \right)_2$$

Electrons—resonance states
$$\left( \frac{\partial N}{\partial t} \right)_1 = C_3 N_e (N_r^\star)_1 \neq \frac{1}{a^3} \left( \frac{\partial N}{\partial t} \right)_3$$

$$\ldots (3.41)$$

All these processes are therefore forbidden. The rate of ionization by the collision of two excited molecules is proportional to the concentrations of both:

Two excited molecules:

$$\left(\frac{\partial \mathcal{N}}{\partial t}\right)_1 = C_4 \mathcal{N}_A^{\star} \mathcal{N}_B^{\star} \neq \frac{1}{a^3}\left(\frac{\partial \mathcal{N}}{\partial t}\right)_2 \qquad \ldots (3.42)$$

where $\mathcal{N}_A^{\star} \ \mathcal{N}_B^{\star}$ is any combination of $\mathcal{N}^{\star}$, $\mathcal{N}_m^{\star}$, $\mathcal{N}_r^{\star}$, hence all possible processes of this kind are forbidden. Ionization by the Penning effect in two gases $X$, $Y$ ($Y$ having $V_i < V_{\mathrm{exc.}}$ of $X$) gives:

Metastable $X$—neutral $Y$:

$$\left(\frac{\partial \mathcal{N}}{\partial t}\right)_1 = C_5 \cdot (\mathcal{N}_m^{\star})_X n_Y = \frac{1}{a^3}\left(\frac{\partial \mathcal{N}}{\partial t}\right)_2 \qquad \ldots (3.43)$$

This is a permitted process, assuming that the ratio $n_X/n_Y$ is the same in both systems, $n_X$ being the density of unexcited atoms, type $X$.

*Electron Attachment and Detachment*

Electrons attach to neutral molecules at a rate proportional to the concentration of both, forming negative ions. Exactly as for ionization by single collisions it follows that

$$\left(\frac{\partial \mathcal{N}^-}{\partial t}\right)_1 = \frac{1}{a^3}\left(\frac{\partial \mathcal{N}^-}{\partial t}\right)_2 \qquad \ldots (3.44)$$

and the process is permitted. Detachment of electrons from negative ions due to collisions with gas molecules follows a similar law, since $\mathcal{N}^-$ transforms with $1/a^2$, $n$ with $1/a$. This also is permitted.

*Photo-ionization*

Photo-ionization proceeds at a rate proportional to the concentration of gas molecules and of photons, $\mathcal{N}_\nu$ (usually from excited molecules of another gas) able to ionize them. $\mathcal{N}_\nu$ is $\propto \dfrac{\partial \mathcal{N}^{\star}}{\partial t} \propto \dfrac{\mathcal{N}^{\star}}{\tau}$. Using either non-resonance [equation (3.35)] or resonance photons [equation (3.39)] gives

$$\left(\frac{\partial \mathcal{N}}{\partial t}\right)_1 \propto \mathcal{N}^{\star}n \quad \text{or} \quad \propto \mathcal{N}_\nu^{\star}n \neq \frac{1}{a^3}\left(\frac{\partial \mathcal{N}}{\partial t}\right)_2 \qquad \ldots (3.45)$$

The process is forbidden.

*Drift (Mobility Motion) and Diffusion*

These can be regarded as processes of gain or loss depending on whether the net flow of particles is in or out of the volume considered. Self-repulsion is a special case of drift in the field, in a region where charges of only one sign are present.

The rate of production or loss in a small element, $dx\,dy\,dz$, due to drift of charged particles in the electric field is given by

$$\frac{\partial N}{\partial t} = \frac{\partial}{\partial x}(Nv) + \frac{\partial}{\partial y}(Nv) + \frac{\partial}{\partial z}(Nv) \qquad \ldots(3.46)$$

where $v$ is the drift velocity; $N$ represents generally the concentration of any type of charged particle. Taking, for example, the $x$ component we obtain, for electrons or ions,

$$\left(\frac{\partial N}{\partial t}\right)_1 = \frac{\partial}{\partial x_1}(N_1 v_1) = \frac{\partial}{a\,.\,\partial x_2}\left(\frac{1}{a^2}N_2 v_2\right) = \frac{1}{a^3}\left(\frac{\partial N}{\partial t}\right)_2 \qquad \ldots(3.47)$$

and similarly for the $y$, $z$ components.

The rate of change of concentration in a similar small element due to diffusion is

$$\frac{\partial N}{\partial t} = -D\left(\frac{\partial^2 N}{\partial x^2} + \frac{\partial^2 N}{\partial y^2} + \frac{\partial^2 N}{\partial z^2}\right) \qquad \ldots(3.48)$$

Now $D$ is $\propto \lambda v$ where $v$ is the random velocity. $D$ could refer to any type of diffusion, e.g. ambipolar. Taking one component for ions or electrons gives

$$\left(\frac{\partial N}{\partial t}\right)_1 = C_6 \lambda_1 v_1 \frac{\partial^2 N_1}{\partial x_1^2} = C_6 a \lambda_2 v_2 \frac{\partial^2 \frac{1}{a^2} N_2}{a^2 \partial x_2^2} = \frac{1}{a^3}\left(\frac{\partial N}{\partial t}\right)_2 \qquad \ldots(3.49)$$

and similarly for $y$, $z$. Both processes are permitted.

*Charge Transfer*

In discharges, charge transfer is of special interest when fast ions hitting neutral molecules exchange their charge but do not share kinetic energy, the collision resulting in a slow ion and a fast neutral molecule. The rate of production of such molecules is proportional to the concentration of ions and gas molecules, i.e. $\propto N^+ n$ and hence transforms to $1/a^3$. Thus $n^0$ the concentration of fast neutral molecules arising from charge transfer is related by $n_1^0 = n_2^0/a^2$. This process is permitted.

The reverse process can occur when a fast neutral molecule picks up a charge from a slow ion and itself becomes a fast ion. The rate of production of such fast ions* is proportional to $n_0$ and to $\mathcal{N}^+$ giving

$$\left(\frac{\partial \mathcal{N}_{\text{fast}}^+}{\partial t}\right)_1 = Cn_1^0 \mathcal{N}_1^+ = C\frac{1}{a^2}n_2^0\frac{1}{a^2}\mathcal{N}_2^+ = \frac{1}{a^4}\left(\frac{\partial \mathcal{N}_{\text{fast}}^+}{\partial t}\right)_2 \quad \ldots (3.50)$$

and hence

$$\mathcal{N}_{1\,\text{fast}}^+ = \frac{1}{a^3}\cdot \mathcal{N}_{2\,\text{fast}}^+ \qquad \ldots (3.51)$$

This process is forbidden.

### Recombination

Between positive and negative ions recombination follows the law

$$\left(\frac{\partial \mathcal{N}}{\partial t}\right) = -\alpha \mathcal{N}^+ \mathcal{N}^- \qquad \ldots (3.52)$$

where $\alpha$ is the recombination coefficient. At high pressure $\alpha \propto 1/p$, and so transforms with the factor $a$, while $\mathcal{N}^+$, $\mathcal{N}^-$ each transform with $1/a^2$; thus finally $\partial \mathcal{N}/\partial t$ transforms with $1/a^3$. The process is then permitted. At low pressure $\alpha \propto p$, $\partial \mathcal{N}/\partial t$ transforms with $1/a^5$ and the process is forbidden.

For recombination between electrons and positive ions $\alpha$ is never $\propto 1/p$, but rather $\propto \sqrt{p}$, hence $\partial \mathcal{N}/\partial t$ never transforms with $1/a^3$ and the process is always forbidden.

### Chemical Reactions

Let there be $n_A$, $n_{A'}$, $n_{A''}$ . . . moles per c.c. of gases $A$, $A'$, $A''$ . . .; similarly $n_B$, $n_{B'}$, $n_{B''}$ . . . of gases $B$, $B'$, $B''$, . . . . Suppose the gases react in the manner

$$x_1 A + x_2 A' + x_3 A'' \ldots = y_1 B + y_2 B' + y_3 B'' \ldots$$

where $x_1$, $x_2$ and $y_1$, $y_2$, etc., are the relative number of reacting moles. The law of mass action gives:

$$\frac{n_A^{x_1}\cdot n_{A'}^{x_2}\cdot n_{A''}^{x_3}\cdots}{n_B^{y_1}\cdot n_{B'}^{y_2}\cdot n_{B''}^{y_3}\cdots} = K \text{ (constant)} \qquad \ldots (3.53)$$

---

* We assume here that the fast neutral molecules are those already formed by the process of charge transfer at some other point in the discharge. If we considered simply the fast molecules of the Maxwellian distribution their concentration would be related as $1/a$ and this process would be permitted. However, the number of sufficiently fast molecules normally present in a gas at ordinary temperatures is negligible.

this constant depending only on gas temperature, and therefore being the same for both systems. Now, since $(n_A)_1 = \dfrac{1}{a}(n_A)_2$, and similarly for the other gases, substitution in the above shows that $K$ can only be the same for both systems provided

$$\Sigma x = \Sigma y \qquad \qquad \ldots (3.54)$$

Chemical reactions are permitted processes provided that the total number of molecules does not change (e.g. $N_2 + O_2 = 2NO$ is permitted; $3O_2 = 2O_3$ is forbidden) and also provided that there is no significant change in gas temperature.

*Thermal Ionization*

The rate of ionization depends only on collisions of gas molecules with each other. Thus

$$\left(\frac{\partial N}{\partial t}\right)_1 = C \cdot n_1 \cdot n_1 = C\frac{n_2}{a} \cdot \frac{n_2}{a} = \frac{1}{a^2}\left(\frac{\partial N}{\partial t}\right)_2 \quad \ldots (3.55)$$

and the process is forbidden.

*Some Implicit Assumptions*

It is quite obvious in the treatment of diffusion and drift that in taking $v_1 = v_2$ the electron energy distribution was assumed to be the same in both discharges, implying the absence of stepwise ionization. This same assumption is implicit in the derivations for all those processes which have been found to transform correctly, because it has been assumed that the constants of proportionality $(C, C_1, C_2, \ldots)$ do not change from discharge 1 to discharge 2.

It follows that when two-stage ionization occurs in a discharge, not only does that process itself violate the similarity laws (this is the most pronounced effect) but to a smaller extent it upsets the behaviour of normally permitted processes.

PERMITTED AND FORBIDDEN SECONDARY PROCESSES

If the electron current density emitted from a wall or electrode by some secondary process is denoted as $j_e'$, then the process is consistent with equal currents flowing in both discharges if

$$(j_e'')_1 = \frac{(j_e'')_2}{a^2}$$

The results of the last section will now be applied using particularly the relations between the concentrations of the various particles. Secondary electron emission due to the impact of:

(a) *Electrons or ions* (excluding fast ions formed by a double charge transfer process), is permitted, since

$$(j_e'')_1 = \delta (j_e)_1 = \delta \frac{1}{a^2} (j_e)_2 = \frac{1}{a^2} (j_e'')_2 \quad \ldots (3.56)$$

$$(j_e'')_1 = \gamma_i j_1^+ = \gamma_i \frac{1}{a^2} j_2^+ = \frac{1}{a^2} (j_e'')_2 \quad \ldots (3.57)$$

where $\gamma_i$, $\delta$ are the usual secondary emission coefficients.

(b) *Fast ions*, formed by a double charge transfer process [see equation (3.51)], is forbidden since

$$(j_e'')_1 = \gamma_i' N_{1\,\text{fast}}^+ v_1 = \gamma_i' \frac{1}{a^3} N_{2\,\text{fast}}^+ v_2 = \frac{1}{a^3} (j_e'')_2 \quad \ldots (3.58)$$

(c) *Fast neutral molecules*, formed by charge transfer, is permitted

$$(j_e'')_1 = \gamma_n n_1^0 v_1 = \gamma_n \frac{1}{a^2} n_2^0 v_2 = \frac{1}{a^2} (j_e'')_2 \quad \ldots (3.59)$$

(d) *Metastable atoms*, is permitted, since $N_m^\star$ transforms as $1/a^2$

$$j_e'' = \gamma_m \tfrac{1}{4} N_m^\star v \quad \ldots (3.60)$$

and $v$ is invariant.

(e) *Photons*, is usually permitted.

The cathode subtends the same solid angle $\omega$ at corresponding small volumes $\delta x\, \delta y\, \delta z$ in the two discharges. Non-resonance photons fall directly on to the cathode giving a total secondary current $i_e$:

$$(i_e)_1 = \gamma_p \frac{\omega}{4\pi} \frac{N_1^\star}{\tau} (\delta x\, \delta y\, \delta z)_1 = \gamma_p \frac{\omega}{4\pi} \frac{1}{a^3} \frac{N_2^\star}{\tau} \cdot a^3 (\delta x\, \delta y\, \delta z)_2 = (i_e)_2$$
$$\ldots (3.61)$$

This photo-electric effect is therefore permitted.

Resonance photons diffuse and give $j_e'' \propto \dfrac{\partial}{\partial x} (N^\star v)$ but since $N_r^\star$ does not transform as $1/a^2$, neither does $j_e''$. This photo-electric effect is forbidden.

Finally, secondary emission by

(f) *Field emission*, is forbidden since $j_e'' = A V^2 e^{-B/V}$. $V$ and hence $j_e''$ are the same in both discharges. Similarly, thermionic emission is forbidden, since $T$ is the same in both discharges.

## GAS HEATING: SIMILARITY LAW FOR TEMPERATURES

It has so far been conveniently assumed that the temperature of the two discharges is the same. This, however, is not a necessary consequence of the basic assumption that the linear dimensions are in the ratio $a$, since this requires only that the gas densities shall differ by this factor. Generally, since for 1 gram molecule

$$p \times \text{volume} = C \cdot \frac{p}{n} = RT \qquad \ldots (3.62)$$

then

$$\frac{T_1}{T_2} = a \frac{p_1}{p_2} \qquad \ldots (3.63)$$

which is easily satisfied if the temperatures and pressures in both discharges are uniform, independent of their position in the discharge space. But if, due to local heating, the temperatures vary in space, then there will generally be in similar discharges a ratio between $T_1$ and $T_2$ at corresponding points. We assume

$$T_1 = \frac{T_2}{b} \qquad \ldots (3.64)$$

from which must follow

$$p_1 = \frac{1}{ab} \cdot p_2 \qquad \ldots (3.65)$$

We note in passing that the gas densities remain in the ratio $1/a$ and, assuming that the actual motion of the gas molecules does not significantly alter the mean free paths, all the relations previously given [except equations (3.11) and (3.18) for gas molecules only] remain unaffected by this change in temperature.

Now in any volume element of gas the temperature is determined by the balance between the energy given to the gas by the colliding ions and electrons, and that lost due to thermal conductivity. If $s$ is the specific heat per unit volume, and $K$ the thermal conductivity

$$\frac{d}{dt} \cdot (s \cdot T) = jX + K \left( \frac{d^2 T}{dx^2} + \frac{d^2 T}{dy^2} + \frac{d^2 T}{dz^2} \right) \quad \ldots (3.66)$$

assuming the discharge is stationary, and free from oscillations, i.e. $T$ not a function of time.

In the two discharges, if they are assumed to be similar

$$\frac{d}{dt} \cdot (s_1 \cdot T_1) = \text{const.} \frac{d}{dt} \cdot (s_2 \cdot T_2) \qquad \dots (3.67)$$

But $\frac{d}{dt}(s \cdot T)$ is the sum of several terms which must each transform by this same constant factor. It is known that

$$j_1 X_1 = \frac{1}{a^2} \cdot j_2 \cdot \frac{1}{a} X_2 = \frac{1}{a^3} \cdot j_2 X_2 \qquad \dots (3.68)$$

and consequently all terms similar to $K \dfrac{d^2 T}{dx^2}$ must transform accordingly.

$$\left( K \cdot \frac{d^2 T}{dx^2} \right)_1 = \frac{1}{a^3} \left( K \cdot \frac{d^2 T}{dx^2} \right)_2 \qquad \dots (3.69)$$

Now if $K_1$, the thermal conductivity, were independent of temperature and density then, since $x_1 = ax_2$, equation (3.69) would be satisfied with $T_1 = \frac{1}{a} T_2$, i.e. from equation (3.64) $a = b$. In fact the thermal conductivity varies with temperature, and this can be conveniently expressed as

$$\frac{K_1}{K_2} = \left( \frac{T_1}{T_2} \right)^q \qquad \dots (3.70)$$

where $q$, on simple kinetic theory, is $\frac{1}{2}$, but experimentally is found, for many gases, to lie between 0·68 and 0·97. Hence

$$b^{1+q} = a \qquad \dots (3.71)$$

The significance of this result is that two discharges are similar not only when the linear dimensions are in the ratio $a$, and the gas densities $1/a$, but also if, in addition, there is a relationship $T_1 = \frac{1}{b} T_2$ (where $b^{1+q} = a$), between the gas temperatures at any two corresponding points. Furthermore, any changes in temperature caused by the heating effect of the current will preserve this ratio between the systems, i.e. that there is a similarity in their temperature distributions.

### SIMILARITY IN VERY HIGH-FREQUENCY DISCHARGES

MARGENAU[7] has pointed out that in extremely high-frequency discharges, e.g. at microwave frequencies, measurements of current and potential are difficult, and rarely made. He defines discharges as similar when the electron energy distributions at corresponding points in the systems are the same, in addition to the scaling of geometry and free paths by the factor $a$. Apart from its different initial assumption, all the derivations are exactly the same as those already given. For high-frequency discharges to be similar, as is seen from *Tables 3.1* and *3.2*, $pd$, $X/p$ and $f/p$ must be the same.

### SIMILARITY IN FULLY IONIZED GASES PRODUCING NUCLEAR REACTIONS

Similarity, or scaling, laws have recently been extended to apply to thermonuclear reactions occurring in a column of highly ionized gas which has been compressed by its own magnetic field[8] ('pinch effect') in the presence of a longitudinal field. In these conditions, the equations connecting current, particle density, electron and ion temperature, etc. are rather different from those familiar in classical discharge physics, due to the absence of neutral molecules and excited states, and standard works should be referred to for details[9].

In these discharges of toroidal geometry (see Chapter 6) the important parameters are $N$, the number of electrons and ions per unit length of the discharge (line density), $T_e$, $T_i$, the length, $L$, of the discharge and the radius, $R$, of the tube. Another important requirement is that the discharge must compress into a concentrated channel in a time which is short compared with $t$, the time taken for a trapped magnetic field to diffuse out of the plasma. $t$ thus determines how long such a discharge remains stable, and controls the length of the pulse of field applied (see Chapter 6). Provided that shock waves do not contribute to the pinch effect, the analysis shows that the fraction of particles undergoing nuclear fusion per pulse, the product $nt$, and $T_e$ and $T_i$ are all independent of size (i.e. are 'similarity parameters'). The rate of loss of energy to the wall, and the consequent release of impurities, however, depend strongly on size, being large in small containers.

### SUMMARY AND CONCLUSIONS

The results obtained are summarized in *Tables 3.1* and *3.2*, and a list given of those groups of parameters which remain invariant in the two discharges. It should be noted that the invariance of some groups (e.g. $j/p^2$) depends upon more assumptions than that of others (e.g. $X/p$). It should also be noted that although the entire treatment assumes the motion of charges to be determined by collisions with gas molecules, any high-vacuum process in which

*Table 3.1*

| Parameters | Relations | Invariant groups of parameters derived—'similarity parameters' |
| --- | --- | --- |
| Potential<br>All linear dimensions | $V_1 = V_2$<br>$d_1 = ad_2$<br>$R_1 = aR_2$ } Basic assumptions* | $V, i, T$ consequently all $V\text{-}i$ curves |
| Current | $i_1 = i_2$ | |
| Gas temperature | $T_1 = T_2$ ) or $T_1 = \dfrac{1}{b}T_2$ (see p. 73) | |
| Mean free path of any particle | $\lambda_1 = a\lambda_2$ | $X/p, \; pd, \; pR$ |
| Gas density | $n_1 = n_2/a$ | |
| Gas pressure | $p_1 = p_2/a$   or $p_1 = p_2/ab$ (see p. 73) | |
| Electric field | $X_1 = X_2/a$    Derived from the basic assumptions | |
| Wall charge density | $\sigma_1 = \sigma_2/a$ | |
| Volume charge density | $\rho_1^+, \rho_1^- = \dfrac{1}{a^2}\rho_2^+, \dfrac{1}{a^2}\rho_2^-$ | |
| Total mass of gas<br>Total charge in vessel | $m_1 = a^2 m_2$<br>$q_1 = a \cdot q_2$ | |
| Total and partial current density | $(j, j^+, j_e)_1 = \dfrac{1}{a^2}(j, j^+, j_e)_2$ } Derived from above assuming also | $T_e, \; T_+$<br>$H/p$<br>$j/p^2, \; N_e/p^2$<br>and for a.c. discharges<br>$fd, fR, f/p$ |
| Particle density: electrons, $+ve$ and $-ve$ ions, metastables†, fast neutrals (by charge transfer) | $(N_e, N^+, N^-, N_m^\star n^0)_1 = \dfrac{1}{a}(N_e \cdots)_2$ } no stepwise ionization except the Penning effect | |
| Excited states, except resonance | $N_1^\star = N_2^\star/a^3$ | |
| Velocity, energy of charged particles | $v_1 = v_2$<br>$\varepsilon_1 = \varepsilon_2$ | |
| Electron, ion, temperature | $(T_e, T_+)_1 = (T_e, T_+)_2$ | |
| Time interval | $dt_1 = a\,dt_2$ | |
| Collision frequency | $v_1 = v_2/a$ | |
| Applied frequency | $f_1 = f_2/a$ | |
| Magnetic fields | $H_1 = H_2/a$ (applied or due to current) | |
| Rates of current growth | $\dfrac{di_1}{dt} = \dfrac{1}{a} \cdot \dfrac{di_2}{dt}$ | |

\* But see p. 64 for a discussion on the assumption $i_1 = i_2$.
† Provided metastables are produced only by direct excitation, and not by electrons falling from higher levels.

76

Table 3.2. Permitted and forbidden processes

| | Permitted | Forbidden |
|---|---|---|
| In the gas | Ionization by single electron collision<br><br>Penning effect<br>Electron attachment and detachment<br>Drift<br>Self repulsion } of charges<br>Diffusion<br>Charge transfer ion → fast neutral<br>Recombination ion — ion at high $p$<br>Secondary emission by impact of:<br>Electrons ($\delta$)<br>Ions ($\gamma_i$)<br>Non-resonance photons ($\gamma_p$)<br>Metastables ($\gamma_m$)<br>Fast neutrals ($\gamma_n$) | All stepwise ionizations, collisions of second kind<br>except Penning effect<br>Photo-ionization,<br>Charge transfer: fast neutral → ion*<br><br>All recombination except ion — ion at high<br>pressure<br><br>Thermal ionization |
| On the walls | | Electrons emitted by fast ions formed by charge<br>transfer*<br>Photo-electric effect by diffusing resonance<br>photons<br>Field emission |

* See footnote on p. 70.

77

charged particles gain energy in free fall through a potential drop
$[\frac{1}{2}mv^2 = e(V_1 - V_2)]$ also obeys similarity laws.

The greatest care is needed in attempting to infer anything about
physical processes when a given discharge does or does not obey
similarity laws. The derivations given prove only consistency;

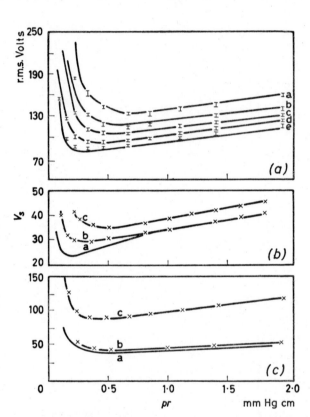

Figure 3.2. (a) Similarity relationship in pure helium. The curves a, b, c, d, e
are with tube C at frequencies, f, of 10, 20, 30, 50, and 70 Mc/s. The points are
obtained with the geometrically similar tube B of twice the linear dimensions at
half the pressure and at frequencies f/2, and lie on the curves within experimental
error; (b) effect of variation in the geometrical parameters: (a) tube A—50 Mc/s
(curve), (b) tube B—50 Mc/s (points X), (c) tube B—25 Mc/s (points X), and
tube C—50 Mc/s; (c) similarity in pure and impure helium with tubes B
(points X) and C (curves): (a) tube C—50 Mc/s, impure helium, (b) tube B—
25 Mc/s, impure helium, (c) tube B—25 Mc/s, and tube C—50 Mc/s, pure helium.
The tubes (coaxial cylinders) A—1·59 mm (inner diameter), 3·945 cm (outer diameter); B—3·18 mm (inner diameter), 3·95 cm (outer diameter); C—1·60 mm
(inner diameter), 2·08 cm (outer diameter). (From F. LLEWELLYN JONES
and G. C. WILLIAMS[11], by courtesy of the Physical Society)

they do not prove, for example, that single-stage ionization causes $N_1^+/N_2^+ = 1/a^2$.

It may, therefore, be logically deduced that if the similarity laws are obeyed then all the forbidden processes can be excluded, but it cannot be assumed that forbidden processes are necessarily present if the laws are broken. However, it is reasonable to infer that if a discharge first obeys, and then progressively deviates from, the laws as some parameter (e.g. discharge current) is varied, then forbidden processes are appearing, or the gas temperature is changing. Similarity relations in discharges with externally produced ionization have also been discussed[10].

Some examples of the use of similarity laws are now given[11]. *Figure 3.2* shows curves of breakdown and maintenance potentials in helium in concentric cylinders at frequencies between 10 and 70 Mc/s. Tube C consists of two concentric cylinders, the inner one of radius, $r$, being the cathode; tube B is geometrically similar, but of twice the linear dimensions, having half the gas pressure and being subjected to a field of half the frequency. In pure helium the curves for the same values of $pr$ and $f/p$ coincide, showing that the similarity laws are obeyed [*Figure 3.2(a)*]. If two tubes, not geometrically similar, are considered the result shown in *Figure 3.2 (b)* is obtained: here, tube A has a central rod half the radius of B, but the outer cylinder is the same size as B. The curve for tube A does not coincide with the other two (here the similarity parameter $rX_0$ is plotted as ordinate, where $X_0$ is the field at the central rod).

In impure helium, contaminated with a slight trace of $H_2$, it may be observed from curves a and b, shown in *Figure 3.2(c)*, that even for the same values of $pr$ and $f/p$ the curves do not coincide. In these experiments it was thought that approximately 1 part in $10^5$ of $H_2$ was present (the Penning effect was certainly present), but it seems possible that dissociation of $H_2^+$, being essentially a chemical reaction, upsets similarity. The interesting point is that quite a small fraction of impurity produces a noticeable deviation from the similarity laws.

Recently these measurements have been repeated in uniform radio frequency fields between metal electrodes. The similarity rules are obeyed except when the electrodes are covered with an oxide layer, and a type of field emission occurs[12].

## REFERENCES

[1] DE LA RUE, W. and MÜLLER, W. H., *Phil. Trans.*, **171** (1880) 65
[2] PASCHEN, F., *Wied. Ann.*, **33** (1889) 69

[3] TOWNSEND, J. S., *Electrician*, **71** (1913) 348

[4] HOLM, R., *Phys. Z.*, **25** (1924) 497; **26** (1925) 412

[5] STEENBECK, M., *Wiss. Veröff. Siemens*, **11** (2) (1932) 36; see also VON ENGEL, A. and STEENBECK, M., *Elektrische Gasentladungen*; Berlin: Springer, 1932

[6] DÄLLENBACH, W., *Phys. Z.*, **26** (1925) 483

[7] MARGENAU, H., *Phys. Rev.*, **73** (1949) 326

[8] BICKERTON, R. J. and LONDON, H., *Proc. phys. Soc. Lond.*, **72** (1958) 116

[9] SPITZER, L., *Physics of Fully Ionized Gases*; New York: Interscience, 1956

[10] FUCHS, W., *Naturwissenschaften*, **35** (1948) 283

[11] LLEWELLYN JONES, F. and WILLIAMS, G. C., *Proc. phys. Soc. Lond.*, **B66** (1953) 17, 345; see also LLEWELLYN JONES, F. and MORGAN, G. D., *ibid.*, **B64** (1951) 560, 574

[12] TOWNSEND, W. G. and WILLIAMS, G. C., *ibid.*, **72** (1958) 823

# 4

# ALTERNATING AND HIGH-FREQUENCY DISCHARGES

## GENERAL CONSIDERATIONS

IONIZATION in a gas subjected to alternating electric fields differs in several important respects from ionization in steady (d.c.) fields. First, since the field reverses direction periodically, the charges may not be swept out of the volume on to the walls or electrodes; with losses thus reduced quite low fields can lead to a slow growth of ionization, resulting in an equilibrium conducting state, i.e. a self-sustained discharge. In these circumstances secondary processes at the electrodes are not a necessary condition for breakdown as they are in d.c. discharges. Secondly, if charged particles, photons and excited atoms striking the walls produce secondary electrons these will not contribute to the growth of the discharge unless they are emitted when the field is in a favourable direction. Thirdly, a.c. discharges can be maintained in insulating vessels, and the drift of ions and electrons to the wall sets up static fields which largely control the equilibrium density of ionization in the space.

The factors which determine the breakdown field, $X_s$, and the subsequent current and ion density, etc. of the fully developed discharge are:

(1) the gas pressure, $p$ (mm Hg), and consequently the mean free path, $\lambda_e$ (cm), of the electrons, and the frequency $\nu$ ($= v_r/\lambda_e$ sec$^{-1}$) with which they hit gas molecules;

(2) the frequency, $f$, and wavelength, $\lambda$, of the applied electric field $X$, where $X = X_0 \sin \omega t = X_0 \sin 2\pi f t = X_0 \sin \dfrac{2\pi c}{\lambda} \cdot t$;

(3) the dimensions of the vessel; in the simplest example the length, $d$ (cm), in the direction of the electric field, and the perpendicular width or radius, $r$.

It is now necessary to distinguish various sets of conditions in which different physical processes are important, thinking always of discharges in vessels a few centimetres in size, such as those commonly used in laboratory experiments.

(1) Very low pressure, $\lambda_e > d, r$; the electrons hit the walls of the vessel more often than they hit gas molecules, and hence

secondary effects at the walls control breakdown. For ordinary vessels this occurs at pressures of about $10^{-2}$ mm Hg or less.

(2) Medium or high pressure, $\lambda_e < d, r$; low frequency, $\nu \gg f$; the electrons make many collisions for each oscillation of the electric field, and drift as a cloud in phase with the field. Their motion may be described by a mobility, and the conditions can be divided into two sub-groups: (a) if the frequency is sufficiently high, the amplitude of oscillation may be less than the dimensions of the vessel. New charged particles are formed by ionizing collisions in the gas, and lost mainly by diffusion to the walls; (b) at lower frequencies and larger amplitudes of oscillation the entire cloud of electrons is driven to the walls in each half cycle of the field. A secondary wall process is then essential to maintain a discharge.

(3) Medium or high pressure, $\lambda_e < d, r$; high frequency, $\nu \ll f$; the electrons make many oscillations of small amplitude between collisions with gas molecules. In these circumstances a cloud of electrons would appear to be stationary (there being no drift motion), spreading outwards only by diffusion. There is, of course, a wide range of conditions intermediate between 2 (a) and 3, in which the applied and collision frequencies are not vastly different, but there is no marked change in the mechanism of the discharge during this transition.

(4) Very high frequency, $\lambda \gtrsim d, r$; here the electrons are not under the influence of an electric field but are under that of a standing wave with oscillatory electric and magnetic components, distributed in space in a manner determined by the frequency of the field, the geometry and the mode of excitation of the vessel (now more commonly called a cavity since it forms part of a microwave guide and resonator system).

In addition, superimposed fields, e.g. a steady magnetic or electric field, or an oscillatory electric field in another direction, can strongly influence the starting and maintenance of the discharge.

### MOTION OF ELECTRONS IN AN ALTERNATING ELECTRIC FIELD

*When the Electron Rarely Hits Gas Molecules ($\nu \ll f$)*

These conditions obtain when the gas pressure is very low or when the applied frequency is high. An electron, starting at the point $x = 0$ with an initial velocity component, $v_0$, in the direction of a uniform electric field, $X$, has the equation of motion

$$m \frac{\mathrm{d}^2 x}{\mathrm{d}t^2} = eX_0 \sin(\omega t + \phi) \qquad \ldots (4.1)$$

82

where $\phi$ is the phase angle of the field at the instant, $t = 0$, when the electron starts. Integration with the boundary condition $dx/dt = v_0$ when $t = 0$ gives the velocity at time, $t$

$$v = v_0 + \frac{eX_0}{m\omega} \left[ \cos\phi - \cos(\omega t + \phi) \right] \qquad \ldots\,(4.2)$$

and the displacement $x$ in the direction of the field

$$x = \left( v_0 + \frac{eX_0}{m\omega} \cos\phi \right) t + \frac{eX_0}{m\omega^2} \left[ \sin\phi - \sin(\omega t + \phi) \right]$$
$$\ldots\,(4.3)$$

There is clearly a steady drift at uniform speed in the direction of the original velocity, superimposed upon which is a sinusoidal oscillation of amplitude $eX_0/m\omega^2$, i.e. proportional to $X/f^2$ or to

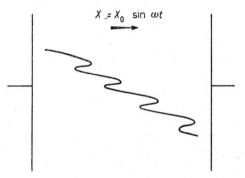

*Figure 4.1. Motion of an electron in an oscillating electric field [equations (4.2) and (4.3)]*

$X\lambda^2$. Only those electrons which happen to be stationary when the phase of the field is zero will oscillate about their mean position. Any initial motion perpendicular to the field is, of course, unaltered.

The velocity of the electron consists of a constant plus an oscillating component; it follows that an electron moving thus without hitting gas molecules will not absorb any power from the field, since the oscillatory component is always 90° out of phase, and the steady component will, in alternate half cycles, absorb energy from, and return it to, the field. A comparison of the uniform velocity due to the field, $eX/m\omega$, with the initial velocity $v_0$ is interesting: an electron having an initial energy of a few eV would have $v_0 \sim 10^8$ cm/sec, whereas an applied field of 30 V/cm at a frequency of 10 Mc/s would produce in its most favourable phase, $\phi = 0$, a steady velocity of nearly $3 \times 10^8$ cm/sec. At higher frequencies and lower fields this contribution would be greatly reduced.

The general motion of an electron in a uniform electric field, including its unchanged motion at right angles to the field, is illustrated in *Figure 4.1*.

*When the Electron Collides Frequently with Gas Molecules* $(\nu \gtrsim f)$

Electrons colliding with gas molecules can gain energy from a high-frequency field, and consideration is given here to elastic collisions in which each electron loses only a very small fraction $(\sim 2m/M)$ of the kinetic energy it has before hitting the molecule. The result is that the phase of the electron's motion has been changed without depriving it of the energy it has already gained from the field, and its ordered motion has been changed to a random motion. This explains the apparent paradox that in d.c. discharges, electrons, in hitting gas molecules, can only lose energy: in high-frequency discharges no energy can be gained without collisions. The energy the electron loses to the molecule is more than replaced on average by its consequent gain from the field due to the change of phase. In this way the energy of a swarm of electrons can increase until an appreciable fraction of them are fast enough to excite or ionize the gas, in doing which, of course, they lose large amounts of energy.

In these conditions it is convenient to consider the motion of an average electron representative of a cloud. Although not as rigorous as a treatment based on the distribution function, it has the merit of making the physical processes clearer. The electrons gain momentum from the field, and lose it in hitting gas molecules, the net rate of gain being the difference. The loss may be represented by a frictional force proportional to the velocity

$$\frac{m \, \mathrm{d}v_{\mathrm{drift}}}{\mathrm{d}t} = eX_0 \sin \omega t - gv_{\mathrm{drift}} \qquad \ldots . (4.4)$$

The drift velocity is the proper quantity here, since this equation describes the motion of a cloud of electrons in the direction of the electric field.

This expression implies no motion except that produced by the field, which is justifiable provided that the velocity gained from the field between collisions is small compared with the random velocity of the electrons. The frictional factor, $g$, requires some consideration; LORENTZ[1] suggested that it should be made equal to $2m/\tau$, where $\tau$ is the average time of free flight of the electron between collisions with gas molecules, $1/\tau = \nu$. This assumption was made to conform with equations derived from electromagnetic theory to describe the absorption of light in a dispersive medium. There are no valid physical arguments to support it, however, especially as, in a gas, the frequency of light waves is much greater than $v$. It is more correct to calculate the average momentum lost when an electron hits a gas molecule. From elementary collision theory (see Chapter 2), assuming that the electron behaves as a very light elastic sphere, and that after a collision with a much heavier gas molecule all directions of motion are equally probable, it follows that on the average an electron loses all its momentum in any given direction at each collision. Thus the rate of loss of momentum in the $x$ direction is $v \cdot (mv_{\text{drift}})$, or $g = m/\tau$. This may be derived indirectly by taking Townsend's expression for the drift velocity of an electron

$$v_{\text{drift}} = C \frac{e}{m} \tau X \qquad \ldots (4.5)$$

where $C$ is a numerical constant close to 1, depending on the energy distribution of the electrons. Rewriting equation (4.5)

$$C' \frac{m}{\tau} v_{\text{drift}} = eX \qquad \ldots (4.6)$$

the right-hand side represents the rate of gain of momentum from the field, and hence in the steady state the left-hand side represents the rate of loss. An experimental test of this derivation was made by CHILDS[2], who measured, by a radio frequency method, the conductivity of an ionized gas (air) between the plates of a condenser; conductivity, being the reciprocal of resistance, depends on the energy abstracted by the electrons from the field, i.e. on the frictional factor. He found that with $p = 1$ mm Hg, $f = 3 \times 10^8$ c/sec, $g$ was approximately equal to $m/\tau$, but tended to smaller values (i.e. $< m/\tau$ for electron energies greater than about 8 eV. APPLETON and CHAPMAN[3] derived the factor $m/\tau$ in a slightly different way, and also checked it experimentally.

It should be noted that these derivations of the frictional factor are valid only when the free paths are distributed according to an exponential law, i.e. determined by chance. This implies that $\lambda_e$ is much less than the dimensions of the vessel. Furthermore, the deduction from the mobility equation implies that, at any instant, the electrons are in a state of near equilibrium with the field, so that the terms on the right-hand side of equation (4.4) are both much larger than the left-hand side.

When electron scattering is not symmetrical, the collision

frequency for momentum transfer, $v_m$, may be used, instead of $v$, where

$$v_m = v(1 - \cos \theta) \qquad \dots (4.7)$$

$v_m$ is the number of collisions per second in which an electron transfers momentum to a gas molecule, and $\theta$ is the angle of scattering as a result of the collision.

Clearly, using average values

$$v_m = \overline{v(1 - \cos \theta)} \qquad \dots (4.8)$$

and the two collision frequencies are equal only when scattering is equally probable into all angles (see Chapter 2, p. 20). It should be noted, however, that for electron energies of a few eV or less, scattering is symmetrical, so that $v = v_m$ in the range under consideration. Furthermore, the collision cross section, or mean free path, determined from diffusion and mobility measurements, which are processes depending on the transfer of momentum, lead to the quantity $v_m$. Experimentally determined values of average random velocity, $v_r$, and electron mean free path, $\lambda_e$, may therefore confidently be used to deduce $g = mv = mv_r/\lambda_e$. However, this is true only for Maxwellian energy distributions, and in some circumstances $g$ should be taken as a complex quantity.

From equation (4.4), the drift velocity of the electron cloud is:

$$v_{\text{drift}} = \frac{dx}{dt} = \frac{eX_0}{m} \frac{\sin(\omega t - \phi)}{\sqrt{v^2 + \omega^2}} \qquad \dots (4.9)$$

where

$$\tan \phi = \frac{\omega}{v} \qquad \dots (4.9a)$$

Further integration gives the displacement, $x$

$$x = \frac{eX_0}{m\omega} \cdot \frac{\cos(\omega t - \phi)}{\sqrt{v^2 + \omega^2}} + \text{constant} \qquad \dots (4.10)$$

Unlike motion in vacuum, this displacement is entirely oscillatory about a mean position. The high-frequency electron current density $j_e$ (due to the drift of $n$ electrons/cm³) is:

$$j_e = nev = \frac{ne^2X_0}{m} \frac{\sin(\omega t - \phi)}{\sqrt{v^2 + \omega^2}} \qquad \dots (4.11)$$

The current lags behind the applied field by the phase angle $\phi$.

These results are often expressed in vector notation. If the applied field is written $X_0 e^{i\omega t}$, where $i$ is the vector operator numerically equal to $\sqrt{-1}$, the electron has a complex mobility.

$$b_e = \frac{e/m}{iw + \nu} \qquad \ldots\ldots(4.12)$$

and

$$j_e = \frac{ne^2 X_0}{m}\left[\frac{\nu}{\nu^2 + \omega^2} - i\frac{\omega}{\nu^2 + \omega^2}\right] e^{i\omega t} \qquad \ldots\ldots(4.13)$$

The instantaneous rate at which the electrons in unit volume gain energy is given by the instantaneous power, $P$, supplied by the field per unit volume, i.e. by the product $VI$. $V$, the potential across unit cube is numerically equal to the field, $X$, and $I$, the current through unit cube is by definition $j_e$. Hence

$$P = Xj_e = X_0 \sin \omega t \frac{ne^2}{m} X_0 \frac{\sin(\omega t - \phi)}{\sqrt{\nu^2 + \omega^2}} \qquad \ldots\ldots(4.14)$$

$$= \frac{ne^2 X_0^2}{2m}\frac{[\cos\phi - \cos 2\omega t]}{\sqrt{\nu^2 + \omega^2}} \qquad \ldots\ldots(4.15)$$

The steady rate at which electrons gain energy and deliver it to unit volume of the gas is given by the time average of this expression; since $\overline{\cos 2\omega t}$ is zero, and using equation (4.9a)

$$\overline{P} = \frac{ne^2 X_0^2}{2m} \cdot \frac{\nu}{\nu^2 + \omega^2} \text{ i.e. } \propto X_0^2 \qquad \ldots\ldots(4.16)$$

Similar calculation gives an average high-frequency conductivity $\sigma = j_e/X = \frac{ne^2}{m}\frac{\nu}{\nu^2 + \omega^2}$, being greatest when $\nu = \omega$. This is the real part of the complex $\sigma = \frac{ne^2}{m(i\omega + \nu)}$.

Comparing equation (4.16) with the steady drift motion of electrons in a d.c. field, where

$$P_{\text{d.c.}} = X_{\text{d.c.}} j_e = X_{\text{d.c.}} ne\left(\frac{e}{m} \cdot \tau \cdot X_{\text{d.c.}}\right) = \frac{ne^2 X_{\text{d.c.}}^2}{m\nu} \qquad \ldots\ldots(4.17)$$

it is possible to define an effective steady (d.c.) field $X_{\text{eff.}}$ which would transfer energy to electrons at the same rate as the actual applied high-frequency field whose root mean square value is $X_{\text{r.m.s.}} (= X_0/\sqrt{2})$. From equations (4.16) and (4.17) the relationship is:

$$X_{\text{eff.}}^2 = X_{\text{r.m.s.}}^2 \cdot \frac{\nu^2}{\nu^2 + \omega^2} = X_{\text{r.m.s.}}^2 \frac{1}{1 + \omega^2\tau^2} \qquad \ldots\ldots(4.18)$$

This concept has recently been used by American workers[245], but the expression was derived much earlier by TOWNSEND and GILL[7] from a more detailed study of the motion of the electrons in their free flight between collisions. They also noted the striking resemblance between the second form of the expression and the formulae which describe many properties of d.c. discharges in the presence of a magnetic field $H$, when $\omega$ is replaced by the gyro frequency $\omega_H = eH/mc$. The concept of an effective field can be useful over a restricted range of frequency and pressure because it takes account of the frequency of the applied field, and thus reduces the number of parameters required for a coherent description of breakdown and maintenance potentials at various pressures and frequencies in vessels of different geometry.

The concept of a drift velocity, as used in equation (4.4), cannot apply if an electron makes many oscillations before it hits a gas molecule, i.e. $\nu < f$, since the electron cloud as a whole does not drift. The directed motion of an electron must then be calculated by considering its motion between collisions (following Townsend and Gill). If $v_0$ is the component of the random velocity in the direction of the field immediately after a collision, its gain of momentum in free flight (time interval $t$) is derived from equation (4.2). The loss of directed momentum in the next collision is $mv (1 - \cos \theta)$ if the electron is scattered into an angle $\theta$ with the field direction. Provided the average directed motion is small compared with the random motion, the mean value of $v_0$ is zero; similarly, the average value of $\phi$, the phase of the field immediately after a collision, is zero. The time intervals of free flight, $t$, are distributed about the mean value $\tau$ in the same way as the free paths ($e^{-t/\tau}$), and if, in a rigorous treatment, the mean time for momentum transfer, $\tau_m$ is used (corresponding to $Q_m$, $\lambda_m$, $\nu_m$, the cross section, mean free path and collision frequency for momentum transfer—see pp. 20, 21) the average value of $\cos \theta$ is also zero. A calculation of rates of momentum gain and loss on these lines, with proper averaging, leads to an equation formally similar to equation (4.4) and the same value of an effective field.

*When the Electron Collides Very Frequently with Gas Molecules ($\nu \gg f$)*

Since this is an extreme case of the conditions discussed in the preceding section, $\omega$ has only to be neglected in comparison with $\nu$ in the equations, to obtain the motion of the electrons. Physically this motion is determined entirely by their mobility, $b_e$, and is always in phase with the field, so that it may be written

$$v_{\text{drift}} = \frac{dx}{dt} = b_e X_0 \sin \omega t \qquad \dots (4.19)$$

which, taking $\omega \ll \nu$, is the same as equation (4.9) provided the mobility, $b_e$, is equal to $e/m\nu$. The above equation, however, is more general as it can be used with the experimentally determined value of the mobility. Since the electrons are in equilibrium with the field at every instant it follows that their properties, e.g. energy distribution, will be the same as those found in a steady field equal to the instantaneous value of the applied field.

## Non-uniform Fields

An electron oscillating in a field whose value changes with position, as well as varying periodically with time, clearly suffers an asymmetrical force. As it moves in one direction from its mean position, e.g. into a weaker field, it suffers a weaker force, while in the opposite direction it suffers a stronger force. If the electrons move *in vacuo* with approximately simple harmonic motion (the non-uniformity of the field being a second order effect) the force on them is always towards their central position, and it follows that in addition to their oscillatory motion they are driven steadily towards the weaker regions of the field. However, if the gas pressure is high and the motion of electrons is determined by mobility, then although their oscillation will be asymmetrical the mean position will not alter, and there will be no net drift towards other regions of the field.

If $X_0 \sin \omega t$ represents the electric field at the mean position $x = 0$, the force on a free electron at some point, $x$, of its path is given in its simplest form by:

$$m \frac{d^2 x}{dt^2} = e \left( X_0 + x \frac{dX_0}{dx} \right) \sin \omega t \qquad \ldots\ldots(4.20)$$

If the term in $dX_0/dx$ is assumed to be small, an approximate solution can be obtained by first ignoring this term, deriving $x = \dfrac{eX_0}{m\omega^2} \sin \omega t$, and substituting in equation (4.20) giving

$$\text{Force} = m \frac{d^2 x}{dt^2} = eX_0 \sin \omega t + \frac{e^2}{m\omega^2} X_0 \frac{dX_0}{dx} \cdot \sin^2 \omega t \quad \ldots\ldots(4.21)$$

Averaged over a complete cycle, the first term gives no net force, the second gives a resultant force whose average value $\overline{F}$ is

$$\overline{F} = \frac{1}{2} \frac{e^2}{m\omega^2} X_0 \frac{dX_0}{dx} = \frac{1}{4} \frac{e^2}{m\omega^2} \frac{dX_0^2}{dx} \qquad \ldots\ldots(4.22)$$

directed towards the weaker regions of the field. This force is independent of the sign of the charge, and it is also proportional to the gradient of the energy density in the field. A more rigorous solution is obtained by adding to equation (4.20) a constant term $f(x)$ representing the force necessary to prevent the centre of oscillation drifting. A Mathieu equation results, which can be solved for small amplitudes of oscillation and small distortions of the field, with the same results as given above. A more general treatment of the motion of charges in a non-uniform electromagnetic wave has also been given[8].

CONDUCTIVITY AND ELECTRON ENERGY DISTRIBUTION IN
IONIZED MEDIA: RIGOROUS TREATMENT

The theory outlined in previous sections assumes that the motion of the average electron can be taken as representative of the whole. It has been applied in various forms by many workers[9-14], with essentially the results given in equations (4.11) and (4.13) for the conductivity of the ionized gas, although not all took account of collisions between electrons and molecules. Rigorous methods have been employed by several authors[4-6, 15-24], who start from the Boltzmann–Maxwell transfer equation. If, of the $n$ electrons per cm³ in the element $x$ to $x + dx$, $y$ to $y + dy$, $z$ to $z + dz$, $dn$ have vectorial velocity $\boldsymbol{v}$ with components $v_x, v_y, v_z$

$$\frac{dn}{n} = f(x, y, z, v_x, v_y, v_z) \, dx \, dy \, dz \, dv_x \, dv_y \, dv_z \quad \dots (4.23)$$

The transfer equation is then[25] (see Appendix V)

$$\frac{\partial f}{\partial t} + \boldsymbol{v} \cdot \nabla_r f + \frac{eX}{m} \nabla_v f = \left(\frac{\partial f}{\partial t}\right)_{\text{collisions}} \quad \dots (4.24)$$

where the right-hand side represents the rate of change of $f$ due only to collisions which the electrons make with other particles and $\nabla_r$ and $\nabla_v$ are the usual gradient vector operators having components $(\partial/\partial x, \partial/\partial y, \partial/\partial z)$ and $(\partial/\partial v_x, \partial/\partial v_y, \partial/\partial v_z)$ respectively. Generally $dn/n$ can be regarded as constant in space, and if the field is restricted to the direction, $x$, the simplest equation may be derived

$$\frac{\partial f}{\partial t} + \frac{eX}{m} \frac{\partial f}{\partial v_x} = \left(\frac{\partial f}{\partial t}\right)_{\text{collisions}} \quad \dots (4.25)$$

The right-hand side can be expressed as a complicated integral involving the function $f$, but there is no general method of solution for the resulting form of the equation. However, in a Lorentzian gas, i.e. a mixture of light particles amongst heavier ones, conditions are much simpler provided that the density of the light particles (electrons) is small, so that their change of motion is due entirely to encounters with heavy particles (gas molecules). The velocity distribution is then nearly isotropic, apart from small directional effects due to the electric field and diffusion. An approximate solution can be found by expanding the function $f$ in spherical harmonics, taking only the first two terms. By substituting in equation (4.25) and equating corresponding terms an expression may be explicitly derived for the isotropic part of the distribution, and a relation between it and the non-isotropic part. The former determines the mean energy or electron temperature, the latter the mean drift, i.e. momentum, whose magnitude and phase determines the conductivity and dispersive effect (change of dielectric constant) of the medium. The actual expressions obtained depend on the assumptions made in deriving the term $\left(\dfrac{\partial f}{\partial t}\right)_{\text{collisions}}$, i.e. the influence of elastic and inelastic collisions, and the variation of $\nu$ with electron energy. Some of the more interesting results obtained by various authors are now quoted.

MARGENAU[4], assuming only elastic collisions and a constant electron mean free path, i.e. $\nu \propto v_{\text{random}}$, found an energy distribution expressed by an expansion whose first two terms represent a Maxwellian and a Druyvesteyn distribution respectively. In a d.c. field the first (Maxwellian) term is zero and the resulting distribution is a modified Druyvesteyn: for small high-frequency fields, in which ionization can be neglected, the distribution is Maxwellian with a temperature

$$T_e = T_{\text{gas}} + \frac{Me^2X_0^2}{6km^2\omega^2} \qquad \dots\dots(4.26)$$

where $M$ is the mass of a gas molecule. For constant mean free time ($\nu = $ constant), a similar result ensues, but with $T_e$ given by:

$$T_e = T_{\text{gas}} + \frac{Me^2X_0^2}{6km^2(\nu^2 + \omega^2)} \qquad \dots\dots(4.27)$$

Thus at high frequencies a Maxwellian distribution is produced at values of the field which would produce a Druyvesteyn distribution in steady field; this applies to uniform fields and electron densities. Holstein includes a small proportion of inelastic collisions, and finds a distribution function which is similar to Druyvesteyn's for a d.c. field; he also shows that, provided $\omega^2\lambda_e^2/eV_i \ll 1$ ($V_i$ being the ionization potential of the gas) the distribution for an a.c. field of amplitude $X_0$ is identical with that obtained in a d.c. field, $X = X_0/\sqrt{2}$. These treatments have been extended to include large electron densities (when the distribution is always Maxwellian), spatially non-uniform electric fields, and charge densities such that the natural resonant frequency of the ions and electrons is close to that of the applied field (see Chapter 7).

In small fields when electrons have a Maxwellian distribution with a temperature, $T \approx T_{\text{gas}}$ an exact expression for the complex conductivity can be given in terms of the tabulated error function. In limiting conditions the expression becomes very simple.

(1) Many oscillations of the field per collision ($\nu \ll \omega$) implying low gas pressure and/or a high frequency. The electron current density, $j_e$, in the presence of an applied field, $X_0 \sin \omega t$, is:

$$j_e = \frac{16}{3} \frac{ne^2}{m\omega^2\lambda_e} \sqrt{\frac{kT}{2\pi m}} X_0 \sin \omega t - \frac{ne^2}{m\omega} X_0 \cos \omega t \quad \ldots (4.28)$$

This is the form which applies to the passage of centimetre waves through ionized gases. The second term is the current due to free electrons. Several authors have recently given simpler treatments of conductivity to microwaves[239,240].

(2) Many collisions per oscillation ($\nu \gg \omega$) implying high gas pressure and/or a low frequency. Then

$$j_e = \frac{4}{3} \frac{ne^2\lambda_e}{\sqrt{2\pi mkT}} X_0 \sin \omega t - \frac{ne^2\lambda_e^2\omega}{3kT} X_0 \cos \omega t \quad \ldots (4.29)$$

The first term here is the usual Langevin mobility formula.

The exact expression leads to a maximum value of the conductivity when

$$\omega\lambda_e \approx 6 \cdot 10^{13} \sqrt{kT} \qquad \ldots (4.30)$$

which is very nearly the same as the condition that the collision frequency and applied frequency are equal, i.e. $\nu = \omega$. The theory can be extended to give a curve similar to the familiar Paschen curve relating the gas pressure to the potential necessary to maintain a given current. For a given frequency the minimum lies at that gas pressure which gives $\nu \sim \omega$.

### AVERAGE ELECTRON ENERGY AND ITS VARIATIONS WITH FREQUENCY AT HIGH GAS PRESSURE

The variation of the average electron energy as the applied field varies periodically has been studied by TOWNSEND[26], and later by VON ENGEL and HARRIES[27]. It is clear that if the frequency is high, so that the electrons lose little energy to the gas molecules between cycles of the field, then the mean energy will be nearly constant with only a small periodic ripple. At low frequencies the mean energy will vary with the field; if $\varepsilon$ is the mean energy at some instant, $t$, the change, $d\varepsilon$, in ensuing time, $dt$, is given by the difference between the gain due to the electrons moving $dx$ in the field, and the loss by collisions with the gas molecules.

$$d\varepsilon = (eX_0 \sin \omega t)\, dx - \kappa . \varepsilon v\, dt \qquad \dots(4.31)$$

Here $\kappa$ is the average fraction of the energy lost in each collision, and $v$ the collision frequency. At high pressure the drift velocity is in phase with the field,

$$\frac{dx}{dt} = b_e X_0 \sin \omega t \qquad \dots(4.32)$$

which leads to

$$\frac{d\varepsilon}{dt} + \kappa \varepsilon v = eb_e X_0 \sin^2 \omega t \qquad \dots(4.33)$$

$\kappa$ is treated as a constant, equal to the value for elastic collisions $(2m/M)$. Townsend assumes that the variation in $\varepsilon$ is small compared with the mean value and, by expansion in a series, derives the approximate result

$$\varepsilon = \varepsilon_0 - \frac{1}{4}\frac{\kappa v}{\omega} . \varepsilon_0 \sin 2\omega t \qquad \dots(4.34)$$

where $\varepsilon_0$ is that constant mean energy which the electrons would have in the r.m.s. value of the applied field, i.e. in a d.c. field $X = X_0/\sqrt{2}$. As would be expected, since the electrons gain

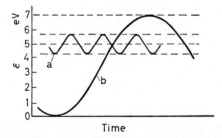

*Figure 4.2. Variation of the average electron energy with time, in helium at $X/p \sim 0.6$ V/cm mm Hg: (a) high frequency; (b) low frequency. (From A. von* ENGEL *and W. L.* HARRIES[27], *by courtesy of the Royal Society)*

93

energy, on the average, independent of the direction of the field, the ripple has twice the frequency of the applied field.

Harries and von Engel apply this equation to the particular example of neon, in which gas $v$ is approximately proportional to $\varepsilon$. The equation then reduces to one which can be solved by the application of Mathieu functions, and a typical result is shown in *Figure 4.2*. At low frequency the ripple is 100 per cent, while at high frequency the ripple is small but the peak energy less, for the same values of the applied field.

It has been known for about fifty years that a gas can be made conducting when placed in a rapidly alternating electric field. Some of the earliest experiments were made by TESLA[28], WIEDE-MANN and EBERT[29] and THOMSON[30], but a systematic study did not begin until about 1920. Low pressures, up to a few cm mercury, and frequencies up to a few Mc/s were used; the starting or mainte-nance potential was measured and its variation with the nature and pressure of the gas, the frequency of the applied field, and the electrode separation noted. The geometry of the apparatus is an important factor, and various workers have used widely differing arrangements. Furthermore, some have placed electrodes inside the discharge vessel, and some outside (exciting the so-called electrodeless discharge); it is essential to distinguish between these types as the properties of the discharges can sometimes be very different. The arrangements most commonly used are:

(1) Parallel plate electrodes (either internal or external) or co-axial cylindrical electrodes, which give a known electric field. Discharges in long cylindrical tubes are often maintained by a non-uniform field applied through short external cylindrical sleeve electrodes at each end.

(2) A solenoid carrying an oscillating current, wrapped around the discharge vessel, usually cylindrical in shape. The electric field, $X$, and the discharge current form a closed path in the gas, and $X$ is determined by the rate of change of magnetic flux through the area enclosed by the path ('ring discharge').

(3) A resonant cavity for fields of very high frequencies (micro-waves). Here the distribution of the field is determined by the method and consequent mode of excitation of the cavity, and its magnitude is deduced from power measurements. Microwave techniques are a rather specialized study, and

their applications to discharge measurements have been fully set out by BROWN, GOULD and ROSE[31,32].

Discharges in arrangements (1) and (2) are frequently called *E* and *H* discharges respectively because of their obvious connections with simple electric and magnetic fields, and their different properties have been extensively discussed[33]. The uniform electric

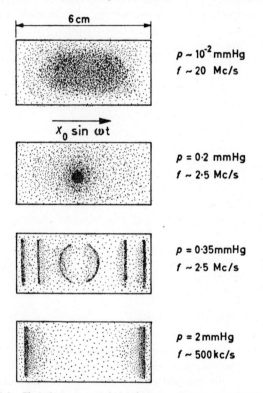

*Figure 4.3. Typical appearance of high-frequency discharges in cylindrical glass vessels. A uniform electric field is applied along the axis*

field (1) clearly provides the simplest condition for the study of high-frequency discharges; in these conditions the field, current, potential, etc. can most easily be measured and the results interpreted.

Several ideas were advanced to explain the mechanism of the discharges studied by early workers. Some were thought to be analogous to the d.c. glow discharge, each electrode or end wall acting in alternate half cycles as cathode and anode. At low frequencies and at not too low pressures the fully developed discharge does in fact show bright and dark regions and sometimes striations very similar to the glow discharge (see *Figure 4.3*). This occurs when the amplitude of oscillation of an electron cloud is greater than the length of the vessel. Working at higher frequencies and in long tubes, Townsend and Gill showed the resemblance between the electrodeless discharge and the positive column of a glow discharge, the only difference being the ionization due to the electron moving in an oscillating field. J. THOMSON[34] developed an elementary theory, considering the motion of a free electron in a gas: according to this, the condition for breakdown is that an electron must, at some point in its path, acquire enough energy to ionize, and must hit a gas molecule before it returns this energy to the field. A similar idea was postulated by J. J. THOMSON[35] in explanation of the electrodeless ring discharge, i.e. a discharge in a cylindrical vessel placed in a solenoid. These theories had some success in explaining qualitatively the properties of the discharges, but were not able to predict absolute values of starting field, etc. Several workers noticed a double minimum in the graph of the starting potential as a function of the pressure: this occurs only at lower frequencies, and GILL and DONALDSON[36] showed that it was connected with the size and shape of the vessel, one of the steeply rising parts being due to large losses when the electrons were driven near to the walls of the vessel. In the earlier literature curves showing spurious maxima, minima and inflexion points can be found, but these were usually caused by the circuits employed.

LOW-PRESSURE DISCHARGE ($\lambda_e >$ dimensions of vessel)

*General Explanation of Breakdown*

The low-pressure discharge has a number of quite distinctive properties. The starting potential is very low (in the region of 100 V), and is determined almost entirely by the material of the electrodes (or the walls in an electrodeless discharge) and the geometry. It is independent of the nature and pressure of the gas. The properties of the fully developed discharge, however, depend on the gas, and hardly at all on the walls. There is also a certain critical frequency, for a particular vessel, called the cut-off frequency, below which it is not possible to start the discharge even when extremely large fields are applied.

The explanation is that, at these low pressures, electrons move along the vessel virtually in vacuum, colliding with the walls much more often than with gas molecules. Electrons can multiply

96

initially only if they move to and fro between the walls of the vessel in resonance with the field, and hit the walls hard enough to eject secondary electrons. The simple theory of such a motion has been outlined by BACKMARK and BENGSTON[37], GILL and von ENGEL[38], and HATCH and WILLIAMS[39]; some refinements have recently been added[43-48,228,229]. (The curious name 'multipacting mechanism' is sometimes used to identify it.)

Clearly, for multiplication, two conditions must be satisfied at the same time: (a) the electrons must cross the tube in half a cycle of the applied field: in angular measure $\omega t = \pi$, where $t$ is the transit time; and (b) the energy of the electrons, when they arrive at an electrode or end wall, must be great enough that at least one secondary electron is emitted for each electron hitting the surface. If $\delta$ is the secondary emission coefficient (ratio of secondary electrons emitted to primary electrons incident), then $\delta \geqslant 1$ is an ideal condition for multiplication between infinite parallel plates: in practical vessels $\delta$ must be somewhat greater than 1 to allow for losses. These are due, first to the angular distribution of the emitted electrons, and secondly to the reflection with almost un-diminished speed of some of the primaries. Thus some of the secondary electrons hit the side walls, and some, by virtue of their very large initial speed, get out of resonance with the field.

Suppose that each secondary electron leaving one wall (or electrode) in the plane $x = 0$ has a velocity $v_0$ in the $x$ direction, along which a uniform high-frequency field $X_0 \sin \omega t$ is applied; if they all leave together when the phase of the field is $\phi$, and take half a cycle (time $t = \pi/\omega$) to reach the opposite wall $x = d$, arriving with velocity $v$, then conditions (1) and (2) can be written:

$$\omega d = \left( v_0 + \frac{eX_0}{m\omega} \cos \phi \right) \pi + \frac{2eX_0}{m\omega} \sin \phi \quad \ldots (4.35)$$

$$v = v_0 + \frac{2eX_0}{m\omega} \cos \phi \geqslant v_{\text{critical for } \delta=1} \quad \ldots (4.36)$$

In general, for a given frequency, this pair of equations has two solutions, two different values of $\phi$ giving rise to two different values of starting field $X_0$. However, this is not of great importance because the equations given are applicable only over certain ranges determined by other physical considerations.

*Secondary Electron Emission*[40-42]

Some of the important facts of secondary electron emission which are relevant to low-pressure, high-frequency breakdown, are sum-marized in *Figure 2.9* (see also Chapter 2, pp. 34, 35). The curve of $\delta$ against energy of the primary electrons falling normally is of a similar shape for all materials, with an ill-defined maximum for electrons of several hundred volts energy. Metals which have a layer of gas on the surface give high yields; rough surfaces, e.g. soot, give very low yields, with $\delta_{max.} < 1$. If the line $\delta = 1$ is drawn across the curve, it is clear that for substances with large yields, equation (4.36) can be satisfied over a wide range of energies, and conversely for substances with maximum yields only slightly

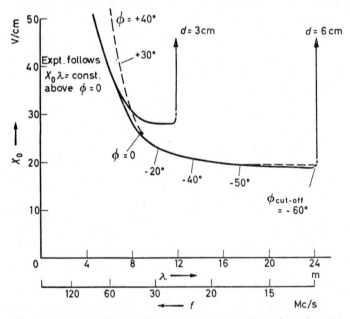

Figure 4.4. Peak starting field, $X_0$, as a function of wavelength, $\lambda$, for flat-ended glass cylindrical tubes of length, d. Field parallel to axis of vessel: gas hydrogen, $p = 1 \times 10^{-3}$ mm Hg. (———) experiment; (- - - - -) simple theory. $X_0\lambda \cos \phi = constant$ for $d = 6$ cm and velocities (expressed as energies) $v_0 = 7$ eV, $v = 93$ eV, $k = v/v_0 = 3\cdot7$. (From E. W. B. GILL and A. VON ENGEL[38], by courtesy of the Royal Society)

greater than 1. Yields are greatly increased when the primary electrons fall at an angle to the surface, increasing by 50 per cent or more when the angle between the primary beam and the normal is 60°. It follows that in the discharges described here electrons glancing on to the side walls can sometimes make an appreciable contribution to the multiplication.

The energy distribution of the emitted secondary electrons is approximately Maxwellian with a most probable energy between

2 and 5 eV for most materials. In addition, a small fraction of the primary electrons are reflected. Neglecting these, the number of true secondaries emitted per unit solid angle in the direction $\theta$ to the normal is proportional to $\cos \theta$, and this is independent of the angle of the primary electrons. Hence most come out normally to the surface.

### Experimental Results

The main experimental results are now given, showing the variation of starting field with frequency or wavelength. *Figure 4.4* shows mainly the measurements of Gill and von Engel in cylindrical

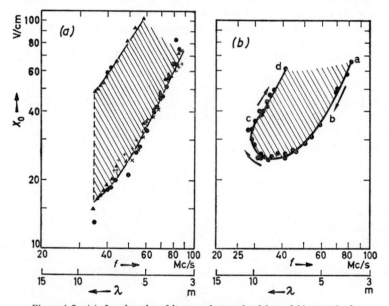

*Figure 4.5.* (a) *Log–log plot of lower and upper breakdown field strengths for alclad electrodes in $O_2$, $p \sim 10^{-3}$ mm Hg. Electrode separation 3 cm; diameter 7·5 cm; broken line indicates cut-off frequency. The breakdown region is shaded;* (b) *log–log plot of closed breakdown curve for silver–copper electrodes in $H_2$, $p \sim 10^{-4}$ mm Hg. Electrode separation 3 cm; diameter 6·5 cm; data taken in order indicated by arrows. The breakdown region is shaded.* (From A. J. HATCH and H. B. WILLIAMS[39], by courtesy of Journal of Applied Physics)

vessels with external electrodes, and *Figure 4.5* those of Hatch and Williams with internal electrodes. The latter find two breakdown potentials, one measured in the usual way by slowly increasing the applied field, the other by suddenly applying a large field and slowly reducing it. Other workers using internal electrodes found that by increasing the potential they could put out a fully developed discharge, and these experiments show that on a graph of field versus frequency there are closed regions, outside which a low-pressure discharge can be neither started nor maintained. Experiments with external electrodes, i.e. 'electrodeless' discharges, have not shown either an upper starting potential or the extinction of the discharge by an increasing field (except at extremely low pressures), for reasons which are explained on p. 110. Breakdown potentials are measured with a valve voltmeter or a system of diodes attached to an electrostatic voltmeter which thus reads the peak value of the applied field. When a discharge starts, a glow appears and the applied potential shows a sudden drop due to the reaction on the oscillator and coupling circuit. At extremely low pressures ($< 10^{-4}$ mm Hg) the discharge current is so small that more sensitive methods to detect breakdown may be necessary.

### Comparison with Theory

Theoretically, for a detailed explanation of the results, the number of parameters must first be reduced by making the assumption that since $v$ and $v_0$, i.e. velocity of impact and emission, are both approximately constant, their ratio

$$k = \frac{v}{v_0} = \sqrt{\frac{\varepsilon_{\text{primary}}}{\varepsilon_{\text{secondary}}}} \qquad \dots (4.37)$$

is also constant.

Equations (4.35) and (4.36) can now be written

$$v = \frac{k}{k-1} \cdot \frac{2eX_0}{m\omega} \cos \phi; \quad \text{or} \quad X_0 \lambda \cos \phi = \text{const.} \times v \quad \dots (4.38)$$

$$X_0 = \frac{\omega^2 d}{\dfrac{e}{m}\left(\dfrac{k+1}{k-1} \cdot \pi \cos \phi + 2 \sin \phi\right)} \qquad \dots (4.39)$$

For any arbitrary, but reasonable, value of $k$ (Gill and von Engel take $k = 10$ or $5$ as examples) the above equations can be solved by numerical trial and error to give a graph of $X$ against $\lambda$, closely similar in shape to the experimental ones except for the cut-off. The cut-off occurs because, at lower frequencies (longer wavelengths) the electrons must leave the wall in more negative phases in order that they take half a cycle to travel the length of the tube. For negative values of $\phi$, the field, until it reverses, opposes the motion of electrons in the $x$ direction. Their initial velocity takes them a little distance against this force, and then they turn back, accelerating towards $x = 0$, until the reversal of the field decelerates them and turns them finally in the proper direction (see *Figure 4.6*). The largest permissible value of $-\phi$ is that which just returns the electrons to the wall, i.e. the second turning point is $dx/dt = 0$ at $x = 0$. (In more negative phases this second turning point is theoretically at negative values of $x$, which means that the electrons are driven back to the wall at very low speed and stick there, so that no multiplication can take place.) This limiting condition

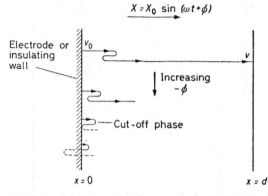

*Figure 4.6. Paths of electrons starting from $x = 0$ when the phase $\phi$ of the field is negative. (After E. W. B. GILL and A. VON ENGEL[38])*

when inserted in equations (4.38) and (4.39) leads to expressions which can again be solved numerically by trial and error to give the cut-off phase and frequency. However, only relative values can be obtained since $k$ is an adjustable parameter, and in order to compare theory with experiment it is necessary to fit the two at one point. For example Gill and von Engel note that since $X_0\lambda \cos \phi$ is a constant, $X_0\lambda$ will be a minimum when $\phi = 0$. The experimental values of $X_0$ and $\lambda$ which give a minimum product $X_0\lambda$ were inserted in the equations with $\phi = 0$, from which they derived $k \approx 4$, and found excellent agreement, within a few per cent, with the experimental curve and cut-off wavelength, but only for negative phases. For positive phases the theoretical curve was too steep, the experimental curve following the law $X_0\lambda = $ constant. The reason was that in the vessels used electrons could often be multiplied by striking the side walls, and in travelling shorter distances required a smaller field to multiply. In tubes with side walls far removed theoretical and experimental curves were much closer.

In spherical vessels placed in a uniform field, the breakdown curve agrees with this theory between cut-off and approximately the wavelength for which $\phi = 0$. For shorter wavelengths $X_0\lambda$ remains constant, the reason being that a spherical vessel offers the

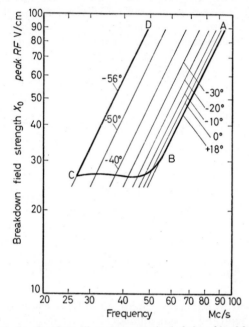

*Figure 4.7. Log–log plot to illustrate theoretical calculation of breakdown region, for 3 cm electrode separation, $v = 60\,eV$, $v_0 = 6\cdot6\,eV$ $(k = 3)$. Light lines represent conditions of half-cycle electron transit time at indicated phase angles. Heavy curves represent boundary of theoretical breakdown region. (From A. J. HATCH and H. B. WILLIAMS[39], by courtesy of Journal of Applied Physics)*

electrons a continuous range of $d$, measured along a chord, from zero to the diameter of the sphere. From $\lambda_{\text{cut-off}}$ down to the wavelength at which $\phi = 0$ the electrons cross the diameter, but at shorter wavelengths the necessary speed of arrival, $v$, can be achieved with the least field if $\phi$ remains zero [equation (4.38)]. Equation (4.35) shows that as $\lambda$ decreases with $\phi$ remaining zero the electrons travel a shorter distance, say $d'$, in half a cycle and thus multiply along that chord whose length is $d'$.

The theory given above arises from a consideration of equation

(4.36), implying that the most severe condition to be satisfied is that the electrons shall hit the wall with enough energy to release more than one secondary. Agreement with experiment indicates that, in the conditions of these experiments, this is probably true; it is not always so, however, and following Hatch and Williams we consider the field necessary to satisfy the resonance condition.

Equation (4.39) gives, at a fixed value of $\omega$ and $d$, a minimum $X_0$ when the bracket in the denominator is a maximum. This occurs when

$$\phi = \tan^{-1}\left(\frac{k-1}{k+1} \cdot \frac{2}{\pi}\right) \qquad \ldots\ldots(4.40)$$

Equation (4.39), when plotted as $\log X_0$ against $\log \omega$ (or log of frequency), gives a straight line of slope 2, for a fixed phase. Assuming that the linear part of the lower experimental breakdown curve corresponds to the least field which can move the electrons

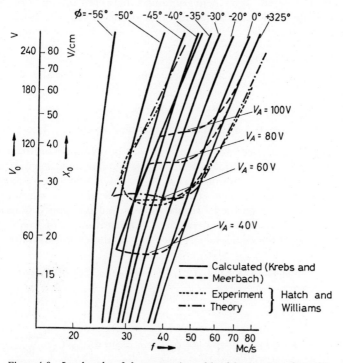

*Figure 4.8. Log–log plot of electron transits and breakdown regions, for various energies of arrival, $V_A$, at the wall. (From K. KREBS and H. MEERBACH[43], by courtesy of Annalen der Physik)*

103

across in half a cycle, theory and experiment can be made to agree by choosing $k = 3$, $\phi = + 18°$ (for electrodes 3 cm apart). For phases more negative than $+ 18°$ similar linear $\log X_0 - \log f$ graphs can be drawn, each of which denotes transit in half a cycle for electrons starting at the chosen phase (see *Figure 4.7*). A limiting condition is reached at the cut-off phase: at a given frequency the application of a field greater than that plotted would require electrons to start in a phase more negative than cut-off in order to cross in half a cycle. This limiting line is found to fit well with the upper breakdown curve, and it can be shown that over most of the range of these lines the condition that $\delta \geqslant 1$ is easily satisfied. However, for each phase, as both field and frequency are decreased, a limit is reached below which the field is not large enough to give the electrons sufficient energy of impact. By joining these points the curve BC in *Figure 4.7* is obtained, and the space enclosed by the limiting conditions denotes the breakdown region. *Figure 4.8* shows the good agreement obtained between this theory and experiment, and also similar theoretical curves due to KREBS and MEERBACH[43].

### The Cut-off Frequency

Here again, theory and experimental results of many workers agree in giving

$$\left.\begin{array}{l} f_{\text{cut-off}} = C/d \ (\simeq 79/d, \quad f \text{ in Mc/s, } d \text{ in cm}) \\ \lambda_{\text{cut-off}} = C' \cdot d \ (\simeq 3 \cdot 8 \cdot d, \quad \lambda \text{ in m, } d \text{ in cm}) \end{array}\right\} \dots (4.41)$$

where $d$ is the electrode separation or the distance between the walls. This can be deduced from general similarity or algebraically from the equations, noting that $\phi_{\text{cut-off}}$ is independent of frequency, and that at cut-off both conditions, $\omega t = \pi$ and $v = \text{constant} = v_{\text{critical for } \delta=1}$, are satisfied. It follows also that the applied potential at cut-off is a constant, independent of separation, $d$, or frequency.

If $\varepsilon_{\text{critical}}$ is the critical energy for $\delta = 1$, the expressions are

$$V_{\text{cut-off}} = \frac{\varepsilon_{\text{critical}} (k - 1)^2 \left[\dfrac{k + 1}{k - 1} \cdot \pi \cos \phi_{\text{cut-off}} + 2 \sin \phi_{\text{cut-off}}\right]}{2k^2 \cos^2 \phi_{\text{cut-off}}}$$

$$\dots (4.42)$$

$$f_{\text{cut-off}} = \frac{(k - 1) \left[\dfrac{k + 1}{k - 1} \pi \cos \phi_{\text{cut-off}} + 2 \sin \phi_{\text{cut-off}}\right] \sqrt{\dfrac{\varepsilon_{\text{critical}}}{8m}}}{k\pi d \cos \phi_{\text{cut-off}}}$$

$$\dots (4.43)$$

*Extensions of Experiment and Theory*

*Effect of lateral motion*—Here, distinction must be made between arrangements with internal and external electrodes. If internal electrodes are used in a vessel whose side walls are far away, then electrons moving laterally simply escape from the discharge space. This source of loss becomes greater as the diameter of the electrodes is reduced, their separation being kept constant; a higher starting field is required to compensate, and in consequence the cut-off frequency is increased. The general shape of the $X_0 - \lambda$ or $X_0 - f$ curves is unaltered. In the electrodeless discharge, however, the side walls are not only a source of loss, but in certain favourable conditions a source of secondary electrons, offering the electrons an oblique path shorter than the length of the vessel. Thus the electrons never start in positive phases, but whenever possible in the phase $\phi = 0$, giving the curve $X_0\lambda =$ constant at higher frequencies.

It is extremely difficult, experimentally, to obtain ideal conditions for comparison with one-dimensional theories. If a cylindrical vessel is placed between large, flat, parallel electrodes the field is uniform but the side walls play a part in the mechanism of the discharge; if the electrodes are placed inside a wide vessel the side walls play no part, but the field is non-uniform at the edges. In measuring starting potentials this cannot be overcome by using guard rings; it is always possible that the discharge starts in the non-uniform region and spreads inwards but this could only be decided by time measurements showing whether a discharge between guard rings preceded that in the main gap.

*Very high frequencies*—At very high frequencies extremely large fields are required to satisfy the resonance conditions as previously given but, in general, multiplication can continue if the transit time is any odd multiple of half a cycle ($\omega t = n\pi$, where $n = 1, 3, 5 \ldots$). *Figure 4.9* shows the theoretical breakdown curves, with their several cut-off wavelengths, for $n = 1, 3, 5$; the dotted curve, giving experimental results in a cylindrical glass vessel, obeys the law $X_0\lambda =$ constant over much of its length, showing that electrons choose the combination of mode and path length which avoids starting in positive phases.

*Superimposed fields*—It has been found that by superimposing a d.c. electric field parallel to the high-frequency field, starting can be made more difficult. A small static magnetic field perpendicular to the h.f. electric field causes a general increase in breakdown field, and a lowering of the cut-off frequency, but leaves the general shape of the $X_0$–$\lambda$ curve unaltered[44,45] (see *Figure 4.10*). This is

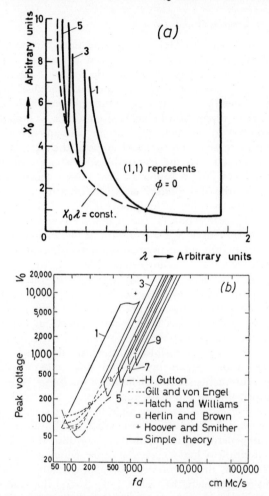

*Figure 4.9. (a) Starting field as a function of wavelength calculated for electron transit times of 1, 3 and 5 half periods (k = 10). (From E. W. B. GILL and A. VON ENGEL[38], by courtesy of the Royal Society); (b) comparison of various data (including some very recent work[228],[229]) with simple theory, giving breakdown regions corresponding to electron transits taking 1, 3, 5, 7, 9, . . . half cycles. (From A. J. HATCH and H. B. WILLIAMS[228], by courtesy of Physical Review)*

consistent with increased losses due to lateral motion caused by the curvature of the electron paths, and similarly the increased transit time equivalent to a lengthening of the vessel. In large magnetic

106

fields the starting potential is almost independent of frequency. A discharge at very low pressure ($\sim 10^{-5}$ mm Hg), once started, can

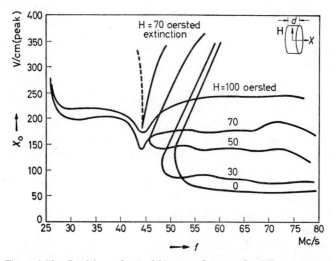

*Figure 4.10. Breakdown electric field versus frequency for different magnetic fields, H, in a cylindrical discharge tube, diameter 1·6 cm. The double-valued curves bound the discharge region. (By courtesy of Hughes Aircraft Company)*

be put out by either increasing the electric field or decreasing the magnetic field.

### Verification of Theory

*Pressure range*—The theory would be expected to break down when the electron mean free path becomes comparable with the length of the vessel; for vessels a few centimetres in size this is at $p \sim 10^{-2}$ mm Hg for most gases and has been confirmed[46]. At frequencies above cut-off the graphs of starting potential against pressure for air, He and $H_2$ follow approximately the Paschen curve, but break off on the low-pressure side into a horizontal section ($X_0$ independent of $p$) stretching from $10^{-2}$ to $10^{-6}$ mm Hg.

*Electrode material*—Coating the electrodes or end walls with a poor secondary emitter (palladium black or soot) necessitates a much higher starting field, or makes it completely impossible to start the discharge.

*Electron energies*—The energy with which electrons arrive at the electrodes has been measured by allowing some to pass through a small hole and applying retarding potentials to a collector[46-48]. Energies of 100 eV have been found when 150 V peak h.f. is applied; groups of electrons have been found with energies corresponding to a transit time of 3/2 cycles, and the spread of electron energies compares well with theory.

## Growth and Maintenance of the Low-pressure Discharge

The theory and experiments, from which the starting condition is derived, do not explain the transition from the initial wall process to the final state in which the spectrum of the gas is emitted from a luminous region, and the walls apparently play little or no part. Experiments have been devised to measure the current flowing through an electrodeless discharge[49], a bridge circuit being used to eliminate the relatively large capacitive currents flowing between the external electrodes. A pulsed high-frequency source, synchronized with an oscilloscope, was used to measure the rate of growth of current. *Figure 4.11* shows the envelope of the growing high-frequency current in hydrogen and helium at two different pressures, the same potential (starting potential) being applied to all four discharges. Clearly, although the starting conditions are the same for all, the rate growth of current and its final values increase with gas pressure, and is greater in the gas which has the steeper ionization probability curve. It has also been shown that the current rises faster and to a larger value with excess potential, and an increase in frequency of the applied field (see *Figure 4.12*).

The explanation of these results is briefly as follows[49-51]. Electrons multiply initially by secondary emission from the end walls. Account must be taken of the effect of the positive wall charge left behind when more electrons leave the wall than hit it ($\delta > 1$); this delays their subsequent crossing and so alters their distribution in phase. It can be shown that for multiplication to continue not only must the total number of electrons be maintained, but also their distribution in phase. In a number of transits each electron will occasionally hit and ionize a gas molecule, those ions which are relatively heavy remaining almost stationary, and after a number of half cycles a concentration of positive ions is built up in the vessel; detailed analysis shows that it has a slight maximum in the centre of the vessel. Up to this point the effective multiplication of the electrons at every crossing of the vessel is $\delta'(1 - a)$ where $\delta'$ is the secondary emission coefficient necessary to overcome losses to the side walls, and those due to the spread in energies of the emitted electrons. The factor $a$ represents the small fraction of electrons ($a \ll 1$) which are lost by falling out of phase when

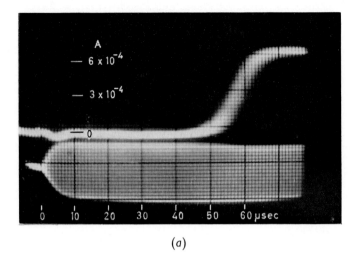

(a)

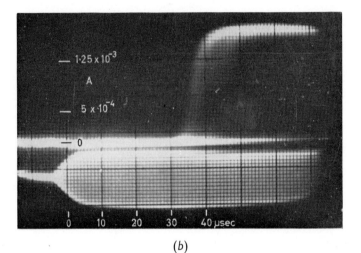

(b)

*Figure 4.11. The rate of growth of current in electrodeless discharges in hydrogen and helium, in a cylindrical Pyrex vessel placed between parallel plates. Length of vessel = 6 cm; frequency = 17 Mc/s ($\lambda \sim 18$ m). Starting potential applied (114 volts): (a)* He, $p = 12 \times 10^{-3}$ mm Hg; *(b)* $H_2$, $p = 12 \times 10^{-3}$ mm Hg.

(From G. Francis and A. von Engel[49], by courtesy of the Royal Society)

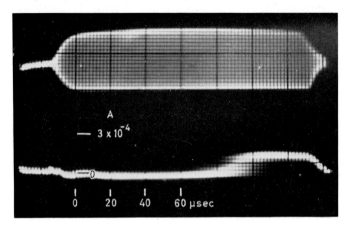

(c)

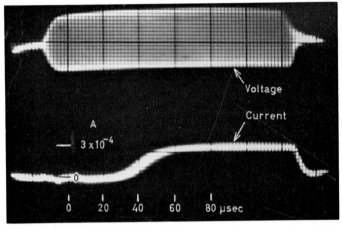

(d)

Figure 4.11—continued: (c) He, $p = 2 \times 10^{-3}$ mm Hg; (d) $H_2$, $p = 2 \times 10^{-3}$ mm Hg.

(From G. FRANCIS and A. VON ENGEL[49], by courtesy of the Royal Society)

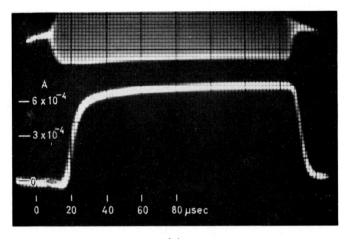

(a)

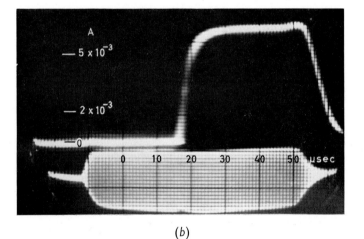

(b)

*Figure 4.12. Effect of excess potential and change of frequency on the rate of growth of current: (a) He, $p = 2 \times 10^{-3}$ mm Hg, $\lambda = 18$ m, 20 per cent excess potential. Compare Figure 4.11 (c) and note the much faster growth and reduced scatter with increased potential; (b) $H_2$, $p = 12 \times 10^{-3}$ mm Hg, $\lambda = 15$ m ($f = 20$ Mc/s). Starting potential applied (116 volts). Compare Figure 4.11 (b) and note the very much faster rate of rise of current and its greater equilibrium value at the slightly higher frequency.*

(From G. FRANCIS and A. VON ENGEL[49], by courtesy of the Royal Society)

they ionize a gas molecule. The rate of growth of current is thus given by

$$i \propto [\delta'(1 - a)]^t \qquad \dots (4.44)$$

A second stage of the growth occurs when the positive ion space charge is large enough to affect the motion of the electrons. The result is that their speed in the gas, and hence the rate of ionization, increases whilst their speed of impact on the walls, and hence the secondary emission, decreases. Production of new electrons by

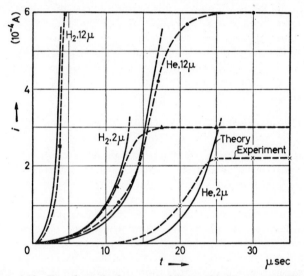

*Figure 4.13. Rate of growth of currents in helium and hydrogen at two different pressures, from theory and experiment. (From G. Francis and A. von Engel[49], by courtesy of the Royal Society)*

these two processes are of equal importance, and the results of the theory are shown in *Figure 4.13*.

Finally all the electrons originally produced by secondary emission are lost to the end walls and replaced by those due to ionization, which execute forced oscillations in phase with the field about the central positive space charge. They move in a layer with an amplitude rather less than the length of the vessel; the layer widens slowly by self repulsion and electrons are deposited on the end walls at the same rate as they are reproduced by ionization in the gas. The rate of these processes, and their dependence on the frequency and amplitude of motion of the electrons, can be calculated and agrees well with the measured currents. This third stage is reached only at the higher pressures in the range $p \sim 10^{-3}$ mm Hg. At pressures less than about $10^{-4}$ mm Hg the ion cloud is not dense enough to control the oscillation of the electrons.

This theory would explain why an increase in field at these pressures will extinguish a discharge between internal electrodes, but not an electrodeless discharge. The strong negative wall charge in the latter helps the ion space charge to diminish the amplitude of the electrons, reducing losses and giving a rapid rise of current. Electrons swept on to metal electrodes, however, do not give rise to these strong fields. Similarly, it is probably very difficult to measure the upper breakdown potential of an electrodeless discharge, because the applied field cannot easily be made to rise so rapidly that the discharge does not start during the transient. At low gas pressure ($\sim 10^{-5}$ mm Hg) the discharge continues largely as the initial wall process and the extinction potential can then be measured[44].

### THE HIGH-PRESSURE, HIGH-FREQUENCY DISCHARGE: DIFFUSION THEORY[245]

Discharges of this type occur when both the mean free path and the amplitude of oscillation of the electrons are appreciably less than the length of the vessel, so that both gas pressure and applied frequency must exceed certain critical values for a given geometry. In ordinary vessels this means $p > 10^{-2}$ mm Hg and $f > 100$ Mc/s, approximately. In many ways these are the simplest of all high-frequency discharges, because only two processes occur (at least in discharges of low charge concentration), namely, ionization due to electrons hitting gas molecules, and diffusion of electrons and ions to the walls. In certain gases electrons can be effectively removed by attachment to gas molecules; loss by recombination is usually negligible, except when the concentrations of charges are large.

*Breakdown*

The condition for the starting of the discharge is that on the average each electron must create one new electron by an ionizing collision in the time it takes to diffuse to the walls. If $D_e$ is the diffusion coefficient of electrons and $\nu_i$ the number of ionizing collisions made by each electron per sec, i.e. the ionization collision frequency, then the critical condition for the multiplication of a small concentration, $n_e$, of electrons, i.e. for a discharge to occur, is

$$D_e \nabla^2 n_e + \nu_i n_e = 0 \qquad \ldots . (4.45)$$

The first term is the rate at which electrons are lost to the walls by diffusion, and the second the rate at which new electrons are produced by ionization in the gas. Consider, for example, a gas between infinite parallel plates a distance, $d$, apart, in which by external irradiation a small number, $Q$, electrons and ions per cm³ are produced uniformly throughout the volume. The rate of rise of electron density is given by

$$\frac{\partial n_e}{\partial t} = Q + v_i n_e + D_e \frac{\partial^2 n_e}{\partial x^2} \qquad \ldots (4.46)$$

where $n_e$ is, of course, a function of position and time. Usually $Q$ is regarded as small and the approach to breakdown so slow that $\partial n / \partial t$ can be ignored. Measuring $x$ from the mid-plane and assuming that the electron density is zero at the walls, gives the solution

$$n_e = \frac{\frac{4}{\pi} Q \cdot \cos \frac{\pi x}{d}}{D_e \left(\frac{\pi}{d}\right)^2 - v_i} \qquad \ldots (4.47)$$

The electron density will rise to a very high value, independent of the external irradiation, when

$$D_e \left(\frac{\pi}{d}\right)^2 = v_i \qquad \ldots (4.48)$$

which is the solution of equation (4.45).

It must be noted, however, that if $Q$ is not small and uniform the full solution of equation (4.46) may give a rapid rise, though not theoretically to infinity, before condition (4.47) is reached. Other processes, e.g. ambipolar diffusion, may then assist complete breakdown. Thus the breakdown conditions may be expected to depend on the amount of external irradiation, and this has, in fact, been found[53-55].

At high pressures, where the electrons drift as a body in the field, the ionization frequency may be expressed in terms of Townsend's ionization coefficient, $\alpha$, since

$$v_i = \alpha v_{\text{drift}} = \alpha b_e X \qquad \ldots (4.49)$$

where $b_e$ is the electron mobility. Equation (4.48) then assumes the form due to Holstein,

$$(pd)^2 = \frac{\pi^2 k T_e}{e \left(\frac{X}{p}\right) \left(\frac{\alpha}{p}\right)} \qquad \ldots (4.50)$$

111

provided that the applied frequency is greater than the frequency of elastic collisions and less than the frequency of inelastic collisions. The energy distribution of the electrons is the same as for a static field, equal to the r.m.s. value of the applied field, so that values of $\alpha/p$, $T_e$ measured in static fields may be used.

More generally, the solution for a vessel of any geometry in a uniform field is:

$$\nu_i = \frac{D}{L^2} \qquad \dots (4.51)$$

where $L$ is a quantity known as the diffusion length[56]. If $\tau$ is the mean lifetime of an electron before it arrives at the wall,

$$\tau D = L^2 \qquad \dots (4.52)$$

For some geometries $L$ reduces to simple expressions, e.g. a cylinder, length $d$, radius $r$

$$\frac{1}{L^2} = \left(\frac{\pi}{d}\right)^2 + \left(\frac{2 \cdot 405}{r}\right)^2 \qquad \dots (4.53)$$

For two parallel plates of separation, $d$, width, $a$, and infinite height

$$\frac{1}{L^2} = \left(\frac{\pi}{d}\right)^2 + \left(\frac{\pi}{a}\right)^2 \qquad \dots (4.54)$$

*Breakdown Curves*

Simple physical arguments indicate how the starting field should vary. The larger the vessel, or the greater the electrode separation, the smaller the field necessary to start the discharge, since an electron then has a greater chance of ionizing before it is lost to the walls.

The shape of the breakdown potential, $V_s$, against pressure curves may also be predicted. At high pressure (many collisions per oscillation) conditions are similar to d.c., the electrons gaining a small amount of energy, $X\lambda_e$, along a free path and losing it in elastic collisions. As pressure increases, the energy gained per mean free path decreases; however, to maintain the rate of ionization a nearly constant mean energy is required and hence $X$ has to be increased so that it is nearly proportional to $1/\lambda_e$, i.e. to the pressure. This is the familiar right-hand part of the Paschen curve. As the frequency is increased this curve will lie at slightly lower potentials, because the amplitude of drift motion of the electrons will be less, and the very small losses to the walls due to this motion will be still further reduced.

Now, as the pressure is reduced, the starting potential will decrease until one of two critical conditions is reached, depending on the size of the vessel and the frequency applied. It may happen that in the space available, the number of molecules is such that an electron makes too few ionizing collisions before diffusing to the walls, whilst the frequency is such that it still makes many elastic collisions per oscillation of the field. Further reduction in pressure then requires an increased field to cause breakdown. This is an exact high-frequency equivalent of the d.c. curve in the sense that the minimum arises from the same physical reasons. From this argument, with increasing frequency the entire curve should lie at lower potential, and the minimum should be shifted towards lower pressures.

However, at appreciably higher frequencies a reduction in pressure might lead first to the condition in which the electron makes many oscillations in the field before colliding with a gas molecule, whilst there is still an ample density of gas in the vessel for it to ionize before diffusing to the wall. Between collisions the electron oscillates at 90° out of phase with the field, and on average gains no energy. The field becomes less and less effective in transferring energy to the electrons as the pressure decreases [see equation (4.18)]. Hence the field must be increased rapidly in order to maintain the rate of ionization and compensate for the increased losses by diffusion. In this region the average electron energy will be large, and a great proportion of the losses will be due to inelastic collisions*. Following Townsend and Gill, it can be shown that, in these circumstances, the breakdown field at high pressure $(\nu \gg f)$ will be almost independent of frequency, whereas at low pressure $(\nu \ll f)$ it will be proportional to the frequency for a given pressure. The minimum occurs when the collision frequency, $\nu$, and applied frequency, $\omega$, are approximately equal. This should be compared with the results on pp. 87–92 which show that in these conditions the gas has also its greatest conductivity. This correspondence with the minimum starting potential has been found experimentally[57, 58].

Thus, within the range of pressure and frequency where diffusion is the main source of loss, two types of breakdown curves are found, superficially very similar. There are many examples of the first kind in pre-war literature[59-64]: in vessels having dimensions

---

* This explains why, at low pressures $(p \sim 20 . 10^{-3}$ mm Hg$)$ and high frequencies $(f > 10$ Mc/s$)$, it has sometimes been possible to account for breakdown by assuming that an electron gains ionizing energy $(eV_i)$ in one free path[57]. This theory is obviously not generally true.

of a few centimetres the minimum occurs at pressures of about 1 mm Hg with applied frequencies of about 50 Mc/s or less. At lower pressures the breakdown field increases, due to the shortage of molecules in the space. The second kind of curve is found mostly from post-war microwave measurements ($f \sim 10^9$ c/s, minimum at $p \sim 1$ to 10 mm Hg), and from some earlier work in which large vessels were used. At low pressure the field increases due to the inefficient transfer of energy to electrons, and this becomes worse at higher frequencies. Some workers have measured both breakdown and maintenance potentials as a function of pressure.

*Choice of Variables*

The breakdown field is dependent upon three parameters, the gas pressure, $p$, the frequency, $f$, and the dimensions of the vessel. It has already been shown that the variation of the field with frequency can be expressed by using, as a single parameter, the effective field. Replacing the measured peak value of the starting potential, $V_s$, by the product $X_{\text{eff}}.L$, where $L$ is the diffusion length of the vessel, and plotting its value against $pL$ gives a curve analogous to the d.c. Paschen curve plotted in the similarity parameters, $V_s$ (or $Xd$) against $pd$. Generally, as BROWN[245] pointed out, several groups of similarity parameters lend themselves to the description of high-frequency discharges controlled by diffusion losses. These are

$$XL, \qquad pL, \qquad p\lambda \text{ (or } p/f)$$
or
$$XL, \qquad X/p, \qquad p\lambda$$

where $\lambda$ is the wavelength of the applied field.

A test of high-frequency discharges in similar co-axial systems has been made, at pressures between 0·1 and 20 mm Hg and frequencies between 3·5 and 70 Mc/s[65,66]. It was found that provided $rp$ and $f/p$ were kept constant for all systems, $r$ being a linear dimension, the breakdown potential in air, $H_2$ and pure helium was always the same, and also the minimum maintenance potential, although this was less exactly defined due to instability in the discharge. Conditions were such that the electrons made many oscillations per collision. A direct test with different electrode materials established that they had no influence on breakdown. These results lend support to the idea that breakdown and maintenance are due to single-stage ionization solely in the gas, compensated by diffusion.

114

The similarity laws, it was found, did not hold for breakdown in helium containing traces of impurity ($H_2$): this is discussed in Chapter 3. Very recently a careful test of similarity has been made in uniform fields[67].

*High-frequency Ionization Coefficient*

In a d.c. discharge, ionization is described by Townsend's coefficient, $\alpha$, being the number of ion pairs produced by one electron drifting 1 cm in the direction of the field, or by the coefficient $\eta$, being the number of ion pairs produced by one electron drifting down a potential drop of 1 V. The rate of production of new ion pairs is then:

$$(\nu_i)_{\text{d.c.}} = \alpha v_{\text{drift}} = \alpha b_e X = \eta b_e X^2 \qquad \dots (4.55)$$

In the static electric field, ion production, described by $\eta$, is balanced by loss due to charges drifting away by mobility motion. By analogy a high-frequency ionization coefficient, $\xi$, has been defined[68], to describe ionization in high-frequency fields in those conditions where the only loss is by diffusion.

$$\xi = \frac{(\nu_i)_{\text{h.f.}}}{D_e X^2} \qquad \dots (4.56)$$

by analogy with

$$\eta = \frac{(\nu_i)_{\text{d.c.}}}{b_e X^2} \qquad \dots (4.57)$$

$\xi$, like $\eta$, is a function of $X/p$ and $f/p$. It must be noted, however, that $\xi$ has no simple physical significance and does not even have the dimensions of an ionization coefficient (the dimensions of $\xi$ are $1/V^2$, and of $\eta$ $1/V$). In circumstances where the electron energy distribution is the same in both d.c. and high-frequency fields at the same value of $X/p$, then the rate of ionization, $\nu_i$, is the same, so that $\eta$ and $\xi$ are connected by

$$\frac{\xi}{\eta} = \frac{b_e}{D_e} \qquad \dots (4.58)$$

Combining equations (4.57) and (4.58) it may be seen that if the value of the uniform field for breakdown in a vessel of particular geometry is measured, the coefficient $\xi$ can be reduced from

$$\xi = \frac{\nu_i}{D_e X^2} = \frac{1}{X^2 L^2} \qquad \dots (4.59)$$

The values deduced from these measurements have been used to predict breakdown in non-uniform fields with some success. This further emphasizes the physical difference between $\xi$ and $\eta$, because the use of $\eta$, or $\alpha$, derived from uniform field measurements gives wrong results when applied to ionization in non-uniform static fields.

### Breakdown Measurements: Comparison with Theory

Many measurements of breakdown field have been made in microwave cavities and have been compared with detailed theory worked out by a group of workers at M.I.T.[68-79]. The general results are shown in *Figures 4.14–4.17*; the Boltzmann transport

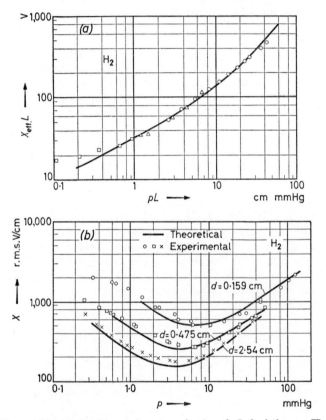

*Figure 4.14.* (a) *Breakdown voltage as a function of pL for hydrogen. The line is theoretical, the points experimental;* $\square$: $\lambda = 10 \cdot 6\ cm$, $L = 0 \cdot 05\ cm$; $\bigcirc$: $\lambda = 300\ cm$, $L = 0 \cdot 2\ cm$; $\triangle$: $\lambda = 10 \cdot 6\ cm$, $L = 0 \cdot 028\ cm$; (b) *experimental and theoretical curves of breakdown in hydrogen at 3,000 Mc/s.* (From S. C. Brown[245], by courtesy of Springer)

116

equation was used to calculate the electron energy distribution and consequently the rate of ionization, and the following assumptions were made:

(a) in hydrogen and helium $v$ = constant for electron energies

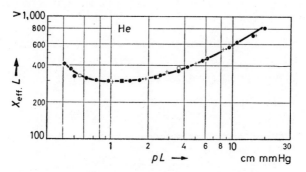

*Figure 4.15. High-frequency breakdown curves in pure helium.*
(From S. C. Brown[245], by courtesy of Springer)

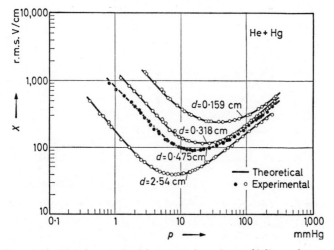

*Figure 4.16. High-frequency breakdown curves in a mixture of helium and mercury.*
(From S. C. Brown[245], by courtesy of Springer)

greater than about 4 eV (i.e. independent of electron energy, but proportional, of course, to pressure);

(b) in helium–mercury mixtures (small proportion of Hg),

$v$ = constant, and no excitation need be considered, all inelastic collisions leading to ionization by the process

$$He^{+}_{metastable\ (19\cdot8\ eV)} + Hg \rightarrow Hg^{+} + e + He$$

(c) in neon, $\lambda_e$ = constant, hence $v \propto v_r$, and, of course, to pressure.

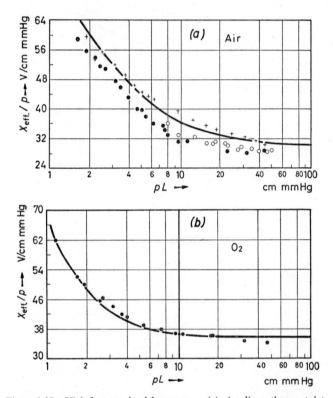

Figure 4.17. High-frequency breakdown curves: (a) air—line: theory; points: experimental. ●: Herlin and Brown (3,000 Mc/s). ○: Pim (2,000 Mc/s). +: Fresh sample of air in each discharge; (b) oxygen—line: theory; points: experimental. (From S. C. Brown[245], by courtesy of Springer)

PROWSE and CLARK[80] have recently tested the diffusion theory and its relation to similarity principles by measuring breakdown fields in cylinders of variable dimensions, $d$, $r$. According to theory the relation between $XL$ and $pL$ should be unique for one gas, and this has been confirmed; it is the use of the diffusion length, $L$, and not the individual dimensions, $d$ or $r$, which result in a single curve. The results given refer to measurements in uniform electric fields to which this theory and the simple breakdown condition applies.

One set of observations on very high-frequency breakdown fields does not apparently conform to the diffusion theory. PROWSE and LANE[55] found that in a parallel plate gap the breakdown field remains constant as the electrode separation is increased, instead of decreasing as might be expected. This was observed in air, $O_2$, $N_2$ and $H_2$, but had previously been noticed only in air[81]. It may be due to their special conditions of measurement in which initial electrons were produced by photo-ionization in the middle of the gap only.

### Non-uniform Fields

The theory has been extended to breakdown in non-uniform electric fields, notably in cylindrical and spherical cavities and between co-axial cylindrical electrodes[68, 78]. A more general breakdown condition must now be used, since the density of electrons and their mean energy vary in space. The transport of momentum is then dependent, by simple kinetic theory, on grad $nv_r$, not simply on grad $n$, i.e. on a temperature as well as a concentration gradient. The general breakdown condition is:

$$\nu_i n + \nabla^2(D_e n) = 0 \qquad \dots (4.60)$$

of which equation (4.45) is a special case, applicable in uniform conditions when $D$ does not vary with position. Written in terms of the high-frequency ionization coefficient $\xi$, and the product $D_e n$ whose gradient determines the flow of electrons,

$$\nabla^2(D_e n) + \xi X^2(D_e n) = 0 \qquad \dots (4.61)$$

The solution of this equation for particular geometries, with the use of $\xi$ derived from uniform field measurements, leads to calculated breakdown fields in good agreement with those found by experiment.

### Breakdown in Electron-attaching Gases

If, in addition to diffusion, electrons are effectively removed from the gas as ionizing agents by attachment to gas molecules (forming heavy negative ions), the breakdown condition must be modified accordingly. Let $\nu_a$ be the frequency at which an electron attaches

119

to a gas molecule, then in a uniform field between parallel plates $d$ cm apart, the simple condition for breakdown is:

$$v_i n = v_a n - D\nabla^2 n \qquad \ldots\ldots(4.62)$$

where $n$ is the electron density. This reduces to

$$v_i = v_a + D\frac{\pi^2}{d^2} \qquad \ldots\ldots(4.63)$$

$v_i$ may be derived from the values of the Townsend coefficient $\alpha$, $v_a$ from the attachment coefficient $\beta$*, both combined with the drift velocity in an a.c. field (taken as $b_e$ . $X_{\text{eff.}}$, $b_e$ being the mobility measured in d.c. fields).

The condition, for electrons having a Maxwellian energy distribution of average energy, $\bar{\varepsilon}$, reduces to

$$\frac{\alpha}{p} = \frac{\beta}{p} + \frac{2}{3}\frac{\bar{\varepsilon}\pi^2}{\left(\dfrac{X_{\text{eff.}}}{p}\right)(pd)^2} \qquad \ldots\ldots(4.64)$$

where $\alpha/p$, $\beta/p$ and $\bar{\varepsilon}$ are all functions of $X/p$ and their values (measured in d.c.) are taken from the literature. *Figure 4.17* shows the agreement between theory and experiment for air and oxygen[68,81]; note the improvement when a fresh sample of air is used for each measurement of breakdown, so that oxides of nitrogen remaining from previous discharges are removed.

### Breakdown in Gas Mixtures: Penning Effect

A few microwave measurements of breakdown potentials in neon, with a small controlled addition of argon, have been made[82,83]. As in d.c. measurements its value is less than in pure neon or pure argon, the reason being that the lowest excited state of neon $(3S^3P_2)$, is metastable and its excitation potential (16·6 eV) is about 0·9 eV greater than the ionization potential of argon. It has a long life in neon gas and, when it hits an argon atom, has a very high probability of ionizing it. A low concentration of argon is thus adequate to ensure a large increase in ionization; if the concentration of argon atoms is too high, the electrons will lose energy in exciting them too, and hence there is an argon concentration giving a minimum breakdown potential. This has been found in these

---

* If $n$ electrons move 1 cm in the direction of the field, $\alpha n$ is the number of ionizations and $\beta n$ the number of attachments resulting in negative ions.

high-frequency measurements but, unlike the effect in d.c., no double minima in the breakdown curve ($X$ against $p$) are found for any percentage of argon. The second minimum disappears in the rapid rise of the field when $v \ll f$.

## Wall Effects in Breakdown

Although in high-frequency breakdown it is usually assumed that secondary effects at the wall play no part whatsoever, this is not always true. At low pressures, when the mean free path is still appreciably smaller than the dimensions of the vessel, say $\lambda_e \sim \frac{1}{10}d$, an electron may hit a wall just as often as it makes an ionizing collision in the gas. This region represents a transition between the low-pressure resonance breakdown and the simple diffusion theory. It has been considered in detail by SALMON[84], for gas pressures below $50 \times 10^{-3}$ mm Hg and frequencies between 20 and 100 Mc/s. He finds that the electrons have a Maxwellian distribution which is unaltered by their frequent collisions with the walls, and that secondary electron emission from the walls, rather than ionization of the gas, is the main source of production. The breakdown condition is then that $\bar{\delta} = 1$, where $\bar{\delta}$ is the effective secondary emission coefficient from all the wall surfaces, averaged over all electron velocities and all angles of impact. Reasonably good agreement is found with the experimental results of CHENOT[64] and HALE[57].

A different process is the photo-electric emission caused when radiation from an excited gas falls on the walls of the vessel. If the flux of radiation is regarded as continuous, then one half of the photo-electrons emitted will find the field in a favourable direction and escape into the gas. The importance of this process clearly depends on the spectrum of the gas, the material of the walls and the consequent photo-electric yield. It has been found to be a dominant process in the breakdown of neon at frequencies up to 10 Mc/s (i.e. in the diffusion region and at lower frequencies), and leads to extremely low starting fields ($X/p \sim 0.6$ V/cm mm Hg) in which ionization by direct impact is negligible[27,85]. The mechanism is thought to be as follows: (a) electrons of relatively low average energy excite neon atoms into metastable and resonance states; and (b) resonance quanta 'diffuse' through the gas, i.e. they are passed on by absorption and re-emission before they finally emit photo-electrons from the wall. The condition for multiplication is that each electron must produce enough quanta to ensure that at least one photo-electron escapes from the wall. Ionization and breakdown results by a two stage process, slow electrons, energy approx. 5 eV, striking the excited and metastable neon atoms.

*Effect of Superimposed Fields*

*Static electric field*—If a small electric field is superimposed upon the high-frequency field, electrons are swept to the walls by their steady drift motion as well as by diffusion, and consequently the amplitude of the high-frequency field must be increased to cause breakdown[60,86]. The electron energy distribution is very similar in both high-frequency and d.c. fields, and it is possible to modify the calculated distribution function for high-frequency fields, and calculate the new rate of ionization in the combined fields. The electron current density $j_e$ to the walls is:

$$j_e = nb_e X_{\text{d.c.}} + D \text{ grad } n \qquad \ldots (4.65)$$

The rate of new production of ions and electrons per cm³ equal to the divergence of $j_e$, is $v_i n$. Equating these gives

$$D\nabla^2 n + \text{div } (nv_{\text{drift}}) + v_i n = 0 \qquad \ldots (4.66)$$

as the breakdown condition. If the static field is uniform and in the $x$ direction, this reduces to the manageable form

$$\nabla^2 n + \frac{b_e}{D} \cdot X_{\text{d.c.}} \frac{\partial n}{\partial x} + \left(\frac{v_i}{D}\right) n = 0 \qquad \ldots (4.67)$$

which can be solved for electron density, $n$, as a function of position, $x$, $r$, in a cylindrical vessel whose axis is also parallel to $x$. It can be shown that the new effective diffusion length, $L_{\text{d.c.}}$, of the vessel in the presence of the d.c. field is shorter than its undisturbed diffusion length, $L$, according to

$$\frac{1}{L_{\text{d.c.}}^2} = \frac{1}{L^2} + \left(\frac{b_e X_{\text{d.c.}}}{2D}\right)^2 \qquad \ldots (4.68)$$

The new breakdown condition is that

$$\frac{v_i}{D} = \frac{1}{L_{\text{d.c.}}^2} \qquad \ldots (4.69)$$

which is equivalent to simple high-frequency breakdown in a smaller cavity. Measurements of breakdown with such a superimposed field have been made, and compared with theory by VARNERIN and BROWN[72] (see *Figure 4.18*). It is interesting to note that the theory given above involves the ratio $b/D = e/kT_e$, which can therefore be determined from these measurements.

YAMANOTO and OKUDA[87] find that transverse high-frequency and d.c. fields give rise to three types of discharge in the pressure range $10-10^{-4}$ mm Hg: a d.c. glow discharge, in which a small amount of ionization is produced by the h.f. field, a typical high-frequency ('diffusion region') discharge in which the d.c. electrodes act as a double probe and collect currents limited by space charges, and an intermediate type in which the h.f. field produces enough ions to alter substantially the cathode fall of the glow discharge. In the absence of a high-frequency field, the cathode region mechanism

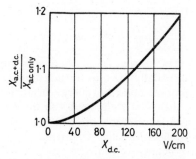

*Figure 4.18. Relative increase of a.c. breakdown field with superimposed d.c. field for air at p = 38 mm Hg.* (From S. C. Brown[245], by courtesy of Springer)

depends on the value of $\gamma$ at the electrode. From the properties of the intermediate type, $\gamma$ can be calculated.

Since the essential breakdown condition is similar in simple high-frequency and in high-frequency plus d.c. fields,

$$\xi = \left(\frac{1}{X^2 L^2}\right)_{\text{h.f.}} = \frac{1}{X_{\text{d.c.}}^2 . L_{\text{d.c.}}^2} \qquad \dots (4.70)$$

where the second expression refers to the values in the combined fields. In vessels of known geometry, $L$ is given; the breakdown fields in simple h.f. and in the combined fields are measured; $L_{\text{d.c.}}$ is thus determined from the above equation, and hence $b/D$ follows from equation (4.68). The values of $\eta$ and of mean energy derived from this type of experiment agree reasonably well with those from d.c. measurements.

*Magnetic fields*—A charge, $e$ (e.s.u.), moving with a velocity component, $v$ (cm/sec), perpendicular to a magnetic field, $H$ (oersted), suffers a force $He\,v/c$ dyn at right angles to both $v$ and $H$. In combined electric and magnetic fields the total force is:

$$F = eX + \frac{e}{c}.v \times H = \frac{mdv}{dt} \qquad \dots (4.71)$$

123

Thus the basic effect of a magnetic field is to cause charged particles not already moving parallel to it, to describe helical paths around the lines of magnetic force. The radius of the helix decreases with increasing magnetic field. In most circumstances only the paths of the electrons are altered, the ions being virtually unaffected. The electrons perform their helical motion with a constant angular velocity $\omega_H$ radians/sec, where

$$\omega_H = \frac{eH}{mc} \qquad \qquad \ldots\ldots(4.72)$$

the gyro frequency. (Strictly, $f_H = eH/2\pi mc$ is the gyro frequency, but the meaning is usually obvious in the context.) An electron in performing this motion takes no energy from the magnetic field, since the force is always at right angles to the motion, but it does move a longer distance through the gas in order to move a given distance along the electric field. It hits gas molecules more often and has a greater chance of ionizing, and thus the presence of a magnetic field acts like an increase in gas pressure, an increase, however, which is apparent only in directions perpendicular to the magnetic field. By considering the curvature of the free path of an ion of molecular weight, $M$, and taking the chord between extreme points as the effective free path, it can be shown[88] that the apparent increase in pressure $\Delta p$ is:

$$\frac{\Delta p}{p} \approx 10^{-2} \frac{\lambda_i}{MT_i} \left(\frac{H}{p}\right)^2 \qquad \ldots\ldots(4.73)$$

where $\lambda_i$ is the mean free path in cm at $p = 1$ mm Hg, $T_i$ is the ion temperature in °K and $H$ the magnetic field in oersted. The numerical factor depends on the assumptions made in the derivation.

When a static magnetic field, $H$, is superimposed upon a static electric field, $X$, the motion of a random swarm of electrons, in the absence of space charge, suffers two effects, as has been shown by Townsend.

(1) The diffusion coefficient, $D_H$, in directions perpendicular to the magnetic field, is reduced:

$$D_H = \frac{D}{1 + \omega_H^2 \tau^2} = D \cdot \frac{\nu^2}{\nu^2 + \omega_H^2} \qquad \ldots\ldots(4.74)$$

where $D$ is the normal diffusion coefficient, $\tau$ the mean time of flight between collisions ($= 1/\nu$, the collision frequency) and $\omega_H$ the gyro frequency; diffusion parallel to $H$ is unaltered.

(2) In perpendicular electric and magnetic fields the mobility, i.e. the drift velocity along the electric field, is reduced by the same factor

$$b_H = \frac{b}{1 + \omega_H^2 \tau^2} \qquad \dots (4.75)$$

The theory assumes that $\tau$ is a constant, i.e. that $\lambda_e \propto v_r$; if $\omega\tau \gg 1$ the result is largely unaffected by the dependence of $\lambda_e$ on $v_r$[89-91].

An extension of this theory[7] shows that superimposing a magnetic field parallel to a static electric field has no effect upon the mean energy of the electrons, but that when a magnetic field is applied perpendicular to the electric field the mean energy is reduced in the ratio

$$\bar{\varepsilon}_H = \frac{\bar{\varepsilon}}{\sqrt{1 + \omega_H^2 \tau^2}} = \frac{\bar{\varepsilon}\nu}{\sqrt{\nu^2 + \omega_H^2}} \qquad \dots (4.76)$$

When a constant magnetic field, $H$, is superimposed upon an alternating electric field, $X_0 \sin \omega t$, the analysis is more complex, but two results can be seen immediately. If $X$ and $H$ are parallel, diffusion perpendicular to $H$ will be reduced [exact theory shows that equation (4.74) still applies], and hence a smaller breakdown field is required. If $X$ and $H$ are perpendicular, not only is diffusion reduced, but for certain values of magnetic field and applied frequency resonance will occur when $\omega = \omega_H$. Physically, this means that the magnetic field reverses the direction of the electron, without loss of energy, as the applied electric field reverses, so that although the magnetic field supplies no energy to the electron, it so alters its direction that the electron can rapidly gain energy from the electric field, provided that the motion is not frequently interrupted by collisions with gas molecules. Thus at low pressure, $\nu \gtrsim f$, a resonance condition should be expected when

$$f_{\text{applied}} = \frac{eH}{2\pi mc} \qquad \dots (4.77)$$

giving very low breakdown fields. At higher pressures the resonance will be masked by collisions, but the losses by diffusion will still be reduced by the presence of the magnetic field.

The theory of these discharges has been given by TOWNSEND and GILL[7] and LAX, ALLIS, and BROWN[92], and the expected behaviour confirmed in experiments by these and other authors[93,94] (*Figure 4.19*). It should be noted that only the rigorous theory, in which the magnetic field is introduced into the Boltzmann transport

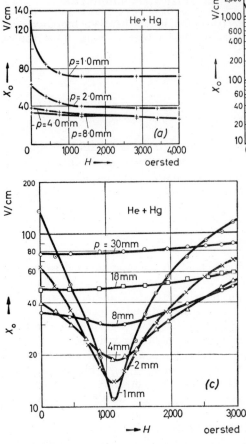

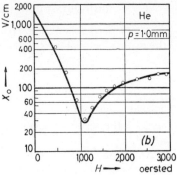

Figure 4.19. High-frequency breakdown in a cylindrical cavity under the influence of magnetic fields: (a) parallel X and H, helium–mercury mixture; (b) transverse X and H, in helium; (c) transverse X and H, helium–mercury mixture; (d) breakdown potential in air, transverse X and H. In (a), (b) and (c) the lines are theoretical and the points experimental; in (d) the lines are measured values. [(a), (b) and (c) from S. C. BROWN[245], by courtesy of Springer; (d) from L. FERRETTI and P. VERONESI[94], by courtesy of Il Nuovo Cimento]

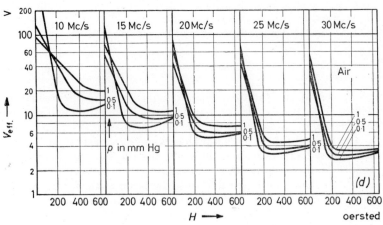

equation and in which the resulting energy distribution and rate of ionization is derived, gives correct numerical results[92]. Theories based on the behaviour of the average electron give correct relative results only but they do give a clearer physical picture of the processes, as will now be seen in the treatment of the motion of an electron in perpendicular magnetic and electric fields. The axes are chosen so that $H$ acts in the $y$ direction and $X_0 \sin \omega t$ in the $x$ direction (*Figure 4.20*); assume that an electron, having suffered a

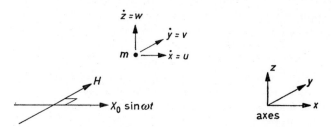

*Figure 4.20. Motion of an electron in transverse electric and magnetic fields*

collision, moves off at $t = 0$, with velocity components $u_0$, $v_0$ and $w_0$ in directions $x$, $y$ and $z$ respectively. The equations of motion are then:

$$m \frac{du}{dt} = eX_0 \sin \omega t - \frac{Hew}{c}$$

$$m \frac{dv}{dt} = 0 \qquad \qquad \ldots (4.78)$$

$$m \frac{dw}{dt} = \frac{Heu}{c}$$

The solution for the velocities at time $t$ ($< \tau$, i.e. before the motion is interrupted by a collision) is:

$$u = w_0 \sin \omega_H t + u_0 \cos \omega_H t - \frac{eX_0}{m} \frac{\omega}{\omega_H^2 - \omega^2} \cos \omega_H t$$

$$+ \frac{eX_0}{m} \frac{\omega}{\omega_H^2 - \omega^2} \cos \omega t$$

$$v = v_0 = \text{constant} \qquad \ldots (4.79)$$

$$w = w_0 \cos \omega_H t - u_0 \sin \omega_H t + \frac{eX_0}{m} \frac{\omega}{\omega_H^2 - \omega^2} \sin \omega_H t$$

$$- \frac{eX_0}{m} \frac{\omega_H}{\omega_H^2 - \omega^2} \sin \omega t$$

If those components of velocity which vary with the gyro frequency $\omega_H$ (the first three terms in the expressions for $u$ and $w$), are separated from those which vary with the applied frequency $\omega$ (the last terms) it may be seen that the motion consists of a helical motion (including $v_0$ with the gyro frequency terms) with its axis along the magnetic field, plus an elliptical motion in the plane perpendicular to $H$. It can easily be shown that the kinetic energy of the helical motion is constant, although the expression is somewhat lengthy to write down. The kinetic energy of the elliptical motion varies with the applied field and is given by

$$\varepsilon = \frac{eX_0^2}{8m} \left[ \frac{1}{(\omega - \omega_H)^2} + \frac{1}{(\omega + \omega_H)^2} + \frac{2 \cos 2\omega t}{\omega_H^2 - \omega^2} \right] \quad \ldots\ldots(4.80)$$

and clearly rises rapidly as $\omega \to \omega_H$. The solution given is not valid when $\omega = \omega_H$, but the exact solution is not of great consequence since, even at the lowest pressures, this motion is occasionally interrupted by collisions; however, it has been discussed by Townsend and Gill. Clearly, $t$ cannot exceed $\tau$, the interval between collisions, and when this motion is interrupted by collisions occurring at a rate of $\nu$ per sec it can be shown that the average energy gained by an electron between collisions is:

$$\Delta\varepsilon = \frac{eX_0^2}{4m} \left[ \frac{1}{(\omega + \omega_H)^2 + \nu^2} + \frac{1}{(\omega - \omega_H)^2 + \nu^2} \right] \quad \ldots\ldots(4.81)$$

This also shows a marked resonance at low pressure ($\nu \ll \omega$) when $\omega \to \omega_H$: at high pressure the resonance is negligible.

The breakdown condition is derived in the usual way by equating the rate of ionization in the gas to the rate of loss by diffusion. Since diffusion perpendicular to $H$ is reduced, lengths in these directions are effectively increased; thus the diffusion length, $L_H$, of a cylinder whose axis is parallel to the magnetic field is:

$$\frac{1}{L_H^2} = \left(\frac{\pi}{d}\right)^2 + \left(\frac{2\cdot405}{r}\right)^2 \cdot \frac{\nu^2}{\nu^2 + \omega_H^2} \quad \ldots\ldots(4.82)$$

It is this modified diffusion length, $L_H$, which must be inserted in the breakdown condition. The theory of the motion of charges in a static magnetic and oscillatory electric field has recently been discussed by HUXLEY[95].

*Time Lags and Mechanism of Growth: Breakdown under Microwave Pulses*

In the simple diffusion theory it was assumed that the approach to breakdown was very gradual and the rate of growth of ionization nearly zero. However, when pulses of high frequency are applied, breakdown can only occur if the ion and electron density grow so rapidly that the discharge reaches a stable state during the time that the pulse is applied. Thus the statistical time lag plus the formative time lag must be less than the length of the pulse; the former can be made negligible by suitably irradiating the gap, but both time lags decrease when the applied potential is increased. The potential necessary to cause breakdown should, therefore, be high when short pulses are applied, and decrease steadily as the pulse is lengthened. The shortest pulse for which the breakdown potential is equal to the value when continuous fields are applied, gives some idea of the formative time lag under simple continuous conditions, and hence the physical processes operating in the growth of the discharge. Experiments by several workers[52-54,96,97,126,230], using gases at relatively high pressure (up to 1 atm) and pulses of microwave field ($f \sim 3,000$ Mc/s) which could be varied up to a few $\mu$sec, show results in accordance with those expected. This is particularly noticeable in the rare gases, argon, helium and especially neon, where the formative time lag is long—even in pulses $1 \cdot 4$ $\mu$sec long ($\sim 4,000$ cycles of the applied field), the breakdown potential is five times greater than in continuous fields. In these short time intervals no electrons diffuse to the walls and the breakdown condition is not given by a balance between production and loss, but by the field necessary to build up a certain critical number of ion pairs within the pulse. Since the energy gained per mean free path is:

$$\varDelta \varepsilon = \frac{e}{2m} \cdot \frac{1}{v^2 + \omega^2} \cdot X_0^2 \qquad \ldots (4.83)$$

the number of ion pairs produced by an electron in time, $t$, should depend upon $X_0^2 \cdot t$, and hence, given constant irradiation of the gap, breakdown should occur at constant values of $X_0^2 t$. This has been experimentally confirmed in neon[96].

In polyatomic gases, however, the formative time lag is so short ($t_f < 5 \times 10^{-8}$ sec for air, $N_2$, $O_2$ and $H_2$) that the breakdown field does not vary with the length of the pulse (with the pulse lengths used $t \sim \mu$sec), and seems to be the same as the continuous breakdown field. Here again the results do not appear to support the idea that breakdown occurs when a relatively slow growth of ionization just exceeds the rate of removal, but rather that a few favourable events, e.g. collisions of a particular type, lead immediately to instability and breakdown. This could happen if a group of oscillating electrons, sweeping repeatedly through a small volume

129

of gas, produce a concentration of excited atoms and then ionize them, in subsequent oscillations. At microwave frequencies ($\sim 3 \times 10^9$ c/s) electrons make about 20 oscillations during the half life of an excited state, and detailed calculation shows that the probability of such a two-stage process is reasonable. It is also consistent with the visible appearance of the discharge, one or several streamers being observed to grow from the middle of the gap, presumably from pockets of initial ionization. In an attempt to check this theory, PROWSE and LANE[98] have applied an auxiliary continuous high-frequency field ($\leqslant 10$ Mc/s) at right angles to the pulsed microwave field; it was argued that the perpendicular drift would prevent electrons sweeping through the concentration of excited atoms, which they had produced in preceding oscillations, and thus cause an increase in the microwave breakdown field. This has been found to be true when the auxiliary field is of sufficiently low frequency to sweep electrons close to the walls, but at higher frequencies the two fields appear to act almost independently. Thus as the amplitude of the auxiliary field is increased, the microwave breakdown field remains constant, despite the fact that the combined field is, of course, greater than either component. This continues until the auxiliary field itself causes breakdown in a manner which is independent of the microwave field: these experiments lend some support to the theory of two-stage ionization but they are not conclusive.

### The Fully Developed Discharge

*Maintenance potentials and fields*—Work on fully developed discharges in which diffusion plays a main role has consisted mainly of the measurement of maintenance and extinction potentials of discharges in vessels of various sizes and shapes. TOWNSEND and his colleagues[36,99–104] and HIEDEMANN[105,106] using long cylindrical tubes, measured the average longitudinal field by the method normally used for positive columns, i.e. measuring the additional potential $\Delta V$ required to sustain an additional length of column at constant current when the electrodes are moved apart a distance $\Delta x$ ($X = \Delta V / \Delta x$). It is important to distinguish between maintenance and extinction potentials: when a discharge is established, the potential falls appreciably below starting potential due to the loading of the oscillator. As the current is decreased, the potential across the electrodes decreases until it reaches a minimum value $V_m$, called the minimum maintenance potential; further decrease of current will cause the potential across the discharge to increase until it reaches the extinction potential, $V_e$, when the discharge will go out. Thus $V_m$ is a property of the discharge itself and $V_e$ depends upon the discharge and the external circuit. Maintenance potentials have also been measured in relatively short flat-ended cylindrical vessels, with internal and external electrodes[60],[63],[107] [*Figure 4.21 (a)*].

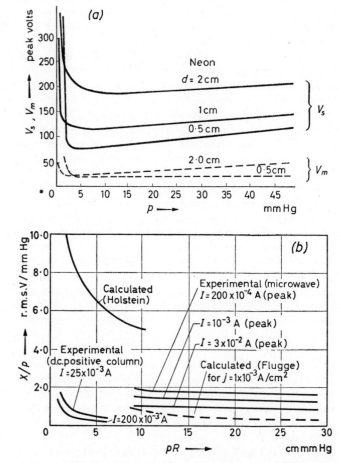

*Figure 4.21. (a) Starting potential, $V_s$, and maintenance potential, $V_m$, in neon for various electrode spacings, d. Frequency 158 Mc/s: glass-covered nickel electrodes; (b) comparison of longitudinal gradient in the positive column with high-frequency maintenance fields. The ordinate $X/p$ is either d.c. field for positive column, or r.m.s. field for high frequency. Calculated curves refer to high-frequency maintenance; positive column data from Klarfeld. R is the radius of the tube or cavity. [(a) from G. M. PATEYUK[107], by courtesy of Journal of Experimental and Theoretical Physics; (b) after S. KRASIK, D. ALPERT and A. O. McCOUBREY[70]]*

The results can be summarized briefly: maintenance potentials are very much smaller than starting potentials, as is to be expected, since the establishment of a space charge of positive ions greatly reduces the loss of electrons by diffusion to the walls (i.e. ambipolar replaces free diffusion), and a smaller rate of production is required to balance this loss. The curves of maintenance potential against pressure are similar in form to those of the starting potential: they show a single minimum, the condition for this being the same as discussed on pp. 112, 113. The minimum maintenance potential can be very low indeed, sometimes less than the ionization potential of the gas, although of course an electron can acquire many times this energy due to random scattering and the frequent reversal of the field. The maintenance potential depends also on the material of the walls, conducting walls giving higher potentials than insulating walls; a superimposed d.c. field necessitates a larger maintenance potential. In long cylindrical tubes containing helium or neon at a pressure of a few mm Hg, the r.m.s. value of the field is the same as that in the positive column of the d.c. glow discharge, and the electron energy distribution is also the same (this was deduced from the variation of spectral line intensities with the mean energy of the electrons)[108]. The potential between the electrodes, however, is much less than in the glow discharge because the cathode region (cathode fall of several hundred volts) which is vital to the maintenance of the d.c. discharge, is not necessary to the high-frequency discharge. In tubes about 30 cm long and a few cm diameter, fitted with external sleeve electrodes and filled with gas at a pressure of 1–30 mm Hg, the potential obeys the empirical law

$$V = X(x + a) + b\lambda i \qquad \ldots (4.84)$$

where $x$ is the separation of the electrodes, $\lambda$ the wavelength of the applied field (40–640 m, $f \sim 0 \cdot 5$–$7 \cdot 5$ Mc/s), $i$ the current (up to 12 mA) and $a$ and $b$ are constants depending on the nature and pressure of the gas and the diameter of the tube. $X$ was found to be constant over this range of currents and frequencies for a particular gas.

There is a marked difference between atomic and molecular gases, the maintenance potential and average field being much greater in molecular than in monatomic gases. For example, in the type of long tubes mentioned, for neon $X/p \approx 0 \cdot 5$, for helium $X/p \sim 1 \cdot 5$ and for $N_2$ $X/p \sim 20$. Under certain conditions of pressure and current, differing for various gases, the column is striated: it has been observed and studied in $H_2$, $O_2$, air and argon, sometimes with mercury vapour as an impurity[104,105,109,110].

132

In mercury vapour, even in discharges using external electrodes, metallic deposits are found on the side walls[111].

*Theory*—The simplest explanation of the properties of the fully developed discharge is that the positive ion space charge retards the diffusion of electrons to the walls. The condition for the steady state is then:

$$v_i n + D_a \nabla_n^2 = 0 \qquad \dots (4.85)$$

which is the same as the breakdown condition with the ambipolar diffusion coefficient $D_a \left( = \dfrac{b_e D^+ + b^+ D_e}{b_e + b^+} \right)$ replacing the coefficient of free diffusion of electrons. This equation, first given by Townsend[112], was applied to cylindrical geometry and to gases at relatively high pressure $(v \gg f)$ in which the rate of ionization can be described by the coefficient $\alpha$. His equation

$$\frac{d^2 n}{dr^2} + \frac{1}{r} \frac{dn}{dr} + \alpha \frac{b_e X}{D_a} \cdot n = 0 \qquad \dots (4.86)$$

gives a solution for the electron concentration, $n$, as a function of the radius, $r$, of the same form as Schottky's solution for the positive column of the glow discharge. In similarity parameters $X/p$ is a function of $pr$. This theory has been found to give the correct dependence of field upon pressure for helium[113]; at pressures below 10 mm Hg there is good agreement between theory and experiment assuming direct ionization, while above 30 mm Hg ionization is assumed to take place by electrons hitting metastable atoms. Theory and experiment are made to fit at one point by an undetermined constant.

The theory has been more rigorously tested for discharges at microwave frequencies between parallel plates by Krasik, Alpert and McCoubrey[70], using Holstein's analysis (see p. 111). Here, again, the form of the $X - p$ curve is correct but the predicted values do not agree well with those measured [see *Figure 4.21 (b)*]. One of the difficulties in an exact solution is the choice of the proper boundary conditions, insulating and metal walls, for example, providing a different potential distribution. A more extensive treatment has been given by Flugge[114] who considers the continuity equations and the average energy balance including elastic, exciting and ionizing collisions. These can be written for parallel plate geometry, in which a static field, $E$, is produced by space charge

$$v_i n_e = \frac{dj_e}{dx} \qquad \dots (4.87)$$

133

$$j_e = - D_e \frac{dn_e}{dx} - n_e b_e E \qquad \dots \text{(4.88)}$$

$$j_+ = - D_+ \frac{dn_+}{dx} + n_+ b_+ E \qquad \dots \text{(4.89)}$$

Poisson's equation

$$\frac{dE}{dx} = 4\pi e(n_+ - n_e) \qquad \dots \text{(4.90)}$$

$$j_e = j_r \qquad \dots \text{(4.91)}$$

and the energy balance equation

$$\frac{d\varepsilon}{dt} = \frac{e^2 X_0}{2m} \cdot \frac{\nu}{\nu^2 + \omega^2} - \frac{2m}{M} \nu(\varepsilon - \varepsilon_{\text{gas}}) - \nu_i(eV_i)$$
$$- \Sigma \nu_{\text{exc.}}(eV_{\text{exc.}}) - n_e b_e E^2 \quad \dots \text{(4.92)}$$

Here, $X_0$ is the peak value of the applied field, $\varepsilon$ the average electron energy (assumed to have a Maxwellian distribution), $\nu_{\text{exc.}}$ the frequency of collisions leading to excitation of the state having energy $eV_{\text{exc.}}$, and $V_i$ the ionization potential. Solution of these equations leads to the values of $n_+$, $n_e$, $\varepsilon$ and $E$ in the centre of the discharge. If $n_e$ is made very small the starting condition is satisfied; if $n_e$ is large and $(n_+ - n_e)/n_e \to 0$ as $n_e \to \infty$ the maintenance condition is satisfied. A comparison with the experimental results shows better agreement for the maintenance condition than the simple theory over a certain range of $pR$ (see *Figure 4.21*), and good agreement for the starting condition, but at lower pressures. SCHNEIDER[115] has pointed out that, in regions close to the wall, electrons may be deposited on the walls by their oscillating drift motion; this loss is small in the middle of the vessel and increases towards the walls, but could be included in the theory by adding a term $an_e x$ to the right-hand side of equation (4.88) where $a$ is a constant and $x$ the distance from the mid-plane.

*Space Charge Effects: Electron Energy and Concentration*

It has been seen that in the fully developed discharge a large space charge develops, leading to appreciable static fields and space potentials. It was natural that the Langmuir probe method should be used in an attempt to measure simultaneously $n_e$, $T_e$ and the space potential, by observing the variation of the current collected by the probe as its potential was altered. The earliest measurements of this type were performed by BANERJI and GANGULI[116] in uniform and striated discharges in air, $O_2$ and $H_2$, in long cylindrical tubes fitted with sleeve electrodes (their discharges showed the dark spaces, etc., characteristic of the cathode regions of a d.c. glow discharge, close to each electrode). There is some difficulty in finding a suitable reference potential for the probe—an electrode cannot be used as in a d.c. charge—and it is possible that the presence of the probe can change the space potential of the plasma itself, since it has no connection to any point at an absolute potential*. However, these early measurements indicate the presence, in the bright regions of the discharge midway between the electrodes, of very large space potentials (several hundred volts) which fall symmetrically to the electrodes and, further outwards, rise and fall again. In the striated discharge there are intermediate maxima and minima, and the electron concentration and average energy behave similarly. More modern measurements of $n_e$ and $T_e$ (but not of course space potential) have been made by the floating double probe method, in which a static potential is applied between two probes placed in the discharge, and the current flowing between the probes is noted as their difference in potential is varied[117].

For example, KOJIMA and TAKOYAMA[118], studying discharges in argon between parallel plates at 200 Mc/s find $T_e \sim 2 \cdot 5$–$2 \cdot 8 \times 10^4$ °K ($\varepsilon \sim 3 \cdot 9$ eV) at $p = 7$ mm Hg; MITANI[119] has made similar experiments in both parallel plate and cylindrical geometry at 2,600 Mc/s. *Figure 4.22* shows the decrease of electron temperature with increasing pressure for weak discharges ($n_e$ at centre of discharge $\sim 10^7$ electrons per $cm^3$). In most discharges, carrying currents of the order of milliamperes, the electron concentration is about $10^9$, and average electron energies at high pressure ($v \gg f$) a few eV. In air at pressures of $0 \cdot 1$–$11$ mm Hg excited at a frequency of $10^8$ c/s the electron temperature has been found to remain constant ($3 \times 10^4$ °K $\approx$ eV) as the electron density varies from $10^{10}$ to $10^{12}$, and the Maxwellian distribution has been confirmed[120]. Energies consistent with those measured by probes have also been found from spectroscopic observations[108,121,231]. A theoretical derivation of the electron energy distribution in the presence of space charge fields has been given by BERNSTEIN and HOLSTEIN[122]. Modern measurements on striated h.f. discharges in long tubes have been made by DZHERPETOV and ZAITSEV[123].

The distribution of electrons in space in the presence of plasma resonance (i.e. when, in certain parts of the discharge, the natural

---

* For a criticism of the method and these measurements and a comparison of d.c. and h.f. columns see H. Beck, *Z. Phys.*, **97** (1935) 355.

frequency of oscillation of the ions and electrons is equal to the applied frequency: $4\pi ne^2/m\omega^2 = 1$) has been discussed and measured by ALLIS and BROWN[124]. The discharge shows greatest luminosity in the regions where resonance occurs and, due to the presence of a large positive space charge and the steady drift by diffusion, appreciable d.c. potentials are built up between probes or electrodes disposed unsymmetrically about the centre of the discharge. In

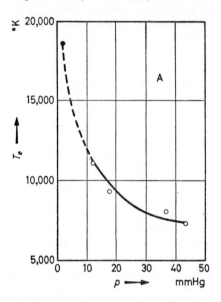

*Figure 4.22. Variation of electron temperature with pressure in argon, in high-frequency fields:* ● *Kojima's value.* (From S. KOJIMA and K. TAKOYAMA[118], by courtesy of the Physical Society of Japan)

this way a high-frequency discharge can be used as a battery, and the properties of such arrangements have been extensively investigated[125]. The current which can be drawn depends on the position and potential of the electrodes, the applied frequency and the gas pressure; sputtering of the electrode material has also been observed in these arrangements. The application of a static field, whether between auxiliary or main electrodes, naturally distorts the appearance of the discharge and the ion and electron distribution, causing the luminous regions to move towards the negative electrode.

The space charge is also a copious source of positive ions, which can be extracted by the application of a d.c. field, usually applied perpendicular to the high-frequency field. Inductively coupled ring discharges (the H discharge), however, are generally found to be more convenient and more copious ion sources.

Chemical reactions have been studied in high-frequency discharges under especially favourable conditions, since there is no possibility of contamination by metal electrodes[127–129]. CORRIGAN and VON ENGEL[130] have shown that in hydrogen much of the electrical energy supplied to the discharge is used in dissociating the molecules, the phase and magnitude of the current being measured by a bridge method[131].

## THE RING DISCHARGE[33,35,147]

An electrodeless ring discharge is excited when a vessel containing gas at low pressure is placed inside a solenoid carrying a high-frequency current. The current in the fully developed discharge forms closed rings, the initial e.m.f. around a ring before space charge develops being given by the rate of change of magnetic flux enclosed by it. THOMSON[132] assumed that the starting condition was satisfied when an electron, moving in this induced electric field, gained ionizing energy in one free path: this leads to

$$rH_0 \frac{e}{m} = \frac{\dfrac{2eV_i}{m} + (\omega\lambda_e)^2}{\omega\lambda_e} \qquad \dots(4.93)$$

where $r$ is the radius of the tube, $H_0$ the maximum value of the magnetic field ($H_0 \sin \omega t$) and $V_i$ the ionization potential of the gas. Thus $H_0$ is a function of $\omega\lambda_e$, i.e. of $f/p$ (a similarity parameter); the field required is large at low and high pressure and is a minimum when $(\omega\lambda_e)^2 = 2e\,V_i/m$. The $H_0/p$ curve for starting is consequently concave upwards and the position of the minimum depends on the frequency: it is thus similar to the $X/p$ curves in ordinary high-frequency discharges.

These properties were qualitatively confirmed by Thomson. The electric field induced in the gas just before breakdown is deduced by measuring the e.m.f. induced in a conductor wrapped around the discharge tube. It must be noted, however, that unless proper electrostatic screening is employed the electric field between the ends of the coil can be much greater than that produced in closed paths by the change of magnetic flux, and there is good reason to believe that it is this field which is responsible for the starting of the discharge. When very large currents pass through the exciting coil, the induced field plays the dominant part[133,134]. Few measurements have been made with proper screening so that no adequate test of the theory of the ring discharge exists. CABANNES[135], however, has made an extensive study of properly screened discharges in Ne, A, Kr and Xe at a frequency of 1 Mc/s and over a wide range of pressures from $10^{-2}$ to 10 mm Hg. He found several different regimes in the discharge having different spectroscopic properties. The curve of induced field against pressure shows two minima, and the double probe method gives values of $T_e \sim 2\cdot8 \times 10^4$ °K in argon and $1\cdot6 \times 10^4$ °K in Kr at the centre of the discharge; discharges between 4 and 8 Mc/s have been studied by Strauss[233]. Probe methods have also been used in earlier work by Smith[135], who found that in mercury vapour forbidden lines can be excited at high electron temperature. The visible light intensity has been found to increase when a magnetic field is applied either parallel or perpendicular to the high-frequency magnetic field[137,138], and in transverse fields the increase can be very large if the applied oscillatory field is approximately in resonance with the gyro frequency.

Although some of the properties of the ring discharge are difficult to measure, they are advantageous for certain purposes. For example, the absence of electrodes and the closed paths of the electrons make precise field and potential measurements almost impossible but, on the other hand, the electrons are presented with an almost infinite path, and, since they move through a positive space charge which is uniform along the length of the path, they suffer no retarding influence and little disturbance of the energy distribution set up by the applied field. In these conditions spectra can be excited by quite low fields and, since the vessel can be electrically isolated, it is used as a spectroscopic source[139,147]. It is also used as a positive ion source for particle accelerators[140], and for the production of very large circulating currents in an insulating vessel in the shape of a torus. These were first studied by Ware[141] and Cousins[142], who discharged condensers through a primary coil to produce the very large change of magnetic flux required. The peak discharge current was greater than $10^4$ A, and rotating camera photographs showed that the current channel contracted periodically ('pinch effect'). Recently, this principle has been used on a larger scale to produce thermonuclear reactions in high-current discharges[143-5] (see Chapter 6).

DISCHARGES AT LOWER FREQUENCIES (electron amplitude ><br>length of vessel)

In some of the earlier measurements of starting potentials it was observed that as the pressure was reduced the $V_s$–$p$ curve sometimes showed several minima, and it was suggested that these were due to resonant oscillations of charges in the gas, but in long cylindrical tubes placed between external electrodes Gill and Donaldson[146] found that when the field is directed along the tube the $V_s$–$p$ curve is normal, having only one minimum, but when it is across the tube, another minimum (at a higher pressure) appeared. They gave the explanation that at high pressure the cloud of electrons oscillates with an amplitude less than the width of the tube, ionization in the gas being balanced by diffusion. As the pressure decreases, the electrons gain more energy from the field due to their longer free paths, so the starting field slowly decreases. However, the amplitude

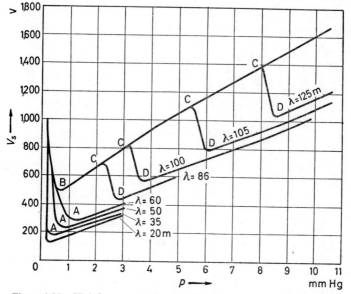

*Figure 4.23. High-frequency starting potential, $V_s$, in a long cylindrical tube fitted with sleeve electrodes 30 cm apart at various wavelengths, λ. (From E. W. B. GILL and R. H. DONALDSON[146], by courtesy of Philosophical Magazine)*

of oscillation of the electron cloud increases and when it becomes approximately equal to the distance between the walls, the loss of electrons increases rapidly and a much greater field is required to start the discharge; this accounts for the minimum at the higher pressure. Calculation using known drift velocities of electrons and the measured fields at this minimum give an amplitude of motion comparable with the diameter of the tube. Since $v_{drift}$ is approximately proportional to $(X_0/p) \sin \omega t$, the amplitude of motion depends on $X_0/\omega p$, and hence, since the minimum of the $V_s$–$p$ curve is given by $X_0/\omega p =$ constant, it moves towards lower pressures as the frequency is increased (points $D$ in *Figure 4.23*). The second minimum (points $A$) at lower pressure occurs, in these experiments,

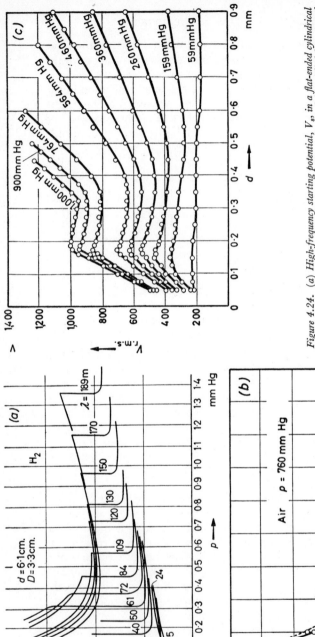

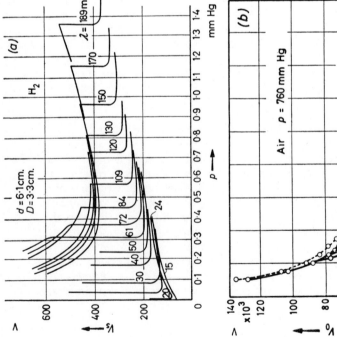

Figure 4.24. (a) High-frequency starting potential, $V_s$, in a flat-ended cylindrical glass vessel, length $d$, diameter $D$, with uniform electric field applied by external electrodes along the axis; (b) and (c) variation of starting potential in air with frequency, gas pressure, and electrode distance, $d$. Breakdown between internal electrodes. [(a) From M. CHENOT[64], by courtesy of Annales de Physique; (b) and (c) from J. A. PIM[81], by courtesy of the Institution of Electrical Engineers]

when $v \approx f$; at pressures lower than this the electrons gain less energy from the field due to their oscillatory motion within a free path, and hence a larger field is required.

Similar curves showing these two minima have been found by CHENOT[64] in extensive experiments using flat-ended glass cylinders filled with gas at low pressure; external plane electrodes were used here [*Figure 4.24 (c)*]. PIM[81], using small gaps ($\gtrsim$ 1 mm) and air at a pressure above 50 mm Hg, found that, with frequencies between 100 and 300 Mc/s, the field increases when the electrodes are brought closer than a critical distance (depending on the frequency). Measurements have been made over a wider range of frequency by GITHENS[148]: they apparently showed various 'modes' of oscillation, but the explanation of his results fits into the general scheme presented here and in subsequent sections. ZOUCKERMAN[147] has also made many measurements of this kind, some on ring discharges.

A detailed study of this transition region has been made in $H_2$, $N_2$, $D_2$, He and Ne by GILL and VON ENGEL[149], who measured the change of starting field in cylindrical glass vessels placed between plane electrodes as the frequency of the applied field is changed. The results are shown in *Figure 4.25*. As the wavelength is increased, a sharp 'cut-off', i.e. discontinuous jump in starting field, is found at all pressures in $H_2$ and $D_2$ and at low pressures ($p < 0.2$ mm Hg) in $N_2$ and the rare gases; at higher pressures it merges into a slower rise of $X$ spread over an appreciable range of wavelengths. The reason is thought to be that in $H_2$ and $D_2$ the electron energy distribution and the spread of the electron cloud in space is narrow, so that losses increase suddenly when it touches the walls; in the other gases the spread is greater, resulting in gradually increasing losses. By coating the walls of the vessel with palladium black it was shown that secondary electron emission is important at gas pressures up to approx. 0.2 mm Hg, and has negligible effect above approx. 0.5 mm Hg. These figures refer to discharges in $H_2$ but give the order of magnitude for other gases.

The electron mobility can be calculated from the position of the discontinuity and the applied field at this point. The peak values of $X/p$ in these discharges are often high, particularly at low pressures, and the drift velocity is known to be proportional to $\sqrt{X}$. Hence, the drift motion of the electrons can be written

$$\frac{dx}{dt} = k\sqrt{X_0 \sin \omega t} \qquad \dots . (4.94)$$

the only error occurring in low fields, as the field passes through zero phase and the square root law does not apply but, since the electrons move only a short distance in these conditions, the error is small. The solution of this equation requires the use of gamma

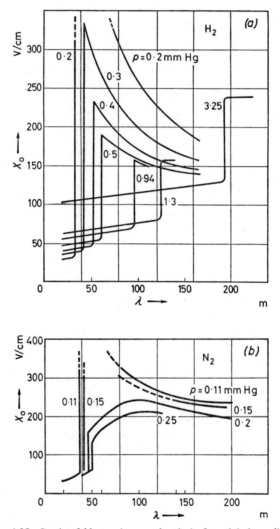

*Figure 4.25. Starting field at various wavelengths in flat-ended glass cylindrical vessels of length 3·55 cm; uniform electric field along axis: (a) hydrogen; (b) nitrogen.* (From E. W. B. GILL and A. VON ENGEL[149], by courtesy of the Royal Society)

functions, and if the extremities of the oscillation, i.e. twice the amplitude, are made equal to the length, $d$, of the vessel

$$\frac{d}{1\cdot2} = 2k \frac{\sqrt{X_0}}{\omega} \qquad \dots (4.95)$$

Hence, if the cut-off wavelength, $\lambda_c$ ($= 2\pi c/\omega$) and the peak field, $X_c$, at the bottom of the discontinuity are measured, the value of $k$ and hence the electron drift velocity at this peak value of $X/p$ can be deduced. At lower $X/p$ (higher pressures) a simple linear relation, $v_{\text{drift}} \propto X_0 \sin \omega t$, is found to fit the results better, and the drift velocity in $H_2$ found for $X_0/p = 20$ is about 30 per cent higher than the measured value in d.c. fields. The analysis in $N_2$, which is less accurate than in $H_2$ due to the spreading of the electron cloud, shows that the drift velocity is proportional to $X/p$ for values between 50 and 100 V/cm mm Hg, and to $\sqrt{X/p}$ between 300 and 500[232].

Some interesting relations concern the cut-off wavelength $\lambda_c$ and the starting field $X_c$ at that wavelength. If the pressure is high enough so that the drift velocity is proportional to $X/p$ the limitation on the amplitude of oscillation of the electrons leads to

$$\frac{X_c \lambda_c}{pd} = \text{constant} \qquad \dots (4.96)$$

Furthermore, the experimental results show that, for any given tube, $X_c$ varies linearly with pressure. This leads to

$$\lambda_c(a + b/p) = \text{constant} \qquad \dots (4.97)$$

where the constant depends on the length of the vessel. $\lambda_c$ tends to a constant value at high pressure.

The interesting point is that the discharge can be started at wavelengths longer than cut-off, but very much higher fields are required. The amplitude of oscillation of electrons would be many times the length of the vessel, and they are all swept to the wall in a fraction of a half cycle. It is clear that a different mechanism must be operating but in only a few examples has this been explained satisfactorily. In $H_2$ at low pressures the rapid fall of $X$ with increasing $\lambda$ suggests that a charged particle is the simplest ionizing agency, since by reason of its inertia it would act differently at varying wavelengths unlike photons or metastable atoms. Assuming the particle to have charge $e$ and mass $M$ the equation of motion is:

$$M\ddot{x} = eX_0 \sin \omega t - \frac{e}{b} \cdot \dot{x} \qquad \dots (4.98)$$

143

where $b$ is the mobility. If it is assumed that the particles must acquire a constant maximum velocity, $v$, the solution of this equation leads to the expression

$$e^2 X_0^2 = v^2 \left( \omega^2 M^2 + \frac{e^2}{b^2} \right) \qquad \ldots (4.99)$$

Thus $X_0^2$ plotted against $\omega^2$ should give a straight line and this is found to be so, experimentally. The intercept and the slope give relations between $e/M$ and the mobility $b$, and it is found, by comparing measured mobilities of known particles, that the ion $H_2^+$ is the effective agent. The amplitude of oscillation of ions at these frequencies and fields is only a fraction of the length of the vessel, and it is believed that positive ions impinging on the walls of the tube with their random velocities release secondary electrons which sustain the initial ionization produced by electrons in the gas. This is a continuous process taking place throughout the cycle and, on average, half of the electrons emitted will find the field in a favourable direction and escape into the gas.

Equation (4.99) shows that, since $v$ is a constant, variations in $\omega$, i.e. in wavelength, cause little change in field, $X$, as $\omega$ becomes smaller (longer wavelength) and as the mobility, $b$, becomes smaller, i.e. as the pressure increases, and this accounts for the main features of the curves in *Figure 4.25*. A few experiments in deuterium show similar results but the mobility of electrons and $D_2^+$ ions is lower than in hydrogen. In nitrogen the effect is not so clear, because the electron cloud is spread out in space and they are not all swept to the walls in one half cycle. In the rare gases the transition region is greatly spread out in frequency. It seems probable that a number of secondary effects occur, the emission of photo-electrons from the walls being dominant.

*Measurements over an Extended Frequency Range*

Relatively few experiments have been made over a wide frequency range. HARRIES and VON ENGEL[27,85] have measured starting potentials in neon and FRANCIS[131] starting potentials and currents in hydrogen, nitrogen and helium, in cylindrical glass vessels with external electrodes, over a frequency range from several Mc/s to a few c/s. The results in neon have been most extensively discussed; here, the starting field plotted against wavelength shows three flat plateaux (*Figure 4.26*), the lowest of which, at shortest wavelength, has already been discussed (see p. 121). The value of $X/p$ ($\sim 0.6$ V/cm mm Hg) is so low that even the most favourable energy distribution fails to give a sufficient fraction of electrons with ionizing energies ($> 21$ eV) to balance losses by diffusion. The starting field is that necessary to create a concentration of excited and metastable atoms in the gas which can be ionized by

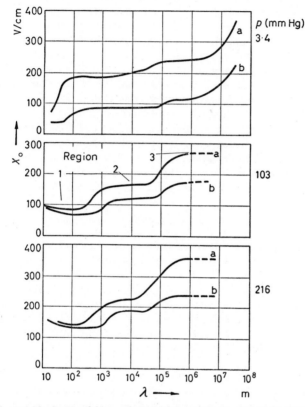

*Figure 4.26. Starting field as a function of the wavelength of the applied field in neon for various gas pressures, with glass vessels of internal length 1 cm (curves a) and 2·2 cm (curves b). (From W. L. HARRIES and A. VON ENGEL[27], by courtesy of the Royal Society)*

electrons of only 5 eV energy, the supply of which is maintained by the release of photo-electrons from the walls. The transition to region 2 takes place in a wavelength range depending on the gas pressure and the length of the vessel and it can be shown that the rise of field is due to electrons being swept to the wall by their drift motion. In the second region the electrons are swept to the walls in a fraction of one half cycle; in the gas, however, they produce a concentration of excited states which decay with the emission of photons. Some of these photons go directly to the walls, but others, from the resonant states, are heavily absorbed by gas atoms which in turn, being raised to resonant states, re-emit the photons. Thus resonance photons ($h\nu \sim 16$ eV) diffuse slowly through the gas and after a relatively long time strike the walls in a continuous stream. A certain fraction, $h$, of them release electrons during that fraction of the following half cycle when the field is large enough to cause multiplication. Let one electron, moving 1 cm in the direction of the field, produce $\varepsilon$ excited atoms, resulting in the emission of $\varepsilon_i$ photons which go immediately to the walls, and $\varepsilon_d$ resonance photons. Each electron then produces $\varepsilon d$ quanta in crossing a vessel of length, $d$. The number of secondary electrons consequently released from each end wall, in a cylinder whose side walls are far away, is $\gamma_p \varepsilon_i d$ immediately, plus those released by the slowly diffusing quanta created in the previous half cycle, i.e. $\gamma_p h \varepsilon_d d$, where $\gamma_p$ is the average photo-electric yield. Hence the starting condition is that

$$\tfrac{1}{2}\gamma_p d(\varepsilon_i + h\varepsilon_d) \geqslant 1 \qquad \ldots (4.100)$$

The factor $\tfrac{1}{2}$ appears because only those electrons from one wall will find the field in a favourable direction and be pulled into the gas.

The next transition, leading to increased fields in region 3 (low frequencies) occurs when the frequency is so low ($< 10^4$ c/s) that the diffusing resonance photons have all reached the wall in the interval between the half cycles of the field. They contribute nothing to the subsequent growth of current, and the starting condition for the third region is simply

$$\tfrac{1}{2}\gamma_p d\varepsilon_i \geqslant 1 \qquad \ldots (4.101)$$

necessitating an increased field. Here the current flows in pulses, occupying only a fraction of the half cycle. Detailed theory gives starting fields in good agreement with experiment for regions 2 and 3 on the assumption that $\gamma_p$ is about 1. There is considerable evidence that photo-electric yields of this order exist with quanta of energy 16 eV, and if, by the presence of any impurity (e.g. argon, which could be ionized by metastable neon) ionization in the gas were greater than that estimated, then lower photo-electric yields would suffice to explain the results. Irradiation by a strong neon light source, which destroys neon metastables did not, however, change the starting field.

In appearance, the discharge is bright and draws large currents in region 1, is a faint, uniformly distributed, brown glow, only

146

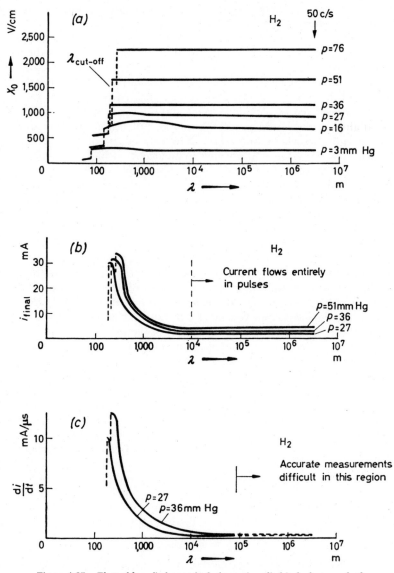

Figure 4.27. Electrodeless discharges in hydrogen in cylindrical glass vessel of length 2 cm: (a) starting field; (b) final equilibrium discharge current; (c) rate of growth of current. (From G. FRANCIS[131], by courtesy of the Physical Society)

147

detectable in complete darkness in region 2, and is similar but slightly brighter in region 3 due to the increased field.

In hydrogen the results are very different (see *Figure 4.27*). Here a sharp 'cut-off' is observed up to the highest pressures studied ($p = 76$ mm Hg) and only two regions are evident from the starting potential. At wavelengths longer than cut-off, $X$ remains nearly constant down to the lowest frequencies. The current, and its rate of rise (measured by a bridge circuit and the application of a pulse of high frequency—see p. 108) are large just beyond cut-off and fall steadily to a constant value. The rate of rise of current has a different significance at varying frequencies: at high frequencies the discharge takes a number of cycles of the field to establish itself, and although the electrons are swept to the walls in a fraction of a half cycle the current is observed to be continuous through the cycle; at low frequencies the current flows entirely in short pulses occurring near the peaks of the cycle. These current pulses were measured by connecting a small resistance in the external circuit in series with the electrodes and amplifying the potential developed across it for display on an oscilloscope. There is a smooth transition from one state to the other, and an intermediate stage showing a small sinusoidal current with a pulse superimposed (see *Figure 4.28*). This has also been observed in $H_2$, Ne and Kr and considered in some detail by Russian workers[150]. The properties of the discharge varied very slightly when vessels of different materials were used, e.g. Pyrex, soft glass and quartz.

At wavelengths shorter than cut-off, the discharge is a pale pinkish-blue glow filling the vessel, being slightly brighter in the centre, and as the wavelength is increased the luminosity varies roughly with the current. Just beyond cut-off the discharge is intensely bright and concentrated in layers near the end walls, while at longer wavelengths these layers become fainter and more diffuse until at 50 c/s they are almost invisible.

In the long wavelength region the growth and peak value of the current pulses have been studied in some detail. A charge, $q$, drifting with velocity $v_{drift}$ in a field, $X$, produces a current in the external circuit which is given by the energy equation

$$iV = qXv_{drift} \qquad \qquad \dots\dots(4.102)$$

Hence by measuring $i$ the number of electrons in a pulse can be deduced. It is found that about $10^9$ electrons are produced in a pulse in 1 $\mu$sec, a rate of growth which requires a fast secondary process. Detailed treatment shows that photo-electrons released from the glass walls, with a photo-electric yield $\gamma_p \sim 5 \times 10^{-2}$

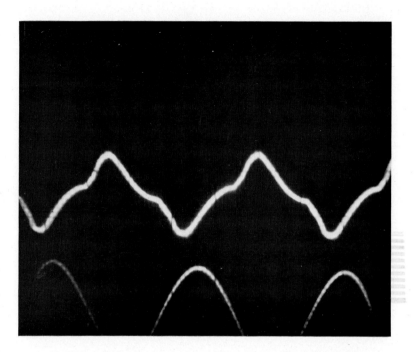

*Figure 4.28. The current (upper trace) and voltage for an electrodeless discharge in* $H_2$ *(p = 27 mm Hg), in a cylindrical Pyrex vessel, length 1·8 cm, placed between parallel plates.* $f = 210$ *kc/s (= 1400 m), peak voltage = 2280. These oscillograms were taken with a double-beam instrument, so that the current trace appears inverted with respect to the voltage trace; thus a positive voltage but a negative current trace appear as upward deflections*

*To face p. 148*

would account for the observed starting potential and rate of growth of current. The charge deposited on the wall of the vessel after the passage of one of these pulses has also been measured by replacing the series resistance with a known condenser. Although the height and rate of growth fluctuate somewhat from one pulse to another, the total charge crossing is constant, and it suffices to reduce the field in the vessel at the end of a pulse to about half the applied field[151].

A common feature of discharges at frequencies lower than cut-off (or its equivalent transition region) is that some ionizing agency remains long after the electrons have been swept out of the space, and either maintains a continuous current or provides initial ionization to restart the discharge in the next half cycle. Some such agencies are positive ions, resonance photons and metastable atoms, all of which can release secondary electrons from walls. At very low frequencies the effect of such an agency is to provide small initial ionization and a consequent regular train of pulses which occur in the same phase in each cycle. In hydrogen discharges this regularity was observed to continue down to frequencies of 1/10–1/100 c/s, simulated by the application of steady d.c. field which could be reversed, i.e. square waves of period 10–100 sec. None of the agencies discussed could account for this effect and it is thought that the electrons deposited on one end wall (the 'anode' wall) in one pulse are loosely bound, and that a few of them can be pulled off by the field in the following half cycle; the electrons are then, of course, on the 'cathode' wall and will have a great chance of ionizing in the gas. Experiments devised to remove these wall charges also destroyed the regularity of the pulses[131].

It is clear from *Figures 4.29* and *4.30* that discharges in nitrogen resemble those in hydrogen, whilst those in helium are similar to those in neon. The theory for these gases has not yet been developed, however.

The presence of wall charges can, of course, affect the measurements of starting potential as well as the regularity of the pulses observed. It is important, when applying continuous fields, to wait an appreciable time between measurements to ensure that all wall charges have leaked away, so that the field in the gas is actually the applied field.

The experiments described above have been made at rather low values of $X/p$ (e.g. in $H_2$ from 30 to 80 V/cm mm Hg) and in vessels with insulating walls: in these circumstances wall charges play an important role, and it is well known that the photo-electric effect, $\gamma_p$, is a dominant secondary process[152,153]. In rather short parallel-plate gaps (low values of $pd$) between metal electrodes, however,

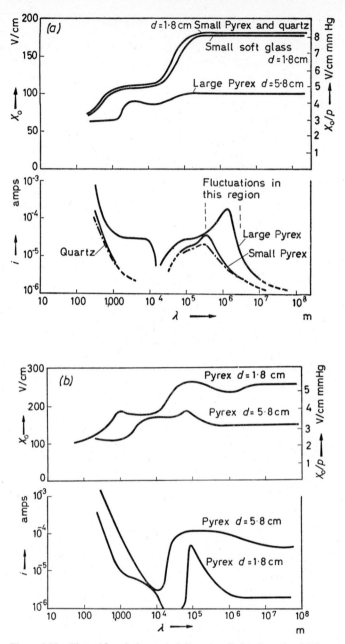

Figure 4.29. *Electrodeless discharges in helium, in cylindrical vessels of different material all of 3 cm diameter, and length d cm. Curves of starting field (peak value $X_0$) and equilibrium current, i, as a function of the wavelength, $\lambda$, of the applied field:* (a) $p = 22$ mm Hg; (b) $p = 47$ mm Hg

wall charges play no part, and the value of $X/p$ is higher so that secondary emission due to the bombardment of positive ions, $\gamma_i$, is the important effect. Here, the curves of starting potential against frequency are different from those found in insulating vessels. The

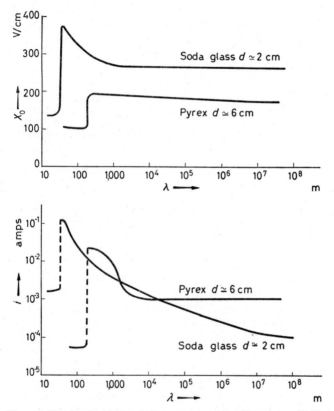

*Figure 4.30. Starting field and discharge current in nitrogen, in cylindrical glass vessels of length d cm (uniform electric field along axis)*

rate of growth of current is governed by the speed with which positive ions drift back to the temporary cathode from the point where they are produced, which is chiefly near the temporary anode. At very low frequencies the half period $T/2$ is so long compared with the transit time, $\tau$, of ions across the gap that the field remains near its peak value long enough for a large density of ionization to grow. At higher frequencies, however, the field may be sufficiently large to give appreciable multiplication long enough only to sustain a few electron avalanches, and therefore in order to produce equivalent ionization, the peak value of the field must be increased; hence the breakdown field increases with frequency. The effect has been studied by FUCHS and his colleagues[154,155], who, in a simplified theory, regard electron avalanches as separate events following each other at intervals of time, $\tau^*$, and deduce the breakdown condition.

$$\gamma_i \left[ e^{\alpha d} \cos \frac{2\pi\tau}{T} - 1 \right] = \gamma_i \left[ e^{\alpha d} \cos \frac{\omega d}{v_{\text{drift}}^+} - 1 \right]$$
$$= 1, \text{ provided } \tau \ll T \ldots . (4.103)$$

This, of course, reduces to the normal Townsend condition when $\omega = 0$ (d.c. fields) but, in general, predicts an increased field as $\omega$ increases. There is a critical frequency, $f_1$, at which the ion transit time becomes comparable with half a period (i.e. $\tau \sim T/2$); ions are no longer swept out of the volume although they move close to the wall and still contribute to the secondary process. The combination of $\gamma_i$ and the ion space charge now leads to a reduction in the starting potential, for $f > f_1$, until the amplitude of oscillation of the ions is so reduced that $\gamma_i$ decreases, at which time the starting potential rises again. A second critical frequency, $f_2$, is reached when the transit time of electrons is comparable with the electrode spacing: above this frequency the diffusion theory applies. Thus the curve of $V_s$ against $f$ is expected to have two maxima between very low frequencies and the diffusion region, which has been confirmed by experiments (*Figure 4.31*). If square waves are used, instead of sine waves, the increase in starting potential at frequencies below $f_1$ disappears[154]. Time lag measurements confirm the important part played by ion oscillations[156]. In Ne–A mixtures the Penning effect causes a reduction in $V_s$ at frequencies above 10 kc/s. Discharges at high pressures ($p > 300$ mm Hg) between internal electrodes have contracted columns: between 300 and 500 mm Hg in argon, for example, both contracted and uncontracted forms exist[158]. In the former the longitudinal effective field is between 20 and 30 V/cm, and in the latter between 25 and 60 V/cm.

---

* This is based on the assumption that it is necessary to wait for the bulk of the ions, formed near the anode in one avalanche, to travel the length of the gap and eject the electrons to start the next avalanche. In fact, $\gamma_i$ is a continuous process and enables current to grow faster than could be imagined on this simple idea (see *Ionization and Breakdown in Gases* by F. Llewellyn Jones, Chapter 8, Methuen, 1957).

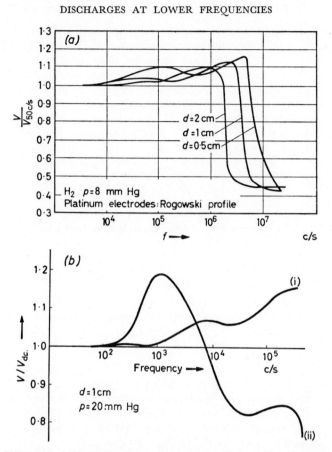

*Figure 4.31. (a) Starting potential relative to that at 50 c/s for electrodes spaced d cm apart; (b) starting potential relative to the d.c. value: curve (i) pure neon, curve (ii) neon–argon mixture. [(a) from W. Fuchs[154], by courtesy of Applied Scientific Research, Hague; (b) from M. T. Vlaardingerbroek[157], by courtesy of Applied Scientific Research, Hague]*

## Discharges at Low Frequencies (50 c/s)

Such discharges, especially between insulating surfaces, are of considerable importance in practical applications, since they occur inside small holes (voids) in insulators subjected to large fields with the subsequent deterioration or breakdown of the dielectric[234,235]. They have been studied in their simplest form in air by HARRIES[159] who used short, wide, cylindrical glass vessels having a uniform field directed along the axis. The current occurs in pulses, whose size and shape was observed by an oscillograph; when starting potential

11  153

is applied, one pulse is observed in each half cycle, occurring near the peak. As the potential is increased, groups of pulses appear, the first of the group appearing at an earlier phase of the cycle. The reason is that when a single pulse occurs, electrons multiply rapidly and, being deposited on the end wall, reduce the field in the gas and stop the current flow. If the external field is still increasing, however, the field in the gas will, again, soon reach a sufficiently high value for another pulse of current to pass. The process is repeated until the applied field passes its peak value: in the next

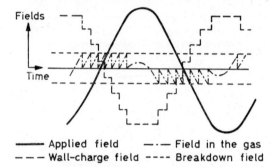

——— Applied field    —·— Field in the gas
— — — Wall-charge field  ---- Breakdown field

*Figure 4.32. The fields at a single discharging area, for an applied voltage much greater than the starting voltage.* (From W. L. HARRIES[159], by courtesy of the Institution of Electrical Engineers)

half cycle the applied and wall-charge fields assist each other; pulses start at an early phase and continue, first discharging the walls and then charging them in the opposite direction (*Figure 4.32*). These and similar experiments show that the mechanism of the discharges is the same as in d.c., primary ionization in the gas being sustained by a secondary wall process (probably photo-electric emission). A single current pulse represents a discharge along a narrow channel, causing wall charges to collect over a small area of the glass. Different areas will not break down simultaneously, because the starting potential, and the subsequent size of the pulse, depends on the secondary emission from the walls and this varies from point to point. Once one pulse has started, however, the voltage drop in the external circuit will stop any others until it is over.

In certain gases, notably the halogens and to some extent water vapour, these pulses are decreased in height when the discharge is irradiated by visible light ($\lambda \geqslant 4,800$ Å in chlorine corresponding to quanta of energy about 2·6 eV or less). The effect was discovered, and has been extensively studied, by JOSHI and his colleagues[160-62] (a few review articles[163],[164] are quoted for reference purposes). Their view is that in the growth of the pulses two secondary effects, release of electrons by positive ions hitting the walls, and photo-ionization in the gas, are important[165]. HARRIES and VON ENGEL[166], who have studied these discharges in $Cl_2$, have shown that the irradiation is effective only near the cathode wall. They believe that an absorbed layer of gas on the walls is dissociated by the external light, and the consequent attachment of electrons to Cl atoms removes them from the avalanche and thus reduces the height of the pulses. The influence of the external irradiation disappears at large over-voltages ($V \sim 2 \times$ starting potential), when pulses follow each other rapidly and some products of one remain to provide ample ionization to start the next when the field recovers.

When a magnetic field is superimposed on a low-frequency electric field, the effective increase in pressure causes an increase in the breakdown field[167].

## SUMMARY OF DISCHARGE MECHANISMS

At low frequencies (a few hundred cycles or less), discharges occur as current pulses almost independently in each half cycle, their starting being governed by primary and secondary processes as in d.c., and the starting potential is, in most gases, the same as for a d.c. discharge in the same conditions. At low values of $X/p$, and especially in insulating vessels, the photo-electric effect is the dominant secondary process. Growth of current is so rapid, compared with the period of the field, that the starting field is independent of frequency over a wide range. At high $X/p$, and when internal metal electrodes are used, positive ions produce the important secondary effect, but growth of current is much slower, and fewer electron avalanches occur in each half cycle. The field must be increased at higher frequency in order to produce the ionization quickly enough. As the frequency is further increased, products of the discharge in one half cycle remain to assist the subsequent discharges, and a decrease of the starting field results. These products may be resonance photons or metastable atoms, as in the rare gases, or ions; in some gases at high $X/p$, between metal electrodes, a decrease in breakdown field occurs at that frequency and pressure when the amplitude of the ion motion becomes less than the length of the vessel. At still higher frequencies the electrons are swept a shorter distance by the field in each half cycle: when their amplitude becomes less than the length of the vessel, losses are greatly reduced and the breakdown field decreases again—this is the diffusion region, since diffusion is now the only source of loss.

155

The transition is abrupt in molecular gases and spread out over a frequency range in the rare gases. Further increase of frequency causes little change in breakdown field until it becomes greater than the frequency with which electrons collide with gas molecules, when the field increases due to the inefficient transfer of energy from the field to the electrons.

Two resonance effects found in the diffusion region, resulting in very low breakdown or maintenance fields are (a) when, in a transverse magnetic field, the gyro frequency equals the applied frequency, and (b) when, in a fully developed discharge, the electron density is such that the frequency of simple plasma oscillations is equal to the applied frequency. At very low pressure, when the mean free path of electrons is greater than the length of the vessel, breakdown is due to secondary emission from the walls in synchronism with the applied field.

For one gas, hydrogen, all the data has been collected into a consistent picture by BROWN[245], in the form of a three-dimensional model whose axes are the similarity parameters, $pL$, $p\lambda$ and $XL$; thus $X$, the breakdown field, is described simultaneously as a function of gas pressure, wavelength of applied field and geometry of the vessel. As we have seen, the surface would be rather different for other gases. A short summary of starting potentials of common gases at atmospheric pressure and at different frequencies is given in *Table 4.1*.

*Table 4.1*. Starting field $X_s$ at 1 atmosphere pressure in various gases (in units of kV/cm)

| Gas | $\lambda = \infty$ $f = 0$ | 300 m 1 Mc/s | $\sim$ 10 cm 3,000 Mc/s |
|---|---|---|---|
| Air | 34 | | 28 |
| $H_2$ | $\approx$ 20 | $\sim$ 22* | 16 |
| $N_2$ | 35 | | 27 |
| $O_2$ | 30 | | 32 |
| He | $\sim$ 10 | 0·75 | 2·5 |
| Ne | $\sim$ 1·4 | $\sim$ 0·5 | 4 |
| A | 2·7 $\pm$ 0·3 | $\sim$ 30 | 10·5 |

\* Extrapolated value.

APPLICATIONS OF HIGH-FREQUENCY DISCHARGES

*Ion Sources*

High-frequency discharges are especially useful for the generation of ions in particle accelerators, first because the insulating glass vessels can be used and the difficulties associated with metal electrodes avoided, e.g. emission of impurities, rapid recombination and the destruction of atomic ions in molecular gases; secondly, because the exciting field need have no d.c. connection to the accelerator. In addition, the fields necessary to maintain the discharge are low and consequently there is a small spread in ion energy. The ions are extracted by a strong d.c. field, which in intense discharges does not greatly affect the maintenance of the plasma. The cylindrical electromagnetic, or ring, discharge, excited by a solenoid with its electrostatic field screened, is especially useful since the electric field is perpendicular, everywhere, to the extracting field, and the long current path results in a large concentration of ions. Conditions of pressure, frequency and size of vessel must be adjusted according to the type of ion required: for example, in a hydrogen discharge, excited at 20 Mc/s in a Pyrex cylinder 3 cm in diameter, the current of protons ($H^+$) extracted is greatest at a pressure of about $2\cdot5 \times 10^{-2}$ mm Hg. (Spectroscopic measurements show this type of discharge to be rich in atomic states[168].) The design of the electrode through which the ions are extracted is also of great importance, and a number of workers have studied these problems[140,168-78].

*Particle Detectors*

BROWN and MCCARTHY[179] have studied the possibility of using gas in a concentric cylindrical cavity excited at 3,000 Mc/s as a counter of ionizing radiation. The h.f. field applied is, of course, smaller than that required for breakdown. If a particle sweeps through the high field region of the cavity, i.e. near the central wire, the ionization produced will multiply rapidly, and cause a mismatching of the microwave line, and a consequent reduction in the transmitted signal. This pulse is rectified and fed to an electronic counting system. In this simple form the counter is insensitive, since only particles passing near the central wire will be counted, and the resolving time is long because the ionization built up in the cavity dies away by ambipolar diffusion. However, the addition of a d.c. field (central wire positive) sweeps initial electrons into the high field region, thus increasing sensitivity, and the resultant ionization can be swept out of the volume by applying another d.c. field after the pulse has been counted. A quenching agent (mostly alcohol) is added to the gas to suppress electron emission from the walls. The counter has a resolving time of about 2 $\mu$sec and a pulse rise time of approx. $10^{-8}$ sec.

It has also been noticed that in an intense microwave field, visible discharges appear, localized along the tracks of $\alpha$ and $\beta$ rays (neon was used, saturated with iodine vapour, at a total pressure of 200 mm Hg)[180].

### High-temperature Welding Torch

Several workers[181-83], using frequencies of $10^8$ c/s or less to excite discharges at atmospheric pressure, have observed the discharge as a torch-like flame attached to one electrode. The effect was studied in detail by COBINE and WILBUR[184], who fed microwave power ($10^9$ c/s) through a co-axial line to an electrode; gas was caused to flow axially out from the electrode. A discharge could be started by touching the electrode with an insulated wire and drawing it away, after which it remained stable, provided the system was suitably tuned, having the appearance of a flame a few cm long. The flame produced by polyatomic gases is able to melt many refractory materials, the energy being produced by association of molecules which have previously been dissociated in the discharge. Probe measurements indicate an electron temperature of about $10^5$ °K (energy $\sim 10$ eV), and estimates from spectroscopic measurements[185], and the vertical displacement of a horizontally directed flame due to convection[186], show that the gas temperature in the outer regions of the flame is about 3,000°K, several kilowatts of microwave power being supplied. The measurements need careful interpretation, since much of the excitation is due to electron impacts—not thermal motion of the gas—and also since the electrons probably have large directed velocities, especially near the electrodes. Temperature measurements of ordinary high-power microwave discharges in cavities with low gas pressures have been made with thermocouples[187].

### MICROWAVE STUDIES OF DECAYING DISCHARGES: DEDUCTION OF STATISTICAL AND ATOMIC CONSTANTS

When the applied field, which maintains a discharge, is switched off, electrons and ions disappear from the discharge region at a rate characteristic of the process by which they are removed; it may be diffusion, recombination, attachment of electrons, or drift if a steady field remains which is insufficient to maintain ionization. Measurements of the electron density, $n$, at various times, $t$, in the decay of the discharge, enable the process to be identified and its value found. $n$ is deduced from the conductivity of the gas in a small microwave field, used as a probing signal (see pp. 87, 92). The conductivity is complex, since the electrons move out of phase with the microwave field, and can be represented as a real and imaginary part corresponding to the currents in phase and at 90° to the applied field. The former absorb power and depend on both $n$ and $\nu$, the collision frequency; the latter absorb no power and to a first approximation, provided $\nu \ll \omega$, depend on $n$ but not on $\nu$. Thus a simultaneous measurement of a resistive effect and a reactive effect enable both $n$ and $\nu$ to be found.

The idea of measuring the electron concentration in an ionized gas by its effect upon a high-frequency field was conceived by VAN DER POL[188], and developed by IMAM and KHASTGIR[189], MAKINSON and his colleagues[190] and others, for steady discharges. More refined modern techniques enable measurements to be made in decaying discharges. Briefly, two methods are used: the ionized gas may be contained in a microwave cavity whose changes in resonant frequency and $Q$ are measured; or a discharge in an insulated, e.g. glass, tube is inserted in the path of a microwave signal whose attenuation and phase shift are measured. The ionization can be produced by any convenient method, not necessarily by a microwave field*, although in the cavity experiments described here, microwave discharges have been used. The method has the great advantage that no solid object need be inserted into the discharge and also that measurements are possible in electrons of very low average energy; however, the measurements give only the average electron density $\bar{n}$ over the region explored.

Depending on the frequencies and experimental technique used these methods are suitable for measuring $\bar{n}$ in the range $10^6$–$10^{12}$ electrons/cm³.

### Experimental Method

The most commonly used method is that devised by BIONDI[191,192] and illustrated in *Figure 4.33*. Ionization is produced in a cavity by a pulsed field, and the resonant (angular) frequency $\omega_0$ of the empty cavity is increased, due to the motion of the electrons, by an amount $\Delta\omega$. Calculations by SLATER[193] give

$$\frac{\Delta\omega}{\omega_0} = 2\pi \frac{\bar{n}e^2}{m\omega_0^2} \cdot \frac{1}{[1 + (\nu/\omega)^2]} G \approx 2\pi \frac{\bar{n}e^2}{m\omega_0^2} \cdot G \quad \ldots\ldots(4.104)$$

and

$$\frac{1}{Q} - \frac{1}{Q_0} = 4\pi \frac{\bar{n}e^2}{m\omega_0^2} \cdot \frac{\nu/\omega}{1 + (\nu/\omega)^2} \quad \ldots\ldots(4.105)$$

where $G$ is a geometrical factor depending on the distribution in space both of the ionization and the field.

---

* For measurements in the d.c. glow discharge see: Francis, G., *Handbuch der Physik*, Vol. 22, Springer, 1956.

A low-power microwave signal of frequency $f$, slightly higher than $f_0$, the resonant frequency of the empty cavity, is fed continuously into the cavity and its transmitted or reflected component observed. As the electron density decays and reaches a value such that, by equation (4.104), the resonant frequency of the cavity is equal to $f$, there is, at that instant, a minimum in the reflected power and a maximum in that transmitted. Thus by repeating the

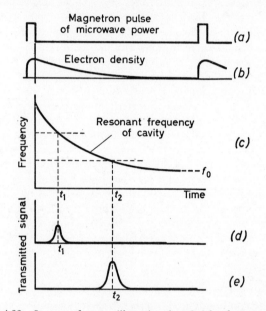

Figure 4.33. Sequence of events, illustrating the principle of measurement of electron densities in afterglows by microwaves. (From M. A. Biondi[195], by courtesy of Applied Scientific Research, Hague)

sequence using different frequencies of probing signals, the decay of electron density with time can be measured. In addition, the decreasing intensities of spectral lines can be measured by using a photomultiplier which is sensitive only for a short selected interval after the discharge has begun to decay[194,195]. By a combination of such measurements the processes by which the electrons are removed can often be deduced.

A word of caution is necessary here concerning the limitations of the method. Persson[196] has pointed out that Slater's result was based on certain simplifying assumptions; for example, that the current due to the motion of the electrons is small compared with the displacement current, so that equation (4.104) is true only when $\Delta\omega$, and hence the electron density, is very small. If this is not true the relation between $\Delta\omega$ and $\bar{n}$ is no longer linear, but can be calculated. An upper limit to the electron density which can be measured is given when

$$\frac{4\pi\bar{n}e^2}{m\omega_0^2} = 1 \qquad\qquad \ldots\ldots(4.106)$$

This gives the frequency of oscillations due to the macroscopic polarization of the plasma. If this expression approaches unity the space charge field is large, and induces other modes of excitation of the cavity; if it exceeds unity the incident field only partially penetrates the plasma. By careful design of the cavity, ensuring that the electric field is perpendicular to electron density gradients, the upper limit can be extended[197]. The change of resonant frequency depends also, to a small extent, on the collisions between electrons and gas molecules. The lower measurable limit of $\bar{n}$ is determined by the sensitivity of the apparatus, i.e. how accurately a change in resonant frequency can be measured. The limits, using the simple theory are $\bar{n} = 5 \times 10^7$ to approx. $5 \times 10^9$ and, with exact theory and suitable design, extends to about $5 \times 10^{10}$ electrons/cm³. Persson points out, however, that a modified technique adapted to frequencies of about 1 Mc/s, measuring the $Q$ of a coil circuit, would permit measurements of $\bar{n} \sim 10^{12}$–$10^{16}$/cm³ at pressures of about 1 mm Hg.

In early experiments using this technique over-simplified theory was applied, leading to values of the electron–ion recombination coefficient (notably in $H_2$) many orders of magnitude too large, although this was sometimes partly due to impurities in the gas[199–201]; these were later corrected[198]. In my opinion microwave measurements differing widely from earlier values should be treated with some reserve, unless deductions of electron density have been made from the exact theory, preferably supported by other (e.g. spectroscopic) evidence. This is not to say that close agreement is to be expected, because in decaying discharges the average electron energy approaches thermal values ($\sim 0{\cdot}03$ eV), whilst in electron swarms in d.c. fields the energies can be several eV.

*Wave Propagation*

Experiments have been made in which the effect of an ionized gas on the propagation of a small microwave signal has been measured[201]. In classical terms the reactive component of conductivity changes the refractive index of the medium and causes a phase shift which can be measured by interferometer methods, and the resistive component changes the extinction coefficient and attenuates the wave (see Chapter 5). The technique and detailed theory has been fully discussed by GOLDSTEIN and others[202-7]. The probing signals can be continuous or pulsed, and several waves of different frequencies and/or amplitudes can be propagated at the same time. The use of millimetre waves has made it possible to measure high electron densities ($\sim 10^{14}$ per cm$^3$)[207].

A variant of this method is to study propagation through an ionized gas in the presence of a static or slowly varying magnetic field, and observe the change in polarization of the wave; combined with a measurement of the absorption it is again possible to find $\bar{n}$ and $\nu$[203,204].

The general theory of propagation of waves through ionized gases is discussed in Chapter 5 and, in more detail, in the reviews of ALLIS[237] and BROWN. Recently DRUMMOND[236] studied microwave propagation through regions having high electron and ion temperatures in a magnetic field.

### Diffusion, Recombination, Attachment, Mobility

When the field exciting the discharge is removed, $\nu_i$ becomes zero, and the electron density, $n$, decays according to the relation:

$$\frac{\partial n}{\partial t} = - D_a \nabla_n^2 - Rn \cdot n_+ - h \cdot \nu_a \cdot n \quad \dots . (4.107)$$

where it may be assumed that electrons are removed by ambipolar diffusion $(D_a)$, recombination (coefficient $R$) and attachment ($h$ is the probability of an attachment and $\nu_a$ is the frequency with which an electron hits an attaching molecule; thus $\nu_a \propto \mathcal{N}$ where $\mathcal{N}$ is the density of such molecules). It may be also assumed that no new electrons are being formed by any process*, and that, by elastic collisions, the electrons have cooled to a constant energy so that $D_a$, $R$ and $h$ do not vary as the measurements are made. If the energy of the electrons needs to be accurately known, two points must be considered: electrons may have constant energy slightly above thermal by absorption of small amounts of power from the constant probing signal, or they may be slightly cooler than the gas because, in ambipolar diffusion, it is the faster electrons

---

* In some rare gases the electron density has been found to increase for a short time after the discharge has been switched off, due to metastable atoms colliding with other metastables, or with neutral atoms of an impurity. Many useful facts about the role of metastable atoms in discharges have been found from these studies[210,211].

which escape to the walls ('diffusion cooling')[208,209]; the latter is noticeable in the heavier rare gases. Since $\kappa$ ($\approx 2m/M$) is small there is slow transfer of energy from atoms to electrons.

Experimental conditions are chosen so that one, or two at the most, of these processes operate; for example high gas pressure will favour recombination. If diffusion is the dominant process, a solution of equation (4.107), neglecting other terms, leads to $n$ as a function of time decaying exponentially in several modes (i.e. different time constants) and it is necessary to wait until all but the one with the longest time constant, corresponding to a characteristic diffusion length, $L$, have died away:

$$n = \Sigma C_1 e^{-t/\tau_1} \cdot f_1(x, y, z) \qquad \ldots.(4.108)$$

where $C_1$ . . . are constants determined by the initial distribution at $t = 0$; $f(x, y, z)$ are functions of space, called modes, and $\tau_1$ . . . the corresponding time constants. When only the lowest-order decay remains, $\log n$ plotted against $t$ gives a straight line of slope[192,200,212]

$$\frac{1}{\tau} = D_a/L^2 \qquad \ldots.(4.109)$$

If recombination is dominant it is usual to have $n = n_+$, and write $- Rn^2$ for the loss term. Then

$$\frac{1}{n(t)} - \frac{1}{n(0)} = Rt \qquad \ldots.(4.110)$$

Hence the $\frac{1}{n} - t$ curve is linear, having a slope $R$[198–201]. If attachment is the only important process then

$$n = n(0) \cdot e^{-h\nu_a \cdot t} \qquad \ldots.(4.111)$$

The slope of the $\log n - t$ curve determines $h\nu_a$[200,213]; this process can be distinguished from diffusion by the dependence on pressure since $\nu_a \propto p$ and $D_a \propto 1/p$. Note also that $h\nu_a = \sigma_a \cdot v_r N$, where $v_r$ is the random velocity of the electrons and $\sigma_a$ the atomic cross section for attachment, which can thus be deduced.

The measurements are often combined with spectroscopic observations, e.g. of recombination lines, and the use of a mass spectrometer to identify the ions present in the discharge[214]. The mobility of ions can be deduced from the ambipolar diffusion coefficient, since if it is assumed that the electrons are at the same temperature as the gas, $D_a = 2D^+$, and $\frac{b^+}{D^+} = \frac{e}{kT}$.

Some interesting results of these measurements show, for example, that ambipolar diffusion is the dominant process of loss in many gases at pressures as high as 20 or 30 mm Hg, and that in the rare gases molecular ions, e.g. $He_2^+$, are important in the afterglow. In helium, at pressures above 20 mm Hg, electrons disappear by dissociative recombination with $He_2^+$. Admixtures of the rare gases favour the production of atomic ions, in which both the Penning effect and charge transfer play a part, and compound ions, e.g. He Ne$^+$, may also be formed.

For a detailed discussion of many of these results reference should be made to the works of GOLDSTEIN[202] and OSKAM[211].

*Atomic Data: Collision Frequencies, Mean Energy Loss*

The collision frequency, $\nu$, of electrons with gas molecules can be deduced from a simultaneous measurement of the real and imaginary parts of the conductivity. This has been performed in the following ways:

(1) Measurement of the change of resonant frequency and $Q$ value of a resonant cavity[215,216,241]. Some results for the cross section for elastic collisions of electrons having energies of 0·039 eV are given below, and compared with older measurements. These refer to gases at $p = 1$ mm Hg, and 0°C.

|  | He | Ne | A | Kr | Xe | H$_2$ | N$_2$ |
|---|---|---|---|---|---|---|---|
| $Q$ (microwave) | 19 | 3·3 | 2·1 | 54 | 180 | 46 | 15 cm²/cm³ |
| $Q$ (older)[217] | 5 | 7 | 8 | 40 | 130 | 4 | 1·6 |

It is clear that there are considerable discrepancies. Another resonant cavity method makes use of a superimposed magnetic field[218] and the results of these and other cavity measurements have been reviewed by GILARDINI[219].

(2) Measurement of the attenuation and phase shift of a propagated wave. The interaction of two waves of different frequencies has been studied, making use on a laboratory scale of an effect first discovered in the ionosphere[220] and interpreted theoretically by BAILEY and MARTYN[221]. When two waves cross the same region of an ionized gas the modulation of the stronger wave can be detected, impressed on the weaker wave ('ionospheric cross-modulation'). The reason is that absorption of the stronger wave increases the mean energy of the electrons, which leads to a change in their collision frequency. This, in turn, changes the absorption of the weaker wave, and hence its transmission is altered by the presence of the stronger ('disturbing') wave. In microwave measurements the stronger wave is applied in a pulse ('pulse modulated') for the purpose of increasing the average electron energy. Thus not only

can $\bar{n}$ and $\nu$ be measured but the variation of $\nu$ with electron energy in the range from approximately 0·04 to 0·5 eV. $\kappa$, the average fraction of energy lost by an electron in hitting a gas molecule, can also be deduced from the relaxation time constant associated with the transmission of the low power wave in the wake of the disturbing pulse[205,206]. For example, in helium $\kappa$ was found to be $2\cdot7 \times 10^{-4} \approx 2m/M$, but in $N_2$ the measured $\kappa$ was about $5\cdot5 \times 2m/M$, indicating that an electron loses small amounts in rotational excitation of the $N_2$ molecule. In helium, at room temperature, the cross section for collisions measured by this method is 24 cm²/cm³, agreeing reasonably with other microwave measurements; but in $N_2$ the measured $Q$ is about 60 cm²/cm³, appreciably larger than cavity measurements or those by older methods.

### Microwave Measurements of Electron Temperature, $T_e$

For completeness, a mention of a microwave method for measuring the electron temperature in a discharge is included, although, to my knowledge, this has so far been applied only to d.c. discharges in which $T_e$ is appreciable, and not to decaying plasma. It has been observed that discharges produce noise (i.e. a continuous spectrum of frequencies) in the microwave region, at frequencies which range within one or two orders of magnitude of those of the average collision of electrons[222,223]. Several empirical laws analogous to the laws of black body radiation (notably Wien's displacement law) have been derived, and it can be concluded that a discharge emits radiation like a black body at a temperature $T_N$ ('noise temperature'). The power radiated in a frequency interval $df$ is $kT_N \cdot df$. The value of $T_N$ has, in some circumstances, been found to agree closely with values of $T_e$ from probe measurements[224-26]. PARZEN and GOLDSTEIN[227] find that the power radiated can be accounted for by fluctuations of electron current in the plasma. By calculating the probability that electrons of a given velocity will have a certain collision frequency, they derive the power, $P_f$, radiated in the frequency interval, $f, f + df$:

$$P_f = \left[ kT_e + \frac{P_0}{N\nu} \left( 2 + \frac{\nu^2 - 4\pi^2 f^2}{\nu^2 + 4\pi^2 f^2} \right) \right] df \quad \ldots \ldots (4.112)$$

where $P_0$ is the total power dissipated in the discharge and $N$ the number of gas molecules per cm³; the second term is usually small and $T_e \approx T_N$. This method is analogous to the measurement of thermal radiation intensity from stars.

### REFERENCES

1 LORENTZ, H. A., *Theory of Electrons*; Leipzig: Teubner, 1916
2 CHILDS, E. C., *Phil. Mag.*, **13** (1932) 873
3 APPLETON, E. V. and CHAPMAN, F. W., *Proc. phys. Soc. Lond.*, **44** (1932) 146
4 MARGENAU, H., *Phys. Rev.*, **69** (1946) 508; **109** (1958) 6
5 MARGENAU, H., *Proceedings of the Third International Conference on Ionization Phenomena in Gases*, Venice, 1957
6 MARGENAU, H. and ADLER, P., *Phys. Rev.*, **79** (1950) 970
7 TOWNSEND, J. S. and GILL, E. W. B., *Phil. Mag.*, **26** (1938) 290
8 BOOT, H. A. H. and SHERSBY-HARVIE, R., *Nature, Lond.*, **180** (1957) 1187
9 ECCLES, W. H., *Proc. roy. Soc.*, **A87** (1912) 79
10 LARMOR, J., *Phil. Mag.*, **48** (1924) 1025
11 APPLETON, E. V. and CHILDS, E. C., *ibid.*, **10** (1930) 969
12 MIERDEL, G., *Ann. Phys.*, **85** (1928) 612
13 IONESCU, V. and MIHUL, C., *J. Phys. Radium*, **6** (1935) 35
14 GANGOPADHAYA, S. and KHASTGIR, S. R., *Phil. Mag.*, **25** (1938) 883
15 JANCEL, R. and KAHAN, T., *Nuovo Cim.*, **12** (1954) 573
16 BAYET, M., DELCROIX, J. L. and DENISSE, J. F., *J. Phys. Radium*, **15** (1954) 795; **16** (1955) 274; **17** (1956) 923, 1005
17 GUREVICH, A. V., *J. exp. theor. Phys.*, **3** (1957) 895
18 HOLSTEIN, T., *Phys. Rev.*, **70** (1946) 367
19 MARGENAU, H. and HARTMAN, L. M., *ibid.*, **73** (1948) 297, 309, 316
20 CAHN, J. H., *ibid.*, **75** (1949) 293, 838
21 ALLIS, W. P. and BROWN, S. C., *ibid.*, **84** (1951) 519
22 ROSEN, P., *ibid.*, **103** (1956) 390
23 WOLFF, P. A., *ibid.*, **103** (1956) 845
24 GILARDINI, A. L. and BROWN, S. C., *ibid.*, **105** (1957) 25
25 CHAPMAN, S. and COWLING, T. G., *The Mathematical Theory of Non-uniform Gases*; London: Cambridge University Press, 1952
26 TOWNSEND, J. S., *Phil. Mag.*, **13** (1932) 745
27 HARRIES, W. L. and VON ENGEL, A. *Proc. roy. Soc.*, **A222** (1954) 490
28 TESLA, N., *Elect. Engr, Lond.*, **7** (1891) 549
29 WIEDEMANN, E. and EBERT, H., *Wied. Ann.*, **1** (1893) 549
30 THOMSON, J. J., *Phil. Mag.*, **32** (1891) 321, 445
31 GOULD, L. and BROWN, S. C., *J. appl. Phys.*, **24** (1953) 1053
32 BROWN, S. C. and ROSE, D. J., *ibid.*, **23** (1952) 711, 719, 1028
33 BABAT, G. I., *J. Instn elect. Engrs*, **94** (III) (1947) 27
34 THOMSON, J., *Phil. Mag.*, **10** (1930) 280; **18** (1934) 696; **21** (1936) 1057; **23** (1937) 1
35 THOMSON, J. J. and THOMSON, G. P., *Conduction of Electricity through Gases*; London: Cambridge University Press, 1933
36 GILL, E. W. B. and DONALDSON, R. H., *Phil. Mag.*, **2** (1926) 129
37 ALFVÉN, H. and COHN-PETERS, H. J., *Ark. Mat. Astr. Fys.*, **31** (1944) 1 [quoting results of N. E. BACKMARK and V. BENGSTON (Dipl. Technische Hochschule, Stockholm, 1941)]

[38] GILL, E. W. B. and VON ENGEL, A., *Proc. roy. Soc.*, **A192** (1948) 446
[39] HATCH, A. J. and WILLIAMS, H. B., *J. appl. Phys.*, **25** (1954) 417
[40] KOLLATH, R. in *Handbuch der Physik*, Vol. 21; Heidelberg: Springer, 1956
[41] McKAY, K. G., *Advanc. Electron.*, **1** (1948) 65
[42] BRUINING, H., *Physics and Applications of Secondary Electron Emission*; London: Pergamon Press, 1954
[43] KREBS, K. and MEERBACH, H., *Ann. Phys.*, **15** (1955) 189
[44] HUBER, E. L., OZAKI, H. T. and KLEIDER, A., *Ninth Gaseous Electronics Conference*, Pittsburgh (American Physical Society)
[45] KOSSEL, F. and KREBS, K., *Z. Phys.*, **139** (1954) 189
[46] HATCH, A. J. and WILLIAMS, H. B., *Phys. Rev.*, **100** (1955) 1228
[47] HATCH, A. J. and WILLIAMS, H. B., *ibid.*, **89** (1953) 339
[48] TAMAGAWA, H., *E.T.J., Tokyo*, **3** (1957) 42, 93
[49] FRANCIS, G. and VON ENGEL, A., *Phil. Trans.*, **A246** (1953) 143
[50] FRANCIS, G. and VON ENGEL, A., *Proc. phys. Soc. Lond.*, **B63** (1950) 823
[51] FRANCIS, G., *D. Phil. Thesis*, University of Oxford, 1951
[52] PROWSE, W. A. and COOPER, R., *J. Instn elect. Engrs*, **95** (III) (1948) 342; *Nature, Lond.*, **161** (1948) 310
[53] COOPER, R., *J. Instn elect. Engrs*, **94** (III) (1947) 315
[54] POSIN, D. Q., *Phys. Rev.*, **73** (1948) 496
[55] PROWSE, W. A. and LANE, P. E., *Appl. sci. Res.*, Hague, **B5** (1955) 127
[56] MITCHELL, A. C. G. and ZEMANSKY, M. W., *Resonance Radiation and Excited Atoms*; London: Cambridge University Press, 1934
[57] HALE, D. K., *Phys. Rev.*, **73** (1948) 1046
[58] BRASEFIELD, C. J., *ibid.*, **35** (1930) 1073; **37** (1931) 82
[59] GUTTON, C., *C.R. Acad. Sci.*, **176** (1923) 1871; **178** (1924) 467
[60] KIRSCHNER, F., *Ann. Phys.*, **77** (1925) 287, 298; **7** (1930) 798; *Phys. Rev.*, **72** (1947) 348
[61] GUTTON, C. and GUTTON, H., *C.R. Acad. Sci.*, **186** (1928) 303
[62] GUTTON, H., *Ann. Phys.*, Paris, **13** (1930) 62
[63] RHODE, L., *Ann. Phys.*, **12** (1932) 569
[64] CHENOT, M., *Ann. Phys.*, Paris, **3** (1948) 277 (many earlier references given here)
[65] LLEWELLYN JONES, F. and MORGAN, G. D., *Proc. phys. Soc. Lond.*, **B64** (1951) 560, 574
[66] LLEWELLYN JONES, F. and WILLIAMS, G. C., *ibid.*, **B66** (1953) 17, 345
[67] TOWNSEND, W. A. and WILLIAMS, G. C., *ibid.*, **72** (1958) 823
[68] HERLIN, M. A. and BROWN, S. C., *Phys. Rev.*, **74** (1948) 291, 910, 1650
[69] MACDONALD, A. D. and BROWN, S. C., *ibid.*, **75** (1949) 411
[70] KRASIK, S., ALPERT, D. and McCOUBREY, A. O., *ibid.*, **76** (1949) 722
[71] MACDONALD, A. D. and BROWN, S. C., *ibid.*, **76** (1949) 1634
[72] VARNERIN, L. J. and BROWN, S. C., *ibid.*, **79** (1950) 946
[73] ALLIS, W. P. and BROWN, S. C., *ibid.*, **87** (1952) 419
[74] ALLIS, W. P., BROWN, S. C. and EVERHART, E., *ibid.*, **84** (1951) 519
[75] MACDONALD, A. D. and BETTS, D. D., *Canad. J. Phys.*, **30** (1952) 565; **32** (1954) 812

[76] MacDonald, A. D., *Phys. Rev.*, **88** (1952) 420

[77] Reder, F. H. and Brown, S. C., *ibid.*, **95** (1954) 885

[78] MacDonald, A. D. and Brown, S. C., *Canad. J. Phys.*, **28** (1950) 168

[79] Brown, S. C. and MacDonald, A. D., *Phys. Rev.*, **76** (1949) 1629, 1634

[80] Prowse, A. W. and Clark, J. L., *Proc. phys. Soc. Lond.*, **72** (1958) 625

[81] Pim, J. A., *Nature, Lond.*, **161** (1948) 683; *Proc. Instn elect. Engrs*, **96** (1949) 117

[82] MacDonald, A. D. and Matthews, J. H., *Phys. Rev.*, **98** (1955) 1070

[83] Oskam, H. J., *J. appl. Phys.*, **27** (1956) 848

[84] Salmon, J. E., *Ann. Phys., Paris*, **2** (1957) 827; see also *J. Phys. Radium*, **16** (1955) 210, 384

[85] Harries, W. L. and von Engel, A., *Nature, Lond.*, **171** (1953) 517

[86] Varela, A. A., *Phys. Rev.*, **71** (1947) 124

[87] Yamanoto, K. and Okuda, T., *Appl. sci. Res., Hague*, **B5** (1955) 144

[88] von Engel, A. and Steenbeck, M., *Elektrische Gasentladungen*; Berlin: Springer, 1932, 1934

[89] Ware, A. A., *Phil. Mag.*, **45** (1954) 547

[90] Knoll, M., Ollendorf, F. and Rompe, R., *Gasentladungstabellen*; Berlin: Springer, 1934

[91] Tonks, L. and Allis, W. P., *Phys. Rev.*, **52** (1937) 710

[92] Lax, B., Allis, W. P. and Brown, S. C., *J. appl. Phys.*, **21** (1950) 1297

[93] Brown, A. E., *Phil. Mag.*, **29** (1940) 302

[94] Ferretti, L. and Veronesi, P., *Nuovo Cim.*, **2** (1955) 639

[95] Huxley, L. G. H., *Aust. J. Phys.*, **10** (1957) 240

[96] Prowse, W. A. and Jasinski, W., *Proc. Instn elect. Engrs*, **98** (IV) (1951) 101; **99** (IV) (1952) 194

[97] Labrum, N. R., *C.S.I.R. Australia*, RPR 85, 1947

[98] Prowse, W. A. and Lane, P. E., *Proc. phys. Soc. Lond.*, **B69** (1956) 33; *Nature, Lond.*, **172** (1953) 116

[99] Townsend, J. S. and Donaldson, R. H., *Phil. Mag.*, **5** (1928) 178

[100] Townsend, J. S. and Nethercot, W., *ibid.*, **7** (1929) 700

[101] Hayman, R. L., *ibid.*, **7** (1929) 586

[102] Johnson, P., *ibid.*, **10** (1930) 921

[103] Llewellyn Jones, F., *ibid.*, **11** (1931) 163

[104] McCallum, S. P. and Klatzow, L., *ibid.*, **15** (1933) 829

[105] Hiedemann, E., *Verh. physiol. Ges. Berl.*, **7** (1926) 47; *Ann. Phys.*, **85** (1928) 43, 649

[106] Ebelar, L. and Hiedemann, E., *ibid.*, **5** (1930) 625

[107] Pateyuk, G. M., *J. exp. theor. Phys.*, **3** (1956–7) 14

[108] Townsend, J. S. and Llewellyn Jones, F., *Phil. Mag.*, **11** (1931) 679; **12** (1931) 815

[109] Banerji, D. and Ganguli, R., *ibid.*, **13** (1932) 494

[110] Richards, R. C., *ibid.*, **2** (1926) 508

[111] Banerji, D. and Ganguli, R., *ibid.*, **15** (1933) 676; **17** (1934) 313

[112] Townsend, J. S., *C.R. Acad. Sci.*, **186** (1928) 55

[113] Llewellyn Jones, F., *Phil. Mag.*, **15** (1933) 958

[114] Flugge, W., *Ann. Phys.*, **18** (1956) 251

## REFERENCES

[115] Schneider, F., *Z. angew. Phys.*, **6** (1954) 456; see also **4** (1952) 324

[116] Banerji, D. and Ganguli, R., *Phil. Mag.*, **11** (1931) 410; **13** (1932) 495

[117] Johnson, E. O. and Malter, L., *Phys. Rev.*, **80** (1950) 58

[118] Kojima, S. and Takoyama, K., *J. phys. Soc. Japan*, **4** (1949) 349

[119] Mitani, K., *ibid.*, **7** (1952) 634, 637; **8** (1953) 642; **10** (1955) 391

[120] Bayet, M. and Guerineau, F., *C.R. Acad. Sci.*, **239** (1954) 1029

[121] Brasefield, C. J., *Phys. Rev.*, **35** (1930) 92

[122] Bernstein, I. B. and Holstein, T., *ibid.*, **94** (1954) 1475

[123] Dzherpetov, K. A. and Zaitsev, A. A., *Dokl. obsch. Sobr. Ak. Nauk. S.S.S.R.*, **89** (1953) 825; *J. exp. theor. Phys.*, **24** (1953) 516

[124] Allis, W. P. and Brown, S. C., *Phys. Rev.*, **84** (1951) 519

[125] Chenot, M., *C.R. Acad. Sci.*, **227** (1948) 45; **234** (1952) 608, 1152; *J. Phys. Radium*, **16** (1955) 54, 101; **17** (1956) 842; **18** (1957) 395; *Appl. sci. Res. Hague*, **B5** (1955) 124

[126] Gould, L. and Roberts, L. W., *J. appl. Phys.*, **27** (1956) 1162

[127] Schumb, W. C. and Goldman, L., *Proc. Amer. Acad. Arts Sci.*, **69** (1934) 169

[128] Thomson, J. J., *Proc. phys. Soc. Lond.*, **40** (1928) 79

[129] Finch, G. I., *ibid.*, **A62** (1949) 465

[130] Corrigan, S. J. B. and von Engel, A., *Proc. roy. Soc.*, **A245** (1958) 335; see also McMahon, H. and Marshal, M., *Trans. electrochem. Soc.*, **84** (1943) 109

[131] Francis, G., *Proc. phys. Soc. Lond.*, **B68** (1955) 137

[132] Thomson, J. J., *Phil. Mag.*, **4** (1927) 1128

[133] MacKinnon, K. A., *ibid.*, **8** (1929) 605

[134] Yarnold, G. D., *ibid.*, **13** (1932) 1179

[135] Cabannes, F., *Ann. Phys. Paris*, **10** (1955) 1026

[136] Smith, C. G., *Phys. Rev.*, **59** (1941) 997; **71** (1947) 135

[137] Neuert, H., Stuckenberg, H. J. and Weidner, H. P., *Z. angew. Phys.*, **6** (1954) 303

[138] Hall, R. N., *Rev. sci. Instrum.*, **19** (1948) 905

[139] Nisewanger, C. R., Holmes, J. R. and Weissler, G. L., *J. opt. Soc. Amer.*, **36** (1946) 581

[140] Thonemann, P. C., Moffat, J., Roaf, D. and Sanders, J. H., *Proc. phys. Soc. Lond.*, **61** (1948) 482; see also *Progr. nucl. Phys.*, **3** (1953) 219

[141] Ware, A. A., *Phil. Trans.*, **A243** (1951) 197

[142] Cousins, S. W. and Ware, A. A., *Proc. phys. Soc. Lond.*, **B64** (1951) 159

[143] Thonemann, P.C., *Nature, Lond.*, **181** (1958) 217

[144] Allen, N. L., *ibid.*, **181** (1958) 222

[145] Hagerman, D. C. and Mather, J. W., *ibid.*, **181** (1958) 226

[146] Gill, E. W. B. and Donaldson, R. H., *Phil. Mag.*, **12** (1931) 719

[147] Zouckerman, R., *Ann. Phys., Paris*, **13** (1940) 78 (many earlier references given here)

[148] Githens, S., *Phys. Rev.*, **57** (1940) 822

[149] Gill, E. W. B. and von Engel, A., *Proc. roy. Soc.*, **A197** (1949) 107

[150] Popov, N. A. and Kaptsov, N. A., *J. exp. theor. Phys.*, **27** (1954) 97; **3** (1956) 147

[151] FRANCIS, G., *Conference on Ionized Gases* (Birmingham: Royal Society, Warren Research Committee), 1954

[152] LLEWELLYN JONES, F., *Phil. Mag.*, **28** (1939) 192, 328

[153] LLEWELLYN JONES, F. and DAVIES, D. E., *Proc. phys. Soc. Lond.*, **B64** (1951) 519; **72** (1958) 1061

[154] FUCHS, W., *Z. Phys.*, **103** (1936) 709; *Appl. sci. Res.*, *Hague*, **B5** (1955) 109; *Proceedings of the Third International Conference on Ionization Phenomena in Gases*, Venice, 1957

[155] FUCHS, W., GRAF, L., MUES, G. and MÜLLER, H. G., *Z. Phys.*, **145** (1956) 1

[156] BRIGHT, A. W. and HUANG, H. C., *Proc. Instn elect. Engrs*, **100** (III) (1954) 407; **102** (c) (1955) 42; see also FATECHAND, R., *Nature*, *Lond.*, **167** (1951) 566

[157] VLAARDINGERBROEK, M. T., *Appl. sci. Res.*, *Hague*, **B5** (1955) 139

[158] SOLNSTEV, G. S. and DMITRIEVA, M. M., *J. exp. theor. Phys.*, **29** (1955) 651

[159] HARRIES, W. L., *Proc. Instn elect. Engrs*, **100** (II A) (1953) 132

[160] JOSHI, S. S. and DESHMUKH, G. S., *Nature*, *Lond.*, **147** (1941) 806

[161] JOSHI, S. S. and DEO, P. G., *ibid.*, **151** (1943) 561; **153** (1943) 434

[162] JOSHI, S. S., *ibid.*, **154** (1944) 147; *Proc. Indian Sci. Congr.* (1946)

[163] RAMIAH, N. A., BHATAWDEKAR, M. G. and SUBRAHMANYAM, N., *J. chem. Phys.*, **21** (1953) 1160

[164] SAXANA, A. P. and RAMIAH, N. A., *J. sci. industr. Res.*, **10** (1951) 182; **12** (1953) 130

[165] KHOSLA, B. D. and RAMIAH, N. A., *Z. phys. Chem.*, **204** (1955) 223; see also *J. chem. Phys.*, **21** (1953) 365

[166] HARRIES, W. L. and VON ENGEL, A., *Proc. phys. Soc. Lond.*, **B64** (1951) 916; see also *J. chem. Phys.*, **19** (1951) 514

[167] DEB, S. and GOSWAMI, S. N., *Sci. & Cult.*, **22** (1956) 283; see also **20** (1954) 97 and *Nature*, *Lond.*, **168** (1951) 1006

[168] JENNINGS, K. R. and LINNET, J. W., *ibid.*, **182** (1958) 598

[169] THONEMANN, P. C. and HARRISON, E. R., *A.E.R.E. Rep.* GP/R1190 (1955)

[170] BAYLEY, A. J. and WARD, A. G., *Canad. J. Phys.*, **26** (1948) 69

[171] MOAK, C. D., REESE, H. J. and GOOD, W. M., *Nucleonics*, **9** (1951) 18

[172] SWANN, C. P. and SWINGLER, J. F., *Rev. sci. Instrum.*, **23** (1952) 636

[173] GOODWIN, L. K., *ibid.*, **24** (1953) 635

[174] LAREYMONDIE, M. de L., SALMON, J. E. and WAJSBRUM, J., *J. Phys. Radium*, **15** (1954) 117

[175] EUBANK, H. P., *et. al.*, *Rev. sci. Instrum.*, **25** (1954) 989

[176] ALLISON, S. K. and NORBECK, E., *ibid.*, **27** (1956) 285

[177] ERÖ, J., *Acta phys. hung.*, **5** (1956) 390

[178] KISTEMAKER, J. and FLUIT, J. M., *Proceedings of the Third International Conference on Ionization Phenomena in Gases*, Venice, 1957

[179] BROWN, S. C. and McCARTHY, J. J., *Rev. sci. Instrum.*, **19** (1948) 851

[180] BEVAN, A. R., *Nature*, *Lond.*, **164** (1949) 454

[181] ASAMI, Y. and HORI, T., *ibid.*, **144** (1939) 981

[182] CRITESCU, G. and GRIGOROVICI, R., *Naturwissenschaften*, **29** (1941) 511; *Bul. Soc. Român. Fiz.*, **42** (1941) 37

[183] MOCHALOV, K. N., *Dokl. obsch. Sobr. Ak. Nauk, S.S.S.R.*, **67** (1949) 241

[184] COBINE, J. D. and WILBUR, D. A., *J. appl. Phys.*, **22** (1951) 835

[185] MOCHALOV, K. N., NIKIFOROV, A. Y. and BOGONOSTEV, A. S., *J. exp. theor. Phys.*, **20** (1950) 474

[186] SOLNSTEV, G. S., KHOKHLOV, M. Z. and RODINA, E. A., *ibid.*, **22** (1952) 406

[187] REINGOLD, I. and GAROFF, K., *J. appl. Phys.*, **25** (1954) 537

[188] VAN DER POL, B., *Phil. Mag.*, **38** (1919) 352

[189] IMAM, A. and KHASTGIR, S. R., *ibid.*, **23** (1937) 858

[190] MAKINSON, R. E. B., THONEMANN, P. C., KING, R. B. and RAMSAY, J. V., *Proc. phys. Soc. Lond.*, **B64** (1951) 665

[191] BIONDI, M. A., *Rev. sci. Instrum.*, **22** (1951) 500

[192] BIONDI, M. A. and BROWN, S. C., *Phys. Rev.*, **75** (1949) 1700

[193] SLATER, J. C., *Rev. mod. Phys.*, **18** (1946) 441

[194] McCOUBREY, A. O., *Phys. Rev.*, **93** (1954) 1249

[195] BIONDI, M. A., *Appl. sci. Res. Hague*, **B5** (1955) 157

[196] PERSSON, K. B., *Phys. Rev.*, **106** (1957) 191

[197] BUCHSBAUM, S. J. and BROWN, S. C., *ibid.*, **106** (1957) 196

[198] PERSSON, K. B. and BROWN, S. C., *ibid.*, **100** (1955) 729

[199] BIONDI, M. A. and BROWN, S. C., *ibid.*, **76** (1949) 1697

[200] RICHARDSON, J. M. and HOLT, R. B., *ibid.*, **81** (1951) 153; see also **77** (1950) 239; **80** (1950) 376; **82** (1951) 278, 868, 874; **106** (1957) 83

[201] VARNERIN, L. J., *ibid.*, **84** (1951) 563

[202] GOLDSTEIN, L., *Advanc. Electron.*, **7** (1955) 399

[203] GOLDSTEIN, L., LAMPERT, M. A. and GEIGER, R. H., *Elect. Commun.*, **29** (1952) 243

[204] GOLDSTEIN, L., *et al.*, *Phys. Rev.*, **82** (1951) 956, 1255

[205] GOLDSTEIN, L., ANDERSON, J. M. and CLARK, G. L., *ibid.*, **90** (1953) 151, 486

[206] ANDERSON, J. M. and GOLDSTEIN, L., *ibid.*, **100** (1955) 1037; **102** (1956) 388, 933

[207] WHITMER, R., *ibid.*, **104** (1956) 572

[208] HOLSTEIN, T., *Westinghouse Research Rep.*: R–04411–9–A

[209] BIONDI, M. A., *Phys. Rev.*, **93** (1954) 1136

[210] BIONDI, M. A., *ibid.*, **88** (1952) 660; **90** (1953) 730

[211] OSKAM, H. J., *Thesis*, Utrecht, 1957; *Philips Res. Rep.*, **13** (1958) 335, 401

[212] SCHULZ DU BOIS, E., *Z. angew. Phys.*, **8** (1956) 267

[213] BIONDI, M. A. and FOX, R. E., *Phys. Rev.*, **109** (1958) 2005

[214] PHELPS, A. V. and BROWN, S. C., *ibid.*, **86** (1952) 102

[215] PHELPS, A. V., FUNDINGSLAND, O. T. and BROWN, S. C., *ibid.*, **84** (1951) 559

[216] GOULD, L. and BROWN, S. C., *ibid.*, **95** (1954) 897

[217] FÜCHTBAUER, C., *Z. Phys.*, **90** (1934) 403; **95** (1935) 1

[218] GILARDINI, A. L. and BROWN, S. C., *Phys. Rev.*, **105** (1957) 31

[219] GILARDINI, A. L., *Proceedings of the Third International Conference on Ionization Phenomena in Gases*, Venice, 1957

[220] TELLEGEN, B. D. H., *Nature, Lond.*, **131** (1933) 840

[221] BAILEY, V. A. and MARTYN, D. F., *Phil. Mag.*, **18** (1934) 369

[222] SOUTHWORTH, G. C., *J. Franklin Inst.*, **239** (1945) 285

[223] GOLDSTEIN, L. and COHEN, N. L., *Phys. Rev.*, **73** (1948) 83

[224] KNOL, K. S., *Philips Res. Rep.*, **6** (1951) 288

[225] EASLEY, M. A. and MUMFORD, W. W., *J. appl. Phys.*, **22** (1951) 846

[226] JOHNSON, H. and DEREMER, K. R., *Proc. Instn Radio Engrs, N.Y.*, **39** (1951) 908

[227] PARZEN, P. and GOLDSTEIN, L., *Phys. Rev.*, **79** (1950) 190

[228] HATCH, A. J. and WILLIAMS, H. B., *ibid.*, **112** (1958) 681

[229] HOOVER, C. W. and SMITHERS, R. K., *ibid.*, **98** (1955) 1149

[230] GOLANT, V. E., *Z. tech. Phys.*, **27** (1957) 2071

[231] GRIFFIN, L. R. and DAVIES, T. A., *Proceedings of the Third International Conference on Ionization Phenomena in Gases*, Venice, 1957

[232] LEVITZKY, S. M., *Z. tech. Phys.*, **27** (1957) 970

[233] STRAUSS, H. J., *Ann. Phys.*, **1** (1958) 281

[234] MASON, J. H., *Proc. Instn elect. Engrs*, **98** (1) (1951) 44

[235] WHITEHEAD, S., *Dielectric Breakdown of Solids*; Oxford: Clarendon Press, 1957

[236] DRUMMOND, J. E., *Phys. Rev.*, **112** (1958) 1460

[237] ALLIS, W. P. in *Handbuch der Physik*, Vol. 21; Heidelberg: Springer, 1956

[238] MOLMUD, P., *Phys. Rev.*, **114** (1959) 29

[239] FANG, P. H., *ibid.*, **113** (1959) 13

[240] DESLOGE, E. A., MATTHYSE, S. W. and MARGENAU, H., *ibid.*, **112** (1958) 1437

[241] BEKIFI, G. and BROWN, S. C., *ibid.*, 112 (1958) 159

### GENERAL REFERENCES (REVIEWS)

[242] LLEWELLYN JONES, F., *Rep. Progr. Phys.*, **16** (1953) 216

[243] KIHARA, T., *Rev. mod. Phys.*, **24** (1952) 45 (mathematical theory)

[244] MORGAN, G. D., *Sci. Progr.*, **41** (1953) 22

[245] BROWN, S. C. in *Handbuch der Physik*, Vol 22; Heidelberg: Springer, 1956; see also *Proc. Instn Radio Engrs*, **39** (1951) 1493

### BIBLIOGRAPHY

TOWNSEND, J. S., *Electricity in Gases*; Oxford: Clarendon Press, 1915

LOEB, L. B., *Fundamental Processes of Electrical Discharge in Gases*; New York: John Wiley, 1939

DELCROIX, J. L., *Théorie des Gaz Ionisés*; Paris: Dunod, 1959

# 5

# IONIZATION AND EXCITATION IN THE UPPER ATMOSPHERE

## INTRODUCTION

It has been recognized for a very long time that the atmosphere, which extends for hundreds of miles above the surface of the earth, is not merely an assemblage of neutral gas molecules. In ancient writings there are accounts of displays of the aurora, mostly in northern latitudes, and of the fiery trails of meteors, whilst the common lightning flash points to electrical effects in the lower regions of the atmosphere. More compelling evidence for electrification of layers of the higher regions came from a detailed study of the small daily variations in the earth's magnetic field which, in 1878, led Balfour Stewart[1] to suggest that sheets of electrically charged particles circulate horizontally high above the earth (the 'dynamo theory').

In 1901 Marconi, in his celebrated experiment, succeeded in transmitting radio waves from Cornwall to Newfoundland and receiving them in strength which could not be due to diffraction of the waves around the earth's surface. Independently, Heaviside[2] and Kennelly[3] suggested that the effect was due to reflection of the waves at a conducting layer, and Eccles[4], in 1912, and Larmor[5], in 1924, developed a simple theory showing how regions of charged particles affect the propagation of such waves. Direct evidence of reflection by charged layers was found in carefully designed experiments by Appleton and Barnett[6] and, later, by Breit and Tuve[7]. These disclosed the existence not only of one, but several conducting layers, and indicated their height and charge density.

With the advent of quantum theory and the explanation of many empirical facts of spectra, it was obvious that optical and electrical properties were very closely related, since ionization is only an extreme example of excitation. Thus the light emitted from the aurora was found to be accompanied by ionization, which could be detected when radio waves of suitable frequency were reflected. Careful study[8] of the faint light which comes from the night sky, even on the darkest nights, showed that this was not entirely due to scattered starlight, but that more than half of it was produced in regions high in the atmosphere.

Most of the observed properties of the atmosphere have been found to vary in regular fashion with the rising and setting of the sun, i.e. with the rotation of the earth, and it is natural to expect that radiation from the sun (whether by particles or electromagnetic waves) is largely responsible for them. It has been known since the earliest spectroscopic measurements that the spectrum of the sun's light, observed from the surface of the earth, is cut off sharply at wavelengths below 2,900 Å. Cornu (1878) first suggested that this was due to absorption of the shorter wavelengths by the earth's atmosphere. HARTLEY[9], who discovered strong absorption bands in ozone between 2,100 and 3,200 Å, believed that ozone might be present in the atmosphere, and this view was confirmed by the experiments of FOWLER and STRUTT[10] (Lord Rayleigh), GÖTZ, MEETHAM and DOBSON[11], and most convincingly by measurements of the ultra-violet spectrum taken in a rising balloon by the REGENERS[12]. More and more of the wavelengths below 2,900 Å appeared as it rose to a maximum height of 31 km; the ozone is distributed in a relatively thin layer (in atmospheric terms) between 15 and 40 km.

It will be seen, in the brief survey which follows, how the absorption of the sun's radiation in the upper atmosphere is predominantly responsible for all its main properties. Penetrating ultra-violet and soft X-radiation produce the ionized layers which reflect radio waves; other wavelengths excite oxygen molecules and cause them to dissociate, thus changing the chemical composition of the atmosphere. The strong absorption of energetic quanta in the ozone layer leads to an appreciable rise in temperature in the regions above it, and enables an explanation to be given for the propagation of sound waves over large distances, by their bending and consequent downward reflection in the warmer upper layers[13]; furthermore this rise in temperature determines the density distribution (given by the law of atmospheres $\rho_h = \rho_0 e^{-Mgh/kT}$, where $M$ is the mean molecular weight), and explains how, at heights of 60–160 km, the density of gas molecules is large enough to cause the heating and evaporation of meteors and the consequent tails of excited and ionized gas, which are observed most frequently at these heights[14]. Even the horizontal motion of current sheets (atmospheric tides) and the consequent variation of the earth's magnetic field, which might, at first thought, be ascribed only to gravitational effects, has been found to depend upon this temperature distribution, and thus indirectly upon the absorption of radiation. Unlike the normal (sea) tides these atmospheric tides apparently follow the sun rather than the moon, the reason being that the sun's gravitational pull is in resonance with a natural oscillation of the air which has a period of 12 hours, but the period depends very critically on the temperature distribution. The heating due to the ozone layer gives a distribution which leads to this resonant period, and gives very great speeds of flow at heights between 60 and 90 km where there is also a large density of ionization.

The oxygen molecules, dissociated into atoms by the sun's light during the day, recombine at night; some of them are in excited states and the quanta emitted on recombination largely account for the weak light emitted at a comparatively regular rate, from the night sky. The bright glows frequently observed near the polar regions—the aurorae—are generally believed to be due to excitation and ionization caused by streams of very fast charged particles emitted from the sun during a solar eruption. It is of interest that the spectra of many kinds of light created by processes in the upper atmosphere show forbidden lines, i.e. lines due to transitions which are hardly ever observed in the laboratory, and which do not conform to the selection rules. The reason is that, at very low densities, atoms in an excited state can exist for a long time without being de-excited by hitting another atom. Although the probability of the forbidden transition is extremely small, the event does occur when the lifetime of the state is sufficiently long. (In laboratory experiments such excited states are quickly destroyed on the walls of apparatus, if not in the gas.)

A quite remarkable body of consistent knowledge about the upper atmosphere has been built up from a variety of indirect evidence, and measurements made on, or close to, the earth's surface. Only in the last ten years has it been possible, by the use of rockets and satellites, to take instruments to the regions of interest and to investigate directly the most important factor, namely the radiation which falls from the sun on to the outer regions of our atmosphere.

## THE IONOSPHERE

*Reflection of Radio Waves*

A concentration of $n$ particles per cm³ each of charge $e$ and mass $m$ if subjected to an electric field $X = X_0 \sin wt$, gives rise to a current (90° out of phase with the field) whose density, $j$, is:

$$j = \frac{ne^2}{m\omega} . X_0 \cos wt \qquad \dots (5.1)$$

provided that the motion of the electrons is not interrupted by collisions with gas molecules. In space there is also a displacement current density given by $\dfrac{K}{4\pi} \cdot \dfrac{\partial X}{\partial t}$, and when this is added to the above, the total current density is:

$$j_{\text{total}} = \left(K - \frac{4\pi ne^2}{m\omega^2}\right) \cdot \frac{\omega X_0}{4\pi} \cos wt = \frac{1}{4\pi}\left(K - \frac{4\pi ne^2}{m\omega^2}\right)\frac{\partial X}{\partial t} \quad \ldots (5.2)$$

The effect of the motion of charges in space is thus to reduce the dielectric constant from $K$ to $K - \dfrac{4\pi ne^2}{m\omega^2}$, and hence to increase the phase velocity, $u$, of the waves, since $u = 1/\sqrt{\mu'K}$ ($\mu'$ being the permeability of the region). Thus a wave incident at some angle to the surface of an ionized layer will have its direction of propagation bent away from the normal. This was the basis of the Eccles–Larmor theory of the reflection of radio waves from horizontal ionized layers above the earth; if the concentration, $n$, of charged particles increases upwards then the direction of propagation of the wave becomes more and more horizontal as it proceeds upwards. If the concentration in the layer is sufficiently great, the wave will be propagated horizontally and then reflected by a symmetrical path to earth (see *Figure 5.1*). In optical terms the normal refractive index, $\mu$, in air, where the permeability $\mu' = 1$, is

$$\mu = \frac{c}{u} = \sqrt{K'} = \sqrt{1 - \frac{4\pi ne^2}{m\omega^2}} \quad \ldots (5.3)$$

A wave, or 'ray', incident at an angle, $i$, is reflected at a level whose concentration is $n$ and refractive index $\mu_0$, when by Snell's law

$$\sin i = \mu_0 \sin \frac{\pi}{2} \quad \ldots (5.4)$$

For a ray incident vertically, $i = 0$ and the critical condition for reflection is that $\mu_0 = 0$, or that

$$\frac{4\pi ne^2}{m\omega^2} = 1 \quad \ldots (5.5)$$

In more rigorous treatment, BOOKER[15] analyzed the wave function of the propagating electric field as it passed through the ionized region and showed that a more general condition for reflection is

$$\frac{\mathrm{d}}{\mathrm{d}h}\left(\mu_\phi \cos \phi\right) = \infty \quad \ldots (5.6)$$

where $\phi$ is the angle the ray (i.e. direction of propagation) makes with the vertical at some height, $h$, and $\mu_\phi$ is the refractive index in that direction ($\mu$ being treated as a vector).

It is an essential condition of these and similar theories that the properties of the ionized medium are constant over a wavelength

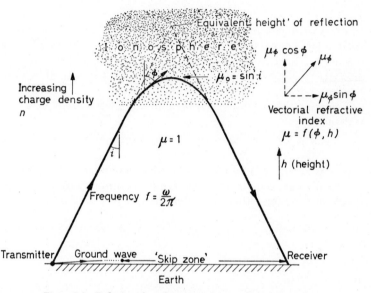

*Figure 5.1. Reflection of an electromagnetic wave from the ionosphere*

of the applied field. The results therefore apply only to sufficiently high frequencies (of the order of 1 Mc/s): at lower frequencies the propagation of the wave must be calculated from first principles using Maxwell's equations in a non-uniform medium.

It may be noted from equation (5.5) that the reflection of a wave depends upon the concentration and mass of the particles, but not upon the sign of their charge, and thus it cannot be decided at once whether electrons or negative or positive ions are responsible. One would naturally expect electrons to be the chief cause, because of their small mass and consequent large speeds, and in fact when the effect of the earth's magnetic field is taken into account, it can be proved that this is true.

The Eccles–Larmor theory is, of course, greatly over-simplified by its neglect of collisions, implying that no energy is absorbed from the wave. In general, the motion of the electrons is retarded as they hit gas molecules with a frequency of $\nu$ collisions per sec, and the

177

resultant current density has a component in phase and one 90° out of phase with the applied field.

This effect is represented by a complex conductivity, having real and imaginary parts $(\sigma_r, \sigma_i)$ (see pp. 87, 158):

$$\sigma = \sigma_r - i\sigma_i \qquad \ldots (5.7)$$

$-i\sigma_i$ is written here since it is already known that the free motion current lags behind the field by 90°, and hence $\sigma_i$ will be numerically positive; $i$ is of course the vector operator (numerically $\sqrt{-1}$), and $X_0 e^{i\omega t}$ is used to represent the field. The general relation between refractive index and conductivity can now be derived.

The refractive index, $N$, of a medium for a wave of frequency, $\omega$, is defined by:

$$X = X_0 e^{i\omega \left(t - \frac{N}{c} \cdot \mathbf{p} \cdot \mathbf{r}\right)} \qquad \ldots (5.8)$$

where $\mathbf{p}$ is the unit vector in the direction of propagation. If Maxwell's equations are solved using equation (5.8) for $X$ and equation (5.7) for $\sigma$ then it is found that

$$N^2 = K' - \frac{i \cdot 4\pi}{\omega} \sigma_r \qquad \ldots (5.9)$$

where $K'$ is the new dielectric constant, given by

$$K' = K - \frac{4\pi\sigma_i}{\omega} \qquad \ldots (5.10)$$

$K$ is the dielectric constant of the non-ionized medium which will now be taken as unity for free space. Putting

$$N = \mu - ik \qquad \ldots (5.11)$$

where $\mu$ is the ordinary refractive index and $k$ the extinction coefficient, then

$$\left.\begin{aligned}
\mu^2 - k^2 = K' &= 1 - \frac{4\pi\sigma_i}{\omega} \\
nk &= \frac{2\pi\sigma_r}{\omega}
\end{aligned}\right\} \qquad \ldots (5.12)$$

Hence

$$\left.\begin{aligned}
\mu^2 &= \frac{K'}{2} \left\{ 1 \pm \sqrt{1 + \left(\frac{4\pi\sigma_r}{\omega}\right)^2} \right\} \\
k^2 &= \frac{K'}{2} \left\{ -1 \pm \sqrt{1 + \left(\frac{4\pi\sigma_r}{\omega}\right)^2} \right\}
\end{aligned}\right\} \qquad \ldots (5.13)$$

Since $\mu$ and $k$ are always real, by definition, the positive sign is chosen when $K' \geqslant 0$, the negative when $K' \leqslant 0$. Note that $\mu = \sqrt{K'}$ is an approximation applicable only when $\sigma_r$ is very small, i.e. when the electrons make very few collisions; note also that when $K'$ is positive the medium is transparent, although refracting to electromagnetic waves; when $K'$ is negative it behaves rather like a metal having definite boundaries particularly at high charge densities. The extreme cases of interest are $\sigma_r/\sigma_i \ll 1$ corresponding to $v/\omega < 1$, which applies to the ionosphere, and $\sigma_r/\sigma_i > 1$ corresponding to $v/\omega \gg 1$ which is sometimes satisfied in the reflection of microwaves from intense plasmas.

Now insert in equations (5.12) and (5.13) expressions for $\sigma_i$ and $\sigma_r$ as set out in Chapter 4, according to the conditions regarding mean free path and its variation with electron energy, etc. In the ionosphere the electron energy is very low so that inelastic collisions can be neglected, and the following expression may be used for the conductivity

$$\sigma = \frac{ne^2}{m} \cdot \frac{v}{v^2 + \omega^2} - i \cdot \frac{ne^2}{m} \cdot \frac{\omega}{v^2 + \omega^2} \quad \ldots . (5.14)$$

If there is little absorption and $k^2 \ll \mu^2$, the simple expression

$$\mu^2 = 1 - \frac{4\pi ne^2}{m(v^2 + \omega^2)} \quad \ldots . (5.15)$$

may be derived.

Experimental observations of reflected radio waves soon showed that the conditions for reflection were more numerous and complicated than could be explained by this theory, even including absorption, and it was evident that the earth's magnetic field strongly affects the propagation of waves through ionized layers especially as the frequency of oscillation of electrons about the earth's field (the gyro frequency $f_H = eH/2\pi mc$) is comparable with commonly used radio frequencies of about 1 Mc/s. This problem had earlier been considered by Lorentz, for simplified conditions (magnetic field parallel or perpendicular to the direction of propagation). APPLETON[16], GOLDSTEIN[17] and HARTREE[18] independently, and by slightly different methods, treated propagation at a general angle to the magnetic field, arriving at the formulae given below. Take a right-handed system of axes, the wave being propagated along O$x$, with $H$ in the $x$–$z$ plane; $H_L$ and $H_T$ are the components of $H$, parallel and perpendicular to O$x$

(longitudinal and transverse fields). Defining the following quantities:

$$\omega_0^2 = \frac{4\pi n e^2}{m} \text{ ('plasma frequency'):} \quad \alpha = -\frac{\omega^2}{\omega_0^2}, \; \beta = \frac{\omega v}{\omega_0^2}$$

$$\omega_H = \frac{eH}{mc}, \; \omega_{L,T} = \frac{eH_{L,T}}{mc}, \; \gamma = \frac{\omega \cdot \omega_H}{\omega_0^2}, \; \gamma_{L,T} = \frac{\omega \cdot \omega_{L,T}}{\omega_0^2}$$

$$\dots (5.16)$$

and $h_y$, $h_z$ the $y$ and $z$ components of the magnetic field associated with the wave, the theory leads to the result:

$$(\mu - ik)^2 = 1 + \frac{2}{2(\alpha + i\beta) - \dfrac{\gamma_T^2}{1 + \alpha + i\beta} \pm \sqrt{\dfrac{\gamma_T^4}{(1 + \alpha + i\beta)^2} + 4\gamma_L^2}}$$

$$\dots (5.17)$$

$$\frac{h_z}{h_y} = -\frac{i}{\gamma_L}\left[\frac{1}{(\mu - ik)^2 - 1} - (\alpha + i\beta)\right] \quad \dots (5.18)$$

A recent critical examination of these formulae has been made by LÉPÉCHINSKY[19], and useful graphical methods of solution devised. There was doubt, for some time, whether the polarization of the medium by the impressed wave affects its propagation: DARWIN[20] showed that it does not, a conclusion supported by many measurements of the absorption of waves near the gyro frequency, and by the propagation of 'whistling atmospherics'[21] (low-frequency waves, which follow the lines of the earth's magnetic field, are reflected at the point where they meet the earth again and return to their starting point).

Equations (5.17) and (5.18) are known as the Appleton–Hartree formulae, and their treatment as the magneto-ionic theory. The first equation describes the dispersion and absorption and the second the polarization of the wave. The $\pm$ sign before the square root shows that the magnetic field splits the wave into two components, having different states of polarization—the ordinary and the extraordinary ray. In certain conditions the equations lead to simple reflection conditions: for example if there is no absorption and no magnetic field ($\beta = 0$, $\gamma = 0$) the condition for reflection ($\mu = 0$) leads again to the Eccles–Larmor expression [equation

(5.5)]. In the presence of a magnetic field, but no absorption, the reflection conditions for a wave incident vertically are:

$$\text{ordinary ray:} \quad \frac{4\pi n e^2}{m\omega^2} = 1 \qquad \ldots (5.19)$$

$$\left. \begin{aligned} \text{extraordinary ray:} \quad \frac{4\pi n e^2}{m\omega^2} &= 1 \pm \frac{\omega_H}{\omega} \text{ provided } \omega > \omega_H \\ \text{or only} \quad 1 &+ \omega_H/\omega \qquad \text{if } \omega < \omega_H \end{aligned} \right\} \ldots (5.20)$$

The rays are therefore reflected at different electron densities, and hence at different heights. In general the reflection conditions are very complicated, and are derived from graphs which relate values of $\mu$, $\omega$ and $n$. It has frequently been supposed that values of the parameters which make $\mu = \infty$ also lead to reflection ('fourth condition' of reflection), but this is not so[22]. A vast amount of experimental evidence on reflected radio waves of different frequencies at different places on the earth's surface and propagated at different angles relative to the earth's magnetic field, have proved the correctness of the theory. Two points of special interest are:

(1) when $\omega = \omega_H$ the wave is heavily absorbed, for the reasons given on pp. 127–128; this is found to occur at frequencies about 1·5 Mc/s ($\lambda \sim 600$ m), proving conclusively that electrons, not heavy ions, are responsible for the effects observed.

(2) when the ordinary ray of one frequency ($f_{\text{ord.}} = \omega_{\text{ord.}}/2\pi$) and the extraordinary ray of another ($f_{\text{ext.}}$) are both reflected from the same level—the level of maximum ionization—equations (5.19) and (5.20) are satisfied by the same $n$, which can thus be eliminated to give $\omega_H$ and hence $H$, the magnetic field at some distance above the earth's surface. It is found that $H \propto \dfrac{1}{r^3}$ where $r$ is the distance from the centre of the earth.

*Experimental Results of Radio Probing and their Interpretation*

An electromagnetic wave can be detected, and its strength measured, by placing a suitable aerial in its path and amplifying, to some convenient level, the e.m.f. generated. If a straight wire is used as the aerial the e.m.f. is induced by the electric field of the wave, and is zero if the length of the wire lies along the direction of propagation; if a loop is used the e.m.f. is induced by the magnetic field and is zero if the loop lies in the plane containing this field and the direction of propagation. Early attempts to measure the angle of a downcoming wave were based on these considerations[23], but gave no conclusive result, because on meeting the earth the wave is partly reflected and such aerials measured the angle of the resultant electric or magnetic field. This depends largely upon the reflecting and absorbing properties of the ground.

With reference to *Figure 5.1*, it is obvious that there exists both a path difference and a time difference between the wave reflected from the ionized layer and that propagated along the ground. Any regular change in path length results in periodic maxima and minima of the received signal (interference effect). This occurs at dusk when, as we shall see, the height of a given ionization density slowly rises; it can be produced artificially in steady ionospheric conditions by steadily changing the wavelength of the transmitted signal—a method used by APPLETON and BARNETT[6] in their classical experiment. They changed their wavelength from 385 to 395 m and, by counting the number of maxima and minima, deduced the path difference between the reflected and the ground ray. Simple triangulation gave the height of the layer as 80–90 km, and from equation (5.5) the electron density was found to be about $2 \times 10^5$ per cm³. Careful comparison of these maxima and minima, as received on a straight wire or a loop aerial, confirmed that the interfering waves lay in a vertical plane, and enabled the angle of the downcoming wave to be deduced; the height of reflection, which could thus be calculated independently, gave the same result. These techniques are now standard ones for probing the ionosphere with radio signals and are known as the frequency change and the angle of incidence methods. The theory takes no account of the change of phase and group velocity in the ionosphere itself and thus gives the height at which the wave would be reflected if it travelled always with velocity, $c$ ('equivalent height'—see *Figure 5.1*).

BREIT and TUVE[7], in devising the so-called group retardation method, which has been especially fruitful in investigating the ionosphere, measured the time interval between the arrival of the ground wave and the sky wave. A pulse of waves of suitable frequency was transmitted, and the received signals displayed on an oscilloscope, the distance between the traces displayed being a measure of the time delay. A repeated train of pulses, synchronized with the time base of the oscilloscope provided a continuous record. This was, of course, the fore-runner of the familiar technique of radar, but much lower frequencies were used within the pulse. The path length is calculated again on the assumption that the group velocity of the wave packet is constant, $= c$, and this leads again to an 'equivalent height', $h'$, for reflection which can be shown to be the same as that given by the frequency change method. Usually, however, vertical reflection is observed, and the distance between the two pulses on the oscilloscope is then directly proportional to the 'equivalent path', $P'$ ($P' = 2h'$), since the ground path is negligible. This method also gave the same height for the reflecting layer as that found by Appleton and Barnett. It is now known that this is the layer which was responsible for Marconi's transmissions, and it is called the Kennelly–Heaviside layer, or the $E$ layer.

Important discoveries were made using the group retardation method, when the frequency of the probing signal was steadily increased; at first the signals were reflected from approximately the same or slightly greater heights. Assuming that a frequency, $f$, is reflected at a layer of electron density, $n = \pi m f^2/e^2$ [equation (5.5)], this result shows that the electron density increases upwards rapidly in a comparatively short distance. At a critical frequency, $f_1$ (usually between 4 and 5 Mc/s), however, the echo disappears and at higher frequencies reappears on the oscilloscope much further from the origin.

This shows, first, that there is a maximum electron density $n_{max.} = \pi m f_1^2/e^2$ in the layer, so that frequencies greater than $f_1$ cannot be reflected by this region; they are reflected, however, at a considerably greater height from a region of greater electron density. In short there exists another reflecting layer above the $E$ layer: this is termed the $F$ layer or Appleton region, and lies about 200–300 km above the earth. If the frequency is further increased, the echo disappears again at a critical frequency of about 9 Mc/s, indicating a maximum electron density in this layer of approximately $6 \times 10^5$ per cm$^3$. By the standards of laboratory experiments these are remarkably low concentrations but, of course, they exist over vast volumes and are free from wall effects.

A graph of $P'$ (or $h'$) against increasing frequency shows almost pictorially the existence of such layers, and automatic equipment has been in use for many years all over the world making continuous records. The frequency of the signal is increased from about 1 to 10 Mc/s in a period of a few minutes, whilst a film, moving perpendicular to the time base sweep, photographs the oscilloscope trace: there appears on the film a complete $P' - f$ curve. The process is repeated regularly, and a typical example is shown in *Figure 5.2*. The curves are frequently very complicated: first, due to splitting of the wave by the earth's magnetic field, reflection is given by the several conditions [equation (5.20)]; secondly, the two layers themselves are not simple structures—the $F$ region in particular shows, in daytime, two critical frequencies corresponding to two levels of maximum ionization, which are termed the $F_1$ and $F_2$ layers; thirdly repeated echoes are observed due to multiple reflections (i.e. a wave which bounces several times between an ionized layer and the earth).

The apparent sharp increase in equivalent height near the critical frequencies is due to the very great reduction in group velocity when $4\pi n e^2/m\omega^2$ approaches unity. Waves of frequency greater than the critical, $f_1$ reflected from the $F$ layers must twice traverse the $E$ layer, and hence suffer additional retardation.

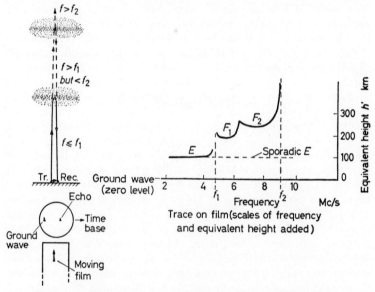

*Figure 5.2. Typical P′–f curves obtained by the group retardation method*

Equivalent heights of the $F$ layers obtained by this method are likely to be overestimated, and indeed recent direct measurements of electron densities by rockets passing through these regions have shown that the layers are lower than previously supposed.

A further limitation is that only levels of increasing electron density can be detected. Maxima and minima of electron density may exist between the $E$ and $F$ levels, but these will not produce echoes unless $n_{max.}$ is greater than that in the $E$ layer, since any frequency capable of penetrating the lower layer will penetrate them too.

Summarizing briefly, the group retardation method has disclosed the existence, and some of the properties, of the following strata in the ionosphere:

(1) The $E$ layer, at about 90 km, with $n \approx 2 \times 10^5$ electrons per $cm^3$, sometimes splitting into two closely spaced layers $E_1$ (the lower) and $E_2$ of slightly greater electron density. The latter occurs mostly in daytime in summer. Very occasionally a layer of dense ionization is formed at about 100 km ('sporadic $E$').

(2) The $F_1$ and $F_2$ layers at about 200–250 km, with $n \approx 5 \times 10^5$, $8 \times 10^5$ electrons per $cm^3$, respectively; these are separate in daytime and coalesce into a single higher $F$ region at night.

(3) By an ingenious combination of the frequency change and group retardation methods (changing the frequency within a pulse and noting the number of undulations in the envelope of the reflected pulse), the approximate thickness of the layers can be calculated[24]. Assuming a parabolic change of electron density with height about the maximum (see pp. 189–191) the semi-thicknesses are found to be: $E$ layer, 20 km; $F_2$ layer, 70–100 km; sporadic $E$ layer, about 100 m (very thin).

(4) The properties of the $E$ and $F_1$ layers (but not sporadic $E$) vary regularly with the position of the sun, the maximum electron density becoming less, and the height of the layers becoming greater after dark referring, of course, to the main variations; there are, in addition, many irregularities due, for example, to wind movements. The properties depend also on latitude and the time of year. The $F_2$ layer does not show such regular variation; in fact its electron density sometimes increases at night.

Several limitations of radio probing from the ground can be overcome by using rockets[25]: a signal transmitted from the ground and received by a rocket, or vice versa, passes only once through the ionized region and need not satisfy any reflection conditions. Measurements of this kind have been made using two different systems: in the first method a pair of pulses is transmitted from the ground, one of very high frequency which suffers no retardation, the other slightly above critical frequency, which is appreciably retarded as it crosses ionized layers. The difference in their times of arrival, $\Delta t$, is recorded in the rocket. A regular succession of pulses is transmitted as the rocket rises, and from the change of $\Delta t$ with the known height of the rocket, the electron density at the height, $h$, can be calculated. In the other method a continuous signal of frequency just above critical, together with one of its harmonics, is transmitted. Due to the motion of the receiver (in the rocket) both suffer a Doppler shift, but the fundamental frequency also suffers a change of phase velocity and, hence, of wavelength. From the difference the electron density can be calculated.

13                    185

These experiments have shown that the 'equivalent heights' obtained by conventional ground radio methods are appreciably greater than the actual heights of the layers, especially the $F$ layers; the true height of the $F_1$ layer is about 180 km, its equivalent height in the same conditions about 220 km.

### Absorption of Radio Waves: Interaction between Several Waves

The reflection and change of phase or group velocity of radio waves is, in regions of low gas density, primarily determined by the electron concentration, $n$. The absorption of energy from the wave depends on $n$ and the frequency, $\nu$, with which electrons hit gas particles, which is proportional to the random velocity of the electrons, $v_r$ ($\propto \sqrt{T_e}$) and the neutral particle density, $N$. It is reasonable to assume that, in the absence of a powerful disturbing electromagnetic wave, the electrons are approximately in thermal equilibrium with the gas particles ($T_e = T_{gas}$), but an estimate of the density, $N$, depends upon an independent measurement or theoretical calculation of the gas temperature in the particular region.

Absorption is naturally greatest in the lower regions where the gas density is large, and is smaller at night than during the day when more electrons are present. It is also greater for waves of low frequency [see the real term of equation (5.14)]. Now it is a common experience that distant reception of medium-wave radio stations ($f \sim 1$ Mc/s) improves markedly soon after dusk; similarly it is noticed that echoes from the $E$ layer picked up by group retardation equipment appear in measurable strength only at frequencies above about 2 Mc/s in daytime. These facts led Appleton to suggest that another ionized layer—termed the $D$ layer—of lower electron density but much greater absorptive power, lies below the $E$ layer. It lies at about 80 km during daytime and disappears completely at night; the electron density estimated from absorption measurements* is of the order of 300 per cm³. Occasionally the electron density rises to a considerably higher value during the short period of a solar flare, and the sudden increase in absorption results in a radio fade-out over the whole sunlit region of the earth.

The absorption of a radio wave can be measured by the reflection coefficient of a wave returned from an ionized layer (i.e. the ratio

---

* At these heights independent measurements—propagation of sound waves and atmospheric samples recovered by balloons and rockets—determine the gas density and temperature and hence $\nu$. Thus $n$ can be derived from measurements of absorption.

186

of the intensities of the reflected and incident waves). This depends not only on $\nu$, but on the distribution of electron density with height, the angle of incidence of the wave, and the direction of the earth's magnetic field, since the ordinary and extraordinary rays suffer different absorptions. The theory has been discussed in detail by BOOKER[26], and measurements by this method have been made mostly in the $F$ region[27].

An important effect of absorption is the interaction between two waves traversing the same ionized region, especially when one of them is of large amplitude. In 1933 it was noticed that broadcasts from Beromünster received at Eindhoven often carried, impressed on their modulation, the programme sent out by the powerful Luxembourg transmitter (the 'Luxembourg effect')[28]. The explanation, first given by BAILEY[29,30], is that the field of the powerful transmitter increases the random energy and hence the collision frequency of the electrons. $\nu$ varies with the strength of the field (i.e. the modulation). This in turn changes the absorption of the weaker wave, which thus becomes modulated with the variations of the stronger one. Let the strong wave be

$$X = X_0(1 + M' \sin \omega_m t) \sin \omega t \qquad \ldots (5.21)$$

where $M'$ is the depth of modulation. The mean fractional loss of energy, $\varepsilon$, of an electron in a collision is given by

$$- \, \mathrm{d}\varepsilon = G(\varepsilon - \varepsilon_{\text{gas}}) \approx 2m/M \, (\varepsilon - \varepsilon_{\text{gas}})$$

then it can be shown that the depth of modulation $M''$ impressed on the weaker wave is:

$$M'' = \frac{k\omega_0}{\omega_0 + GT_e} \cdot \frac{G\nu}{\sqrt{\omega_m^2 + G^2\nu^2}} \cdot M' \qquad \ldots (5.22)$$

Here $\omega_0 = 4\pi ne^2/m\omega$, $T_e$ is the electron temperature in the absence of the fields, and $k$ is the absorption coefficient of the weaker wave (decrease of amplitude with distance $\propto \mathrm{e}^{-kx}$). Measurements with two different frequencies of modulation, $\omega_m$, on the same disturbing wave enable the product $G\nu$ to be deduced[31]. Values of $\nu \approx 10^5$ per sec were found in the $E$ layer corresponding to a gas particle density of about $10^{13}$ per cm³ at a temperature of 300°K. More elaborate experiments by RATCLIFFE and SHAW[32] gave $\nu = 5 \times 10^5$ at a height of 85 km.

Wave interaction in ionized media has been reproduced on a laboratory scale and used to measure both $G$ and $\nu$ (see p. 164).

187

In the presence of the earth's magnetic field the theory of BAILEY[30,33] indicates that a resonant process should occur, and that appreciable cross modulation is to be expected even between two weak waves, provided that one of them has a frequency close to the gyro frequency, and this effect has been detected by several workers[34].

Detailed study of this so-called 'gyro interaction' enables $v$ and $G$ to be found separately; since $G \approx 2m/M$, one can deduce which gases are present in the atmosphere at that level.

From the theory it should also be expected that a powerful wave, in periodically increasing the energy of the electrons, should itself be deprived of energy and consequently its own modulation should be reduced and distorted ('self-interaction'). This has been observed at frequencies near the gyro frequency[35], and also in laboratory experiments, but the theory of the effect is not entirely satisfactory[36]: reference should be made to the review by BAILEY[37].

## Irregularities in the Ionosphere: Scattering of Radio Waves

The echoes received from the ionized layers vary in amplitude, fluctuating irregularly about 20 times per sec. The pattern of irregularity is sometimes similar, but displaced in time, at neighbouring receivers. Moreover, weak signals can be detected within the skip zone (see *Figure 5.1*), which is that region too close to the transmitter to receive the regularly reflected sky wave[38]. These effects are due to scattering of waves in the ionosphere, and the diffraction patterns observed on the ground indicate the presence of regions of concentrated ionization some 20 m in extent. KAHAN[39] considers that these are due to turbulence in the lower regions ($E$ layer), causing spatial and temporal changes of all ionospheric properties (refractive index and absorption). This would account for the propagation of high-frequency signals ($f \sim 50$ Mc/s) over distances of 1,000–2,000 km. The motion of the diffraction pattern over the ground indicates also the presence of horizontal winds, sometimes rising to about 300 k.p.h., in this layer. Here the pockets of ionization are caused by mass motion of the air; the $F$ layer also shows irregularities but these are more likely to be due to a spontaneous wave motion among the ionized particles themselves since, at the higher temperature and lower gas density, rapid diffusion would destroy regions of high gas pressure. These irregularities are thought to account for the fluctuations in radio signals received from outer space ('twinkling' of radio stars, analogous to the twinkling of ordinary stars). Diffraction effects in the upper atmosphere have recently been reviewed by RATCLIFFE[40].

*Production of Ionized Layers: Simple Chapman Layer*

The regular diurnal variation of the ionization in the $E$ and $F$ layers strongly suggests that radiation from the sun is the agency which produces it. During an eclipse of the sun the electron density falls rapidly to a minimum when the sun is completely obscured, the very short time lag showing conclusively that electromagnetic radiations, rather than charged particles, are mainly, though not necessarily wholly, responsible. It remains then to explain why

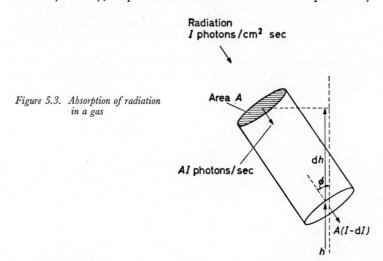

*Figure 5.3. Absorption of radiation in a gas*

ionization appears in fairly well-defined layers, and to account for its distribution in height.

Layers would naturally be formed if the constituent gases in the atmosphere (which are present in varying proportions at different heights) absorb particular wavelengths of light, resulting in photo-ionization. In any particular layer the intensity of this light decreases downwards, whereas the number of gas particles increases downwards; the rate of ionization which is proportional to the product of these factors must therefore have a maximum somewhere. The theory of such a layer was first given by CHAPMAN[41], as set out below.

A beam of monochromatic radiation of unit cross section and intensity, $I$, falls at an angle $\phi$ to the vertical on to a region of the atmosphere at a height, $h$, above the ground* (*Figure 5.3*). The

---

* $\phi$ is, of course, the angle of the sun.

density here is $\rho = \rho_0 e^{-mgh/kT} = \rho_0 e^{-h/H}$ where $\rho_0$ is the density at ground level and $H$ is called the scale height $(H = kT/mg)$. The amount $A \cdot dI$ of radiation absorbed in traversing a slab of gas of area $A$, vertical height $dh$, which absorbs $\alpha$ photons/g is:

$$A \cdot dI = \alpha \cdot I \cdot A \cdot dh \sec \phi \cdot \rho_0 e^{-h/H} \qquad \dots (5.23)$$

This can be integrated to give $I/I_0$ where $I_0$ is the radiation intensity before it enters the atmosphere:

$$\frac{I}{I_0} = e^{-\rho_0 \alpha H \sec \phi \cdot e^{-h/H}} \qquad \dots (5.24)$$

If unit quantity of radiation, when absorbed, produces $\beta$ ion pairs, the rate of production, $q$, of ion pairs per cm³ at the height $h$ is

$$q = \beta \frac{dI}{dh} \cos \phi$$

$$= \beta \alpha I_0 \rho_0 e^{\{-h/H - \rho_0 \alpha H \sec \phi \, e^{-h/H}\}} \qquad \dots (5.25)$$

Differentiation gives the maximum value of $q$:

$$q_{max.} = \frac{\beta I_0 \cos \phi}{H \cdot e} \quad (e \text{ here} = \text{exponential}) \qquad \dots (5.26)$$

And its value $q_0$ at noon, when $\phi = 0$ is:

$$q_0 = \frac{\beta I_0}{He} \qquad \dots (5.27)$$

at a height $h_0 = H \log \rho_0 \alpha H$ [from equation (5.25)]. Reckoning height from this reference level $h_0$, putting $z = \dfrac{h - h_0}{H}$ gives

$$q = q_0 e^{(1 - z \cdot \sec \phi \cdot e^{-z})} \qquad \dots (5.28)$$

(valid for $\phi \leqslant 85°$).

The electron density, $n$, depends, of course, on the equilibrium between the processes of production and removal. If recombination is assumed to be the only process of destruction, described by a coefficient $R$ (regarded as a constant, not changing with height), then

$$\frac{dn}{dt} = q - Rn^2 \qquad \dots (5.29)$$

The densities of positive and negative particles are, of course, assumed equal, since otherwise the electric fields set up would cause movement of charges to establish neutrality. In equilibrium $dn/dt = 0$ hence

$$n = \sqrt{\frac{q}{R}} \qquad \ldots (5.30)$$

which, from equation (5.26), gives for the maximum electron density

$$n_{\text{max.}} = \text{const.} \sqrt{\cos \phi} \qquad \ldots (5.31)$$

In the $E$ layer the value of $dn/dt$ is always very much less than $q$ or $Rn^2$, and thus equilibrium conditions nearly exist throughout the day.

Combining equations (5.28) and (5.30) yields

$$n = n_0 e^{\frac{1}{2}(1 - z - \sec \phi e^{-z}} \qquad \ldots (5.32)$$

where $n_0$ is the electron density at the level of maximum ionization at noon ($\phi = 0$). When $\phi = 0$ and $z$ is small this reduces to a simple parabolic form

$$n = n_0 \left(1 - \frac{z^2}{4}\right) = n_0 \left[1 - \frac{(h - h_0)^2}{4H^2}\right] \qquad \ldots (5.33)$$

$(h - h_0)$ is, of course, the height measured from the level of maximum ionization. This is the justification for the assumption previously mentioned, of a parabolic distribution of ionization with height. It can easily be shown that the same form prevails when $\phi \neq 0$ although of course the actual level $h_0$ also changes. Knowing this distribution in height and assuming that the gas density, and hence the collision frequency, decreases with height exponentially, the absorption coefficient of a simple Chapman layer can be calculated. It must be remembered, however, that the complete equation must be used, since the parabolic distribution applies only for restricted regions around the maximum. In regions where $dn/dt$ is not negligible compared with the separate rates of production and decay the full equation (5.29) must be solved. If $dn/dt$ and $n$ are known and $q$ can be estimated, $R$ can be found; this is often quoted as an 'effective' recombination coefficient even when the process of removal is not a simple single-stage recombination of ions and electrons.

Other workers, in trying to explain the formation of ionized layers, have recognized that the radiation from the sun is continuous, not monochromatic; the results are not much different because only narrow bands of wavelengths are heavily absorbed[42].

*Processes of Ionization and Destruction in the Various Layers*

The factors which control the formation and equilibrium of an ionized layer are:

(1) The nature of the incident solar radiation, in particular the distribution of energy amongst the various wavelengths. Until the advent of rockets and satellites it was impossible to investigate this radiation directly, but these recent experiments have shown that the sun's light is immensely rich in short wavelength radiation ($\lambda < 1{,}000$ Å) particularly in soft X-rays ($\lambda < 100$ Å); most of it is absorbed before it reaches the ground (see *Figure 5.4*).

(2) The composition of the gas at various heights. It is to be expected that nitrogen and oxygen will be the main constituents, but ultra-violet light is known to dissociate oxygen, and the presence of an ozone layer confirms that this process is important (atomic and molecular oxygen combining to form ozone). Although the cross sections for photodissociation of $O_2$, and the concentration of $O_2$ at lower levels ($\sim 50$ km) is well known, the actual concentration of O cannot easily be calculated because of diffusion and vertical and horizontal movements of air.

(3) The actual densities of the constituent gases, i.e. number of atoms or molecules per cm³, at various heights. This is determined primarily by the temperature distribution. If thermal equilibrium is assumed, the density of any one component varies with height according to $\rho/\rho_0 = e^{-mgh/kT}$, and clearly this is most sensitive to the value of $T$. Temperature and average gas density can be deduced from

    (*a*) the propagation of sound waves (reflection of waves transmitted from the ground, and better from the explosion of grenades fired at intervals from a rocket at known heights);

    (*b*) the heights of appearance and disappearance of meteor trails;

    (*c*) the heights of formation of noctilucent clouds: these are clouds formed of tiny ice particles, visible only in the oblique rays of the rising and setting sun when the background of the sky is dark. They move upwards in air currents, and exist only in that region where the temperature is below freezing point; it is found that a minimum temperature occurs at a height of about 90 km;

    (*d*) the absorption, and interaction of radio waves, from

192

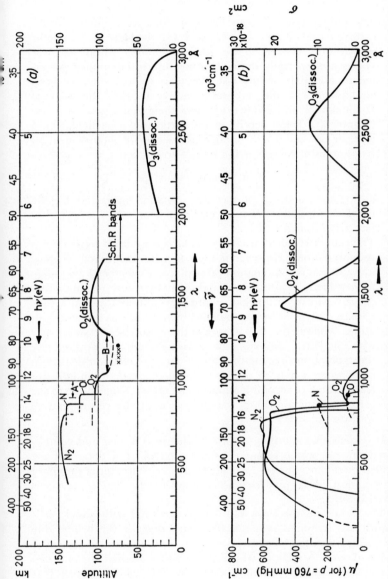

Figure 5.4. (a) The attenuation of the sun's radiation by the constituent gases of the atmosphere. The curves give the altitude at which the constituent gas indicated has attenuated radiation of a particular wavelength by a factor, e. Ionization or dissociation continua are responsible [see Figure 5.4 (b)]. In region A there are strong absorption bands of $N_2$; but numerous windows (i.e. narrow wavelength regions of low absorption) allow the radiation to penetrate below 95 km. Region B denotes oxygen bands and weak continua, with windows marked X extending down to 80 km: the Lyman α line coincides with one of these (marked ●); (b) absorption coefficients and cross sections of the gases responsible for the attenuation curves of Figure 5.4 (a). Dissociation continua are labelled: the others are ionization continua. ⊙ are calculated values for N and O. (From R. W. DITCHBURN[43], by courtesy of the Royal Society)

which the collision frequency and/or the mean energy loss in a collision can be found.

(4) The atomic cross sections for photo-ionization of the various constituents (notably $N_2$, $O_2$ and O) by light of particular wavelengths present in the sun's radiation. Many of these values are especially difficult to measure in laboratory experiments, and only in the last five years or so have they been established with any accuracy, largely through the work of DITCHBURN[43] and WEISSLER[44] and their colleagues (see also Chapter 2). If the density of gas particles of a particular kind is $N$ per cm³ and $\sigma$ is the atomic cross section of photo-ionization by photons of energy $h\nu$ the rate of production $q_\nu$ is:

$$q_\nu = I . \sigma N \text{ ion pairs/cm}^3 \text{ sec} \qquad \ldots . (5.34)$$

if $I$ is the intensity of incident radiation measured by the number of quanta crossing 1 cm²/sec. Thus $\sigma N = \beta$ on p. 190 [see also *Figure 5.4 (b)*].

(5) The rate of removal of charges, which is assumed to be due to recombination. However it must first be established whether ion–electron recombination takes place, or whether a two-stage process firstly of attachment and then of ion–ion recombination occurs. Moreover if negative ions play an important part, they may be destroyed by photo-detachment as well as by recombination. The relative importance of these processes may also vary with height; consequently measurements of atmospheric recombination (e.g. by the rate of decay of electron density at night when $q = 0$, or during an eclipse[45]) leads to an effective coefficient $R$ of recombination for the layer. Some guide to the actual atomic processes is obtained from the recombination spectrum observed.

It is clear that solution of these problems is a long and complicated process, which is not yet finally settled. For details of the evidence reference should be made to the literature, but a summary of the most likely processes accounting for the various layers is given below.

The $D$ layer is the least well documented and understood; it is known that Lyman $\alpha$ radiation penetrates down to this height, due to a 'window' in the $O_2$ absorption spectrum (i.e. a small wavelength range about 1 Å wide in which absorption is negligible), and also that it has a high probability of ionizing NO which is present at this height. Recombination at these low levels, is almost certainly via negative ions.

*Table 5.1*

| | $D$ | $E$ | $F_1$ | $F_2$ |
|---|---|---|---|---|
| Height (km) (radio methods) | 70 | 120 | 220 | 300 |
| Height (km) (rocket data) | 60–90 | ~100 | ~150 | |
| Chief constituents | $N_2$ $O_2$ NO | $N_2$ O ($O_2$?) | $N_2$ O | $N_2$ O |
| Gas density (numbers/cm³) | $4 \times 10^{15}$ | $6 \times 10^{12}$ | $10^{11}$ | $2 \times 10^{10}$ |
| Ionizing radiation | Lyman $\alpha$ | X-rays $hv \sim 300$ eV | X-rays $hv \sim 300$ eV | |
| Process of ionization | $hv + \text{NO} \rightarrow \text{NO}^+ + e^-$ | | $\begin{cases} hv + O_2 \rightarrow O_2^+ + e^- \\ hv + O_2 \rightarrow O^+ + O \\ hv + N_2 \rightarrow N_2^+ + e^- \\ hv + O \rightarrow O^+ + e^- \end{cases}$ | |
| Maximum Rate of ionization (ion pairs per column, of 1 cm² cross section) | | $6 \times 10^8$ | $2 \times 10^9$ | $1.5 \times 10^9$ |
| Process of recombination | | $O_2^+ + e^- \rightarrow 2O$ | $O_2 + O^+ \rightarrow O_2^+ + O$ then $O_2^+ + e^- \rightarrow 2O$ | $O_2 + O^+ \rightarrow O_2^+ + O$ then $O_2^+ + e^- \rightarrow 2O$ |
| Rate of recombination (effective coefficient, in cm³/sec) | | $10^{-8}$ | $4 \times 10^{-9}$ | $8 \times 10^{-11}$ (day) $3 \times 10^{-10}$ (night) |
| Equilibrium electron density | 300 | $1.5 \times 10^5$ (day) $10^4$ (night) | $2.5 \times 10^5$ | $10^6$ (day) $2.5 \times 10^5$ (night) |
| Electron collision frequency (sec⁻¹) | | $2 \times 10^5$ | $4 \times 10^3$ | $1 \times 10^3$ |
| Temperature (°K) | 200 | 200 | ~ 800 | ~ 1,000 |

The $E$ layer is produced by soft X-rays ($h\nu \sim 300$ eV, $\lambda \sim 40$ Å) which ionize both $O_2$ and $N_2$, and produce $O_2^+$, $N_2^+$ and $O^+$. The observed intensity of this radiation, combined with the cross sections for photo-ionization and the best estimates of particle density, gave a rate of ionization which is more than adequate and must be balanced by a rapid removal process, such as dissociative recombination.

In the $F_1$ and $F_2$ layers the ionization process is the same, but the proportion of atomic oxygen increases upward, the reason being that oxygen atoms produced by photo-dissociation will reunite to form $O_2$ only in the presence of a third body. At higher levels and lower gas densities third bodies are less plentiful.

Dissociative recombination can then occur only in two stages: ($i$) charge transfer: $O_2 + O^+ \rightarrow O_2^+ + O$; and ($ii$) dissociative recombination: $O_2^+ + e \rightarrow 2O$. The effective rate of recombination depends on the slower of these two mechanisms. In the $F_1$ layer there are sufficient $O_2$ molecules present for charge transfer to be a fairly rapid process, but in the $F_2$ layer this is not so and the effective recombination coefficient involves the ratio of oxygen molecule to electron concentration, which changes with height. Detailed calculations supported by experiment[46] show that this difference in recombination processes explains the splitting of the $F$ layer into $F_1$ and $F_2$. The properties of the ionized layers are summarized in *Table 5.1*.

### THE NIGHT SKY (AIRGLOW) AND THE AURORA

Consideration is now given, briefly, to radiation actually emitted from the upper atmosphere, as distinct from that which penetrates the earth's atmosphere from the sun. The first of these is the night airglow[47], a very faint light emanating from a widely spread region stretching from 60 to about 600 km in height. It is rather patchy in distribution at any given time and the regions of light move about as though affected by winds, but on average its behaviour is much more regular than that of most other atmospheric phenomena. It is difficult to study with instruments because of its very low intensity (illumination equivalent to 1 candle at 100 m distance in the visible region, but very much stronger in the infra-red). The spectrum shows prominently the forbidden green and red lines of atomic oxygen[48] ($^1S \rightarrow {}^1D$, $\lambda = 5{,}577$; $^1D \rightarrow {}^3P$, $\lambda = 6{,}300, 6{,}363, 6{,}392$ Å), the yellow sodium line[49,50], bands of $O_2$ (blue and ultra-violet region) and a strong infra-red component from excited OH molecules[51]. These and other weaker bands and lines are superimposed on a continuum[52].

The actual process by which the various lines and bands are produced is not known for certain, although it is to be expected that all the light arises from recombination of particles ionized or dissociated during the day by the sun's light. Radiative recombination between electrons and ions would account for a continuum. Molecular oxygen bands are thought to be due to the recombination of oxygen atoms resulting in excited molecules, but the strong lines of atomic oxygen are more difficult to explain. The reaction

$$3O \rightarrow O_2 + O^*$$

has been suggested, the recombination energy being sufficient to excite the remaining atom. At heights of 100 km the concentration and collision frequency of oxygen atoms are large enough to account for the intensity of the red and green lines, but this process fails to explain why their relative intensities vary differently throughout the night. Little is known about the excitation of Na or OH, although various suggestions have been made[53,54]. Very recent rocket measurements have shown that the green oxygen line comes from a layer lying between 80 and 120 km, with a very sharp lower boundary, and the sodium lines from the layer at 85–110 km, with a rather vague upper boundary[55].

The other kind of radiation produced in the atmosphere is the aurora (Aurora Borealis, or Aurora Polaris, or Northern Lights): these are much more intense and spectacular, easily seen by the naked eye and taking many beautiful forms and colours, some being a diffuse glow, others having the structure of rays or draperies. They are seen frequently only in high latitudes, but occasionally nearer the equator. Intense aurorae are associated with solar flares and magnetic storms (i.e. sudden fairly large changes in the earth's magnetic field), but weaker ones occur more regularly. Very many observations of the spectrum and the height at which aurorae appear have been made, notably in Norway by STÖRMER[56] and VEGARD[57]. It is found that when the atmosphere is not lit by the sun's rays aurorae come mostly from heights of about 110 km, but sunlit aurorae* are much more evenly spread out between heights of 120 and 450 km. Aurorae show a strong tendency to recur at 27-day intervals, the period of rotation of the sun.

The spectrum shows certain lines prominently[58], notably the green and red forbidden lines of atomic oxygen, the first and second

---

* Observed when the upper regions of the atmosphere are illuminated by oblique sunlight.

positive bands of $N_2$ in the infra-red and ultra-violet, the Vegard–Kaplan bands of $N_2$, and the first negative band of $N_2^+$, both in the blue-violet and ultra-violet. Forbidden lines of atomic nitrogen (from the decay of a metastable state having a lifetime of many hours), and the hydrogen Balmer lines are also observed. It is especially significant that, when observed in certain directions, the $H_\alpha$ line is shifted, indicating that the emitting atoms are moving at very high speeds (more than $3 \times 10^8$ cm/sec) along the lines of the earth's magnetic field.

It is now regarded as certain that the aurora is caused by streams of very fast particles emitted by the sun, which ionize and excite the atoms in the atmosphere. The Doppler shift of the $H_\alpha$ line is conclusive evidence of the arrival of fast protons, and the 27-day cycle suggests that the earth passes regularly through a jet of matter streaming out in a particular direction relative to the sun as it rotates. Furthermore, a stream of charged particles is affected by the earth's magnetic field.

It was originally believed that streams of fast electrons, focused towards the poles by the earth's magnetic field, were responsible for the ionization and excitation[59]. SCHUSTER[60] pointed out that self-repulsion would rapidly disperse the beam on its way from the sun, and LINDEMANN[61] suggested that, in fact, the stream is electrically neutral, consisting of nearly equal densities of positive and negative particles. Such a stream would be focused by the earth's magnetic field but would suffer little from self-repulsion. Various detailed theories[62–64] have been developed to explain the behaviour of neutral streams as they enter the earth's magnetic field (for details refer to the review by FERRARO[65]); they require particle densities of between $10^{-4}$ and 20 per $cm^3$, and each theory, while explaining many facts about the aurora, is open to certain criticisms. Recently there has been experimental evidence that the particle density in the streams is as high as 500 ion pairs per $cm^3$, and BENNETT[66] has argued that at such densities the self-magnetic field of a singly-charged beam would keep it together and, by a modification of the earlier theories, more convincingly explain the observed phenomena.

### THE RADIATION BELT

Satellite measurements have disclosed the existence of a belt of intense ionizing radiation (consisting of protons of energies mainly between 10 and 100 keV) at about 500 km above the earth[67]. Their origin is uncertain; they may come directly from cosmic rays outside the earth, or from the decay of neutrons formed by cosmic rays in the earth's atmosphere. It is practically certain that they are trapped by the earth's magnetic field, but might, by charge exchange, become energetic neutral atoms before diffusing across the field[68-70].

### REFERENCES

1. BALFOUR STEWART, *Encyclopaedia Britannica* (9th edn.) Vol. 16; 1883
2. HEAVISIDE, O., *Encyclopaedia Britannica* (9th edn.) Vol. 33; 1902
3. KENNELLY, A. E., *Elect. World, N.Y.*, **15** (1902) 473
4. ECCLES, W. H., *Proc. roy. Soc.*, **A87** (1912) 79
5. LARMOR, J., *Phil. Mag.*, **48** (1924) 1025
6. APPLETON, E. V. and BARNETT, M. A. F., *Nature, Lond.*, **115** (1925) 333; *Proc. roy. Soc.*, **A109** (1925) 621; see also SMITH ROSE, R. L. and BARFIELD, R. H., *ibid.*, **A110** (1925) 580; **A116** (1926) 682
7. BREIT, G. and TUVE, M., *Phys. Rev.*, **28** (1926) 554
8. DUFAY, J., *Thesis*, Paris, 1928; *Reun. Inst. Opt., Paris*, June 13 (1933) 6
9. HARTLEY, W. N., *J. Chem. Soc.*, **39** (1881) 57, 111
10. FOWLER, A. and STRUTT, R. J., *Proc. roy. Soc.*, **A93** (1917) 577; **A94** (1918) 260
11. GÖTZ, F. W. P., MEETHAM, A. R. and DOBSON, G. M. B., *Proc. roy. Soc.*, **A145** (1934) 416
12. REGENER, E. and REGENER, V. H., *Phys. Z.*, **35** (1934) 788
13. WHIPPLE, F. J. W., *Nature, Lond.*, **111** (1923) 187; *Quart. J.R. met. Soc.*, **61** (1935) 285
14. LINDEMANN, F. A. and DOBSON, G. M. B., *Proc. roy. Soc.*, **A102** (1923) 411
15. BOOKER, H. G., *Phil. Trans.*, **A237** (1938) 411
16. APPLETON, E. V., *Proc. phys. Soc. Lond.*, **37** (1925) 16D; *J. Instn elect. Engrs*, **71** (1932) 642
17. GOLDSTEIN, S., *Proc. roy. Soc.*, **A121** (1928) 260
18. HARTREE, D. R., *Proc. Camb. phil. Soc.*, **25** (1929) 47
19. LÉPÉCHINSKY, D., *Ann. Télécomm.*, **12** (1957) 60, 74
20. DARWIN, C. G., *Proc. roy. Soc.*, **A146** (1934) 17; **A182** (1943) 152
21. STOREY, L. R. O., *Phil. Trans.*, **A246** (1953) 113
22. BUDDEN, K. G., *Report of Cambridge Conference*; London: Physical Society, 1954
23. SMITH ROSE, R. L. and BARFIELD, R. H., *Proc. roy. Soc.*, **A107** (1925) 587
24. APPLETON, E. V., *Nature, Lond.*, **133** (1934) 793
25. ROCKET PANEL (U.S.), *Phys. Rev.*, **88** (1952) 1027; see also JACKSON, J. E. and SEDDON, J. C., *J. geophys. Res.*, **63** (1958) 197
26. BOOKER, H. G., *Proc. roy. Soc.*, **A150** (1935) 267
27. MARTYN, D. F., *Proc. phys. Soc. Lond.*, **47** (1935) 323
28. TELLEGEN, B. D. H., *Nature, Lond.*, **131** (1933) 840
29. BAILEY, V. A. and MARTYN, D. F., *Phil. Mag.*, **18** (1934) 369
30. BAILEY, V. A., *ibid.*, **23** (1937) 774
31. VAN DER POL, B. and VAN DER MARK, I., *U.R.S.I. Rep.*, Sept. 1934
32. RATCLIFFE, J. A. and SHAW, I. J., *Proc. roy. Soc.*, **A193** (1948) 311

[33] BAILEY, V. A., *Nature, Lond.*, **139** (1937) 68

[34] CUTOLO, M., *ibid.*, **166** (1950) 98; see also BAILEY, V. A. *et al.*, *ibid.*, **169** (1952) 911

[35] CUTOLO, M., *ibid.*, **167** (1951) 314

[36] CARLEVARO, M., *Nuovo Cim.* (Suppl.) **4** (1956) 1422

[37] BAILEY, V. A., *ibid.*, **4** (1956) 1430

[38] MÖGEL, H., *Wireless Engr*, **8** (1931) 604; ECKERSLEY, T. L., *Nature, Lond.*, **140** (1937) 846; **143** (1939) 33

[39] KAHAN, T., *Nuovo Cim.* (Suppl.) **4** (1956) 1352

[40] RATCLIFFE, J. A., *Rep. Progr. Phys.*, **19** (1956) 188

[41] CHAPMAN, S., *Proc. phys. Soc. Lond.*, **43** (1931) 26, 433

[42] PANNEKOEK, A., *Proc. Amsterdam Acad.*, **29** (1926) 1165

[43] DITCHBURN, R. W., *Proc. roy. Soc.*, **A236** (1956) 216; see also MANDELSHTAM, S. L. and EFREMOV, A. I., *Usp. fiz. Nauk*, **63** (1957) 163

[44] WEISSLER, G. in *Handbuch der Physik*, Vol. 21; Heidelberg: Springer, 1956

[45] SAYERS, J., *J. atmos. terr. Phys.* (Suppl.) 1956

[46] RATCLIFFE, J. A. *et al.*, *Phil. Trans.*, **A248** (1956) 621

[47] ELVEY, C. T., SWINGS, P. and LINK, W., *Astrophys. J.*, **93** (1941) 337

[48] McLENNON, J. C. and SHRUM, G. M., *Proc. roy. Soc.*, **A108** (1925) 501

[49] BERNARD, R., *Nature, Lond.*, **141** (1938) 788

[50] CABANNES, J., DUFAY, J. and GAUZIT, J., *Astrophys. J.*, **88** (1938) 164; *Nature, Lond.*, **141** (1938) 1054

[51] MEINEL, A. B., *Astrophys. J.*, **113** (1951) 50

[52] DOBRONRAVINE, P. P. and KHVOSTIKOV, I. A., *C.R. Acad. Sci. U.R.S.S.*, **23** (1939) 233

[53] CHAPMAN, S., *Proc. roy. Soc.*, **A132** (1931) 353; *Phil. Mag.*, **3** (1937) 657

[54] HERZBERG, G., *J. R. astr. Soc. Can.*, **45** (1951) 100; see also BATES, D. R. and NICOLET, M., *J. geophys. Res.*, **55** (1950) 301; ANDRILLOT, Y., *J. Phys. Radium*, **17** (1956) 442, and BATES, D. R. and MOISEIWITSCH, B. L., *J. atmos. terr. Phys.*, **8** (1956) 305

[55] HOPPNER, J. P. and MEREDITH, L. H., *J. geophys. Res.*, **63** (1958) 51

[56] STÖRMER, C., *Vid. Selsk. Skrift.*, **1** (1911) No. 17

[57] VEGARD, L., *Handb. exp. Phys.*, **25** (I) (1930) 385

[58] VEGARD, L. and KVIFTE, G., *Geofys. Publ.*, **16** (1945) No. 7

[59] BIRKELAND, K., *Arch. Sci. phys. nat.*, **4** (1896) 497

[60] SCHUSTER, A., *Proc. roy. Soc.*, **A85** (1911) 45

[61] LINDEMANN, F. A., *Phil. Mag.*, **38** (1919) 669

[62] ALFVÉN, H., *K. svenska VetenskAkad. Handl.*, **18** (1939) 3; **18** (1940) 9

[63] CHAPMAN, S. and FERRARO, V. C. A., *Terr. Magn. atmos. Elect.*, **36** (1931) 77, 171; **37** (1932) 147, 421; **38** (1933) 79; **45** (1940) 245

[64] MARTYN, D. F., *Nature, Lond.*, **167** (1951) 62

[65] FERRARO, V. C. A., *Advanc. Phys.*, **2** (1953) 265

[66] BENNETT, W. H., *Astrophys. J.*, **27** (1958) 731; see also ALFVÉN, H., *Tellus*, **10** (1958) 104

[67] VAN ALLEN, J. A., McILWAIN, C. and LUDWIG, G., *J. geophys. Res.*, **64** (1959) 271

## BIBLIOGRAPHY

[68] SINGER, F., *Phys. Rev. Lett.*, **1** (1958) 171, 181
[69] KELLOGG, P. J., *Nuovo Cim.*, **11** (1959) 48
[70] STUART, G. W., *Phys. Rev. Lett.*, **2** (1959) 417

REVIEWS (see also references 22, 40, 43 and 65)

LOVELL, A. C. B., *Sci. Progr.*, **38** (1950) 22
DÈJARDIN, G., *Rev. mod. Phys.*, **8** (1936) 1
MEINEL, A. B., *Rep. Progr. Phys.*, **14** (1951) 121
GERSON, N. C., *ibid.*, **14** (1951) 316
LOVELL, A. C. B. *et al.*, *ibid.*, **11** (1946) 389
Gassiot Committee of the Royal Society, *ibid.*, **9** (1942–3) 1

## BIBLIOGRAPHY

RATCLIFFE, J. A., *The Magneto-ionic Theory;* London: Cambridge University Press, 1959
MASSEY, H. S. W. and BOYD, R. L. F., *The Upper Atmosphere*; London: Hutchinson, 1958
MITRA, S. K., *The Upper Atmosphere*; Calcutta: Royal Asiatic Society of Bengal, 1948 (2nd edn. 1952)
BATES, D. R. (Ed.), *Space Research and Exploration*; London: Eyre and Spottiswoode, 1957
VAN ALLEN, J. (Ed.), *Scientific Uses of Earth Satellites*; London: Chapman and Hall, 1957
RAWER, K., *The Ionosphere*; London: Crosby Lockwood, 1956 (translated from the German: *Die Ionosphäre*, 1952)
ARMSTRONG, E. B. and DALGARNO, A. (Eds.), *The Airglow and the Aurorae*; London: Pergamon Press, 1955
BOYD, R. L. F. and SEATON, M. J. (Eds.), *Rocket Exploration of the Upper Atmosphere*; London: Pergamon Press, 1954
KUIPER, P. (Ed.), *The Earth as a Planet*; Chicago: The University Press, 1953
CHAPMAN, S. and BARTELS, J., *Geomagnetism*; Oxford: Clarendon Press, 1940
KAISER, T. R. (Ed.), *Meteors*; London: Pergamon Press, 1955
NEWELL, H. E., *High Altitude Rocket Research*; New York: Academic Press, 1953
WHITE, C. S. and BENSON, O. O. (Eds.), *Physics and Medicine of the Upper Atmosphere*; New Mexico: The University Press, 1952
MASSEY, H. S. W., *Negative Ions*; London: Cambridge University Press, 1950
ALFVÉN, H., *Cosmical Electrodynamics*; London: Oxford University Press, 1950
GERSON, N. C., DONALDSON, R. J. and KATZ, L. (Eds.), *Proceedings of the Conference on Ionospheric Physics*; Massachusetts: Air Force Cambridge Research Centre, 1952
WEEKES, K. (Ed.), *Polar Atmosphere Symposium (Part II)*; London: Pergamon Press, 1957

# 6

# HIGH-CURRENT DISCHARGES
# AND THERMONUCLEAR EFFECTS

## GENERAL

WHEN a large current passes through an ionized gas or, more precisely, when the motion of the ions and electrons results in a large current density, several important effects occur. They are separated here, for convenience although, of course, it is possible for any combination to be found in particular conditions of gas pressure, current, applied potential, etc.

(1) Ions and electrons, driven by the electric fields, hit gas molecules imparting momentum and energy to them, and increasing the gas temperature. If the density or the speed of the charged particles is very large, a high temperature and large temperature gradients result. Thermal ionization, evaporation and thermionic emission from electrodes, excitation of ions, two-stage processes and convection currents in the gas are important processes in the maintenance of the discharge. In addition to the large current density there is a large flux of radiation and excited states, which are the well-known properties of arc discharges; these have been extensively described in many books and journals[1-7] and will not, therefore, be considered here.

(2) At large current densities the pressures due to the random motion of ions and electrons ($p_i = n^+kT_i$; similarly for $p_e$) tends to drive gas molecules, if they are at a lower temperature, out of the current channel, and the ratio of charged to neutral particles is large. At very high temperatures the random motion of all the particles is so large that, due to the processes mentioned above, only a very small fraction of the particles in the entire discharge space remain neutral: the gas is then said to be fully ionized. The motions of the individual particles are now governed by much simpler laws, first because they are of only two kinds, positively and negatively charged, and secondly because the complicated reactions between electrons and atomic structures, described

by wave mechanical equations, are absent. Short-range atomic forces are now replaced by long-range electrostatic repulsion and attraction. The laws governing such systems have been fully discussed by SPITZER[8]. When these conditions are created in gases of the lightest elements it is probable that all the electrons are removed from the atoms ('stripped atoms') so that a gas mixture consisting only of electrons and nuclei is obtained. If two of these nuclei collide violently enough a nuclear rearrangement resulting in different particles is possible—this is a thermonuclear reaction.

(3) A large current through an ionized gas creates a large magnetic field; if the current flows, for example, in a cylindrical channel the field lines form circles concentric with the cylinder, as in the case of a current flowing in a straight wire. The lateral repulsion between the lines exerts a pressure radially inward, the value at any point being given by the energy density $H^2/8\pi$. Here, however, the charged carriers are free to move in space (not being restricted by a lattice structure as in a solid conductor), and the discharge is consequently compressed inwards. This is the 'pinch effect', one of the most powerful methods of confining a very hot plasma in space away from walls, and can sometimes itself contribute to further ionization.

### THE PINCH EFFECT

*Figure 6.1* illustrates the force exerted at some point $(r, \theta)$ on a current element flowing along the $z$ axis of cylindrical geometry, due to the magnetic field, $H$, created by the current flowing within the circle of radius, $r$ (in later applications this field will be referred to as $H_\theta$ but as there are, at the moment, no $r$ and $z$ components the suffix will not be used). It is clear that the force is radially inwards: if $j_r$ is the current density at radius $r$, the value of $H$ can be found by taking the imaginary unit pole in opposite directions around the perimeters of rings radii $r$, $r + dr$, and applying Ampère's rule:

$$2\pi(r + dr)(H + dH) - 2\pi rH = 4\pi(2\pi r \, dr \, . \, j_r)$$

whence

$$\frac{1}{r}\frac{d}{dr}(rH) = 4\pi j_r = \frac{4\pi e}{c}(n_e v_e + n^+ v^+) \qquad \ldots (6.1)$$

where $n_e$, $n^+$, $v_e$, $v^+$ are the electron and ion densities and drift velocities.

203

The inward force on unit volume of charged particles (following ALFVÉN[9]) is:

$$\left.\begin{aligned} f &= j_r \times H \quad (j_r \text{ in e.m.u.}) \\ &= j_r \cdot \frac{2}{r} \cdot \int_0^r j_r \cdot 2\pi r \, dr \\ &= \frac{1}{4\pi} \left( \frac{H^2}{r} + H \frac{\partial H}{\partial r} \right) \end{aligned}\right\} \quad \dots (6.2)$$

When the current is small the magnetic force is negligible, and

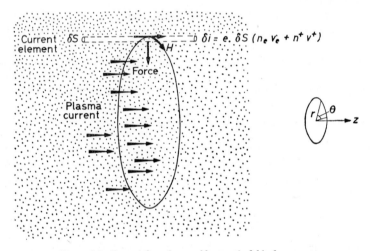

Figure 6.1. Inward force due to self-magnetic field of a current

the radial motion of charges is governed by ambipolar diffusion, the rapid outward diffusion of electrons setting up small space and wall charges resulting in a radial electrostatic field, $E_r$, which equalizes the outward flow of oppositely-charged particles (the classical Schottky theory of the positive column). It is assumed that the gas pressure is large enough to ensure that the charged particles make more collisions with gas molecules than with the wall, and that the plasma is nearly neutral ($n^+ - n_e \ll n_e$, $n^+$, thus $n_e = n^+ = N$, say), and also that the electron and ion temperatures are independent of the radius. The common radial drift velocity is then:

$$v = -\frac{D^+}{N} \cdot \frac{dN}{dr} + b^+ E_r = -\frac{D_e}{N} \cdot \frac{dN}{dr} - b_e E_r \quad \dots (6.3)$$

solving for $E_r$, using the equation $D_e/b_e = kT_e/e$ gives

$$E_r = -\frac{\mathrm{d}V}{\mathrm{d}r} = -\frac{kT_e}{e} \cdot \frac{1}{\mathcal{N}} \cdot \frac{\mathrm{d}\mathcal{N}}{\mathrm{d}r} \qquad \ldots(6.4)$$

$$\therefore \qquad \frac{\mathcal{N}_r}{\mathcal{N}_0} = \mathrm{e}^{-\frac{e(V_0 - V_r)}{kT_e}} \qquad \ldots(6.5)$$

where $\mathcal{N}_0$ and $V_0$ refer to conditions at the axis. This is the Boltzmann distribution. The presence of an appreciable magnetic field, however, adds an additional force to equation (6.3) and hence changes the radial distribution of electrons and ions.

It must be noted that the magnetic field, unlike the electrostatic, exerts an inward force on both ions and electrons, thus compressing the entire plasma. The effect was first treated theoretically for neutral beams of electrons and ions (the electrons moving at relativistic speeds) by BENNETT[10], and has recently been extended by LAWSON[11] to beams in which the particles are accelerated by a longitudinal electric field. TONKS[12] first calculated the magnetic compression in a normal plasma, where the thermal motions of the particles greatly exceed their drift speeds; his treatment was later extended with fewer arbitrary assumptions by BLACKMAN[13]. The derivation of THONEMANN and COWHIG[14] is considered first, since it shows most clearly the physical process, and follows naturally from the normal positive column theory. The inward force acting on an electron current stream of density $n$ at a radius $r$ is:

$$F = -ne \cdot E_r + H \cdot (ne)v_{\mathrm{drift}} \qquad \ldots(6.6)$$

where $v_{\mathrm{drift}}$ is the drift velocity of the electrons parallel to the $z$ axis. In equilibrium this inward force is balanced by outward diffusion of the electrons which, as has been seen, may be written as

$$F = -\frac{\mathrm{d}p}{\mathrm{d}r} = -\frac{\mathrm{d}}{\mathrm{d}r} nkT_e \qquad \ldots(6.7)$$

Equating these expressions and integrating leads to

$$\log\frac{n_r}{n_0} + \log\frac{T_e}{(T_e)_0} = \int_0^r \frac{eE_r}{kT_e} \cdot \mathrm{d}r - \int_0^r \frac{eH}{kT_e} \cdot v_{\mathrm{drift}} \cdot \mathrm{d}r \qquad \ldots(6.8)$$

A 'magnetic potential' $V_m$ is defined by

$$V_m = \int_0^r Hv_{\mathrm{drift}} \cdot \mathrm{d}r \qquad \ldots(6.9)$$

205

Then, provided $T_e$ is also constant, independent of $r$ (as it usually is in low-pressure columns)

$$\frac{n_r}{n_0} = e^{-\frac{e(V_r - V_m)}{kT_e}} \qquad \qquad \dots (6.10)$$

For large currents ($\sim 100$ A) the electrostatic inward force can be neglected, compared with the magnetic one ($V_r \ll V_m$). If the total current flowing within a cross section of radius $r$ is $i$, $H$ is given by

$$H = \frac{2i}{r} = \frac{2}{r} \int_0^r 2\pi r \, . \, n_r e v_{\text{drift}} \, . \, \mathrm{d}r \qquad \dots (6.11)$$

These last three equations can be solved by eliminating $H$ and ignoring $V_s$, to give, for the new electron distribution:

$$\frac{n_r}{n_0} = \frac{1}{(1 + C \, . \, r^2/r_0^2)^2} = \frac{1}{\left(1 + \dfrac{\pi n_0 e^2 v_{\text{drift}}^2}{2kT_e} \, . \, r^2\right)^2} \qquad \dots (6.12)$$

where $r_0$ is the radius of the tube, and $C$ is a constant. This is a distribution of exactly the same form as that found by Bennett. This can be combined with the expression for the current to give both $n_0$ and $n_r/n_0$ in terms of the total discharge current $I$,

$$n_0 = \frac{I}{\pi e r_0^2 v_{\text{drift}} \left(1 - \dfrac{e I v_{\text{drift}}}{2kT_e}\right)} \qquad \dots (6.13)$$

$$\frac{n_r}{n_0} = \left[1 + \left(\frac{I v_{\text{drift}}}{\dfrac{2kT_e}{e} - I v_{\text{drift}}}\right) \frac{r^2}{r_0^2}\right]^{-2} \qquad \dots (6.14)$$

$$= \left[1 + \left(\frac{I v_{\text{drift}}}{2 \times 10^9 V_e - I v_{\text{drift}}}\right) \frac{r^2}{r_0^2}\right]^{-2}$$

in practical units $I$ amps, $V_e$ volts.

The interesting point is that as $I$ increases, and $I v_{\text{drift}} \to \dfrac{2kT_e}{e}$, $n_0 \to \infty$, from equation (6.13). This can of course only mean that $r_0$ no longer represents the radius of the tube but the radius of the ionized region which must decrease rapidly as the current approaches this limiting value. This pulling away of the plasma from the walls is termed the 'pinch effect', and is illustrated in *Figures 6.2* and *6.3* for increasing values of the current. In the simplest terms the stability of such a discharge channel unattached to the walls would seem to depend upon whether $T_e$ increases or decreases as $I$ increases, the latter giving an unstable discharge. It will be seen later, however, that the stability conditions are very much more complicated.

The treatment of TONKS[12] and, later, of BLACKMAN[13] is rather more general, beginning with the equations of motion of electrons

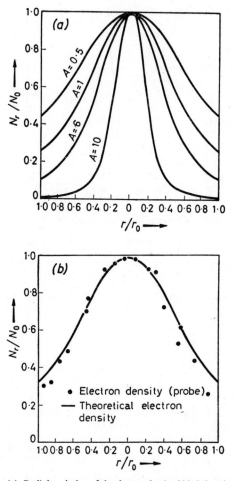

Figure 6.2. (a) Radial variation of the electron density ($N_0$ being the value at the centre), calculated from equation (6.14) for various values of $A$ [$A = Iv_{\text{drift}}/(2kT_e/e - Iv_{\text{drift}})$]; (b) calculated radial variation compared with probe measurements, in mercury vapour ($A = 0.72$ from the following data: current 150 amps, $T_e = 31,500°K$, drift velocity $= 1.5 \times 10^7$ cm/sec). (From P. C. THONEMANN and W. T. COWHIG[14], by courtesy of the Physical Society)

in the presence of electric and magnetic fields and concentration gradients[15], assuming that the electrons have a Maxwellian energy distribution. If a magnetic field, $H$, is applied along the $z$ direction,

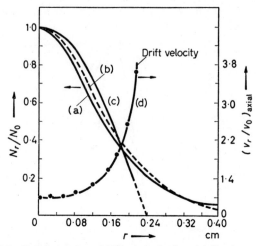

*Figure 6.3. Radial variation of drift velocity in the axial direction and electron density. Curve (a) calculated from $N_r/N_0 = 1/(1 + Cr^2)^2$, ignoring multiplication by collisions; curve (b) measured values of $N_r/N_0$; curve (c) calculated $N_r/N_0$ including multiplication by collision; curve (d) measured values of electron drift velocity in axial direction. (After M. BLACKMAN[13])*

the drift velocities $v_x$ and $v_y$ of electrons (concentration $n$ per cm³) along the $x$ and $y$ directions are given by:

$$\left.\begin{aligned}
v_x &= C_1 \frac{1}{1 + \omega_H^2 \tau^2}\left(b_e X_x + D_e \frac{1}{n}\frac{\partial n}{\partial x}\right) \\
&\quad + C_2 \frac{\omega_H \tau}{1 + \omega_H^2 \tau^2}\left(b_e X_y + D_e \frac{1}{n}\frac{\partial n}{\partial y}\right) \\
v_y &= C_1 \frac{1}{1 + \omega_H^2 \tau^2}\left(b_e X_y + D_e \frac{1}{n}\frac{\partial n}{\partial y}\right) \\
&\quad - C_2 \frac{\omega_H \tau}{1 + \omega_H^2 \tau^2}\left(b_e X_x + D_e \frac{1}{n}\frac{\partial n}{\partial x}\right)
\end{aligned}\right\} \quad \dots (6.15)$$

where $b_e$ and $D_e$ are the normal electron mobility and diffusion coefficients in the absence of a magnetic field, and

$$D_e = \tfrac{1}{3}\lambda_e v_{\text{random}}; \quad \omega_H = \frac{eH}{mc}; \quad \tau = \frac{1}{\nu} = \frac{\lambda_e}{v_{\text{random}}} \quad \dots (6.16)$$

208

$C_1$ and $C_2$ are correction factors (functions of $\omega_H \tau$) close to unity. It will be noted that, since the magnetic field causes the paths of all charged particles to be curved, a drift due to an electric field or a concentration gradient in, say, the $x$ direction creates a component perpendicular (along $y$), and vice versa. In certain simple conditions (e.g. $X_x$, $X_y = 0$, $\partial n/\partial y = 0$) the equations reduce to the Townsend expression for diffusion perpendicular to a magnetic field, except for the numerical factor which arises from a different averaging process. Using the Townsend relation that $D_e/b_e = kT_e/e$, equations can be simplified by defining a 'potential function'

$$V' = - \left( \frac{eV}{kT_e} + \log n \right) \qquad \ldots (6.17)$$

where $V$ is the electric potential at some point. Then

$$\left. \begin{array}{l} v_x = D_e \left[ C_1 \cdot \dfrac{1}{1 + \omega_H^2 \tau^2} \cdot \dfrac{\partial V'}{\partial x} + C_2 \dfrac{\omega_H \tau}{1 + \omega_H^2 \tau^2} \cdot \dfrac{\partial V'}{\partial y} \right] \\[3mm] v_y = D_e \left[ C_1 \cdot \dfrac{1}{1 + \omega_H^2 \tau^2} \cdot \dfrac{\partial V'}{\partial y} - C_2 \dfrac{\omega_H \tau}{1 + \omega_H^2 \tau^2} \cdot \dfrac{\partial V'}{\partial x} \right] \end{array} \right\} \ldots (6.18)$$

These equations are expressed in cylindrical form, assuming that the main current flow (axis of cylinder) is along $x$, and remembering that $\partial n/\partial x = 0$, and that $X_r = -\dfrac{\partial V}{\partial r}$ is everywhere perpendicular to $H$. Thus $n_e$, $n^+$, $H$ and $V$ are functions of $r$ only. Two further equations are required, which are the connection between the magnetic field and axial drift velocity at any radius, given by equation (6.1), and the continuity equation for ions, which can be written (writing $v^+$ for the radial drift velocity of the ions):

$$\frac{\partial}{\partial r} (n^+ v^+ r) = v_i n_e r \qquad \ldots (6.19)$$

where $v_i$ is the number of ion pairs formed by each electron per second. (The left-hand side, if multiplied by $2\pi$, gives the net loss of ions by drift from an annular ring $r$, $r + dr$, the right-hand side gives the rate of production, as the electrons within this ring ionize gas molecules by virtue of their random velocity.) The radial drift of the ions is assumed to be unaffected by the magnetic fields, and therefore given (in cylindrical co-ordinates) by

$$v^+ = b^+ X_r - \frac{D^+}{n^+} \frac{\partial n^+}{\partial r} \qquad \ldots (6.20)$$

209

The solution of equations (6.1), (6.18), in cylindrical co-ordinates, (6.19) and (6.20) is possible only by numerical methods, and depends on the boundary conditions. Tonks, for example, assumed a conducting wall held negative so that there is no radial flow of electrons; Blackman assumed an insulating wall which is closer to actual experimental conditions; a somewhat simpler treatment, by SCHLÜTER[16] leads to an explicit solution for the radial electron distribution, provided $v_i = 0$. The exact theories give $n_r/n_0$ very close to $1/(1 + Cr^2)^2$, and predict that at a critical value of the current the plasma will contract away from the walls and $n_0$ will rise very rapidly. The axial drift velocity also increases rapidly towards the outer edges of the plasma in a pinched discharge[12] (see *Figure 6.3*). When $n_0$ greatly exceeds the local density of neutral gas molecules the inner core is fully ionized and this treatment no longer applies, for reasons given on p. 203.

In a pinched discharge not only is the radial distribution of electrons altered, but also their energy distribution, as shown by ALLEN[17], following an earlier treatment by DAVYDOV[18] and assuming that the electrostatic inward force is negligible compared with the magnetic force. The Maxwellian distribution, found in low-current columns is replaced by one in which there are appreciably fewer fast electrons. Provided the degree of ionization is small, so that elastic collisions predominate, and $\lambda_e$ is independent of electron energy, the new distribution is of the form

$$\mathrm{d}n = f(\varepsilon)\mathrm{d}\varepsilon = A \cdot \left(\frac{\varepsilon}{\bar{\varepsilon}}\right) e^{-B\left(\frac{\varepsilon}{\bar{\varepsilon}}\right)^{3/2}} \cdot \mathrm{d}\left(\frac{\varepsilon}{\bar{\varepsilon}}\right) \qquad \ldots (6.21)$$

However, when the degree of ionization is large the long-range electrical forces between electrons and ions tend to restore the Maxwellian distribution, although even then there are still relatively fewer fast electrons.

These treatments are somewhat limited in their scope, since they ignore the role played by positive ions, assuming them to be in thermal equilibrium with the gas. At very high currents, however, the ions have a temperature not very different from the electron temperature, and the pressure of the ions resisting the inward magnetic force is of more importance than their outward diffusion. In these circumstances theory shows that the centre of the discharge becomes negative. A number of more general treatments, in which the magnetic force and the ion pressure terms are incorporated into the Tonks and Langmuir theory of the positive column, have been given in a series of reports by THOMPSON and his colleagues[19-21].

They refer also to unpublished work by Thomson, who modified Thonemann's and Cowhig's treatment by adding the ion pressure term $k T_i \cdot \dfrac{\partial n^+}{\partial r}$.

## Stable Fully Ionized Column : Current–Temperature Relation

Assuming that a stable cylindrical pinched discharge has been achieved, in which at every point ions and electrons are in thermal equilibrium at the same temperature $T$, let the radius of the column be $R$ cm and the total current $I$ e.m.u. At every point the pressure gradient will be balanced by the inward magnetic force: let the total current enclosed by a cylinder of radius $r$ within the plasma be $i$ (e.m.u.). The balance of the annular ring $r, r + \mathrm{d}r$ is given by:

$$H \frac{\mathrm{d}i}{\mathrm{d}r} = 2\pi r \frac{\mathrm{d}}{\mathrm{d}r} (n^+ k T_i + n_e k T_e) = 2\pi r \frac{\mathrm{d}}{\mathrm{d}r} (n^+ + n_e) k T \quad \ldots (6.22)$$

where $n^+$, $n_e$ are the densities of ions and electrons (numbers per cm³). Putting $H = 2i/r$ and integrating both sides from $O$ to $R$ gives:

$$\left. \begin{aligned} I^2 &= 2\pi R^2 (n^+ + n_e) k T \\ &= 2(\mathcal{N}^+ + \mathcal{N}_e) k T \\ &= 4 \mathcal{N} k T \end{aligned} \right\} \quad \ldots (6.23)$$

where $\mathcal{N}^+$, $\mathcal{N}_e$ (both equal to $\mathcal{N}$) are the total numbers of ions and electrons per unit length of the column. This result could have been more simply obtained by equating the external surface magnetic pressure $H_0^2/8\pi = 1/8\pi \, (2I/R)^2$ to the particle pressure $(n^+ + n_e) k T$. In plane plasmas carrying sheet currents, where lines of magnetic force are straight and parallel, it can be shown that at all points:

$$\frac{H^2}{8\pi} + p = \text{constant} \quad \ldots (6.24)$$

If there is a trapped magnetic field inside the plasma the external field must compress both the internal field and the gas. Let $\beta = \dfrac{p}{H_0^2/8\pi}$, then equation (6.23) becomes, in general,

$$\beta I^2 = 4 \mathcal{N} k T \quad \ldots (6.23a)$$

Equation (6.23) (first derived by Bennett) applies only to stable pinched discharges in thermal equilibrium—as will be seen, these are rarely found.

So far only the equilibrium state of a pinched discharge has been considered; however, if a large current is established in an ionized gas very rapidly, the discharge channel quickly contracts, and one must consider, at the same time, the motion of the fluid (the ionized gas), given by the gas laws and hydrodynamic equations, and its reaction on the magnetic field described by the electromagnetic equations. The study of such motion is called magnetohydro-dynamics, or hydromagnetics[9,22,23].

### THE COLLAPSE OF THE PINCHED DISCHARGE

The previous pages refer to the pinching of an initially uniform and steady discharge as the current is increased. In normal laboratory apparatus it is difficult to attain steady currents of more than a few hundred amperes at the voltages necessary to maintain the discharge because of the large amounts of power which have to be dissipated and, in order to study very much higher currents, pulse methods must be used. This was first carried out by WARE and COUSINS[24,25] who observed the predicted effect, that the luminous discharge channel (which was assumed to carry the entire current) became separated from the walls and concentrated in the central regions. They used a glass torus coated externally with a layer of copper, through which was discharged a bank of condensers. An electrode-less ring discharge resulted (see pp. 137, 138), the electric field being given by the change of magnetic flux through the torus. The lines of electric field and current flow form closed circles in this arrange-ment and, by virtue of the infinite path thus presented to the electrons, the current can grow to very large values. The current in the gas was deduced from the potential induced in a small loop poked into the torus, the contribution due to the current flowing in the copper being balanced out by suitable circuitry. The dis-charge was observed through a small window diametrically opposite the point where the condensers were discharged into the copper coating, by means of a spectroscope and photomultiplier, or a rotating mirror camera.

The measurements showed that the discharge of a 2 $\mu$F con-denser, having a potential about 15 kV, produced a peak current of about 10,000 A in the gas, and from the broadening of spectral lines it appeared that in hydrogen up to 70 per cent of the gas was ionized. Rotating mirror photographs showed that the discharge first con-tracted into a thin channel at the axis of the tube, then expanded and contracted again several times symmetrically about this axis. These movements were accompanied by oscillations in the discharge current, which decreased slightly when the discharge was concen-trated. The oscillations of the luminous channel were not sinusoidal,

212

but the contraction and expansion proceeded at almost constant velocities. It is probable that this motion is due to initial shock waves moving radially inwards, being reflected outwards as they meet at the axis and afterwards being reflected at the walls of the tube; the period of these pinch oscillations varies as $1/\sqrt{M}$, where $M$ is the molecular weight of the gas, increases with increasing gas pressure, and decreases when the applied potential and gas current are increased. Typical results in argon at $p = 0.5$ mm Hg give a period of about 5 $\mu$sec for the pinch oscillations when 2 $\mu$F charged to 10 kV is discharged through the copper coating (peak current 13 kA). This behaviour is compatible with the propagation of shock waves.

At pressures below about 0·1 mm Hg a general lateral motion of the discharge occurs simultaneously with the pinch oscillations, while at higher pressures it occurs slightly later; this is quite a separate effect, due to the general instability of the pinched discharge which is discussed later (see p. 221). Similar periodic contractions and expansions of the discharge channel have been observed by KURCHATOV, ARTSIMOVITCH and their colleagues[26-29], and also by COLGATE[30] working in straight tubes: condensers of several hundred $\mu$F at potentials up to 50 kV were connected to electrodes at the ends of the tube, and their energy discharged through the gas. Here the current rises to about a million amperes in several $\mu$sec, the rate of rise depending, of course, on the inductance of the circuit (plus that presented by the gas discharge) which must therefore be kept to a minimum. In these intense discharges the instants of maximum contraction are marked by sudden changes in the current, and even more marked changes in the voltage across the electrodes.

A number of observations on these transient properties were made by high-speed photography, showing the motion of the luminous gas, by magnetic probes* and piezo crystals placed at various points in the tube giving the magnetic field and gas pressure, and by spectroscopic measurements from which the degree of ionization and the gas temperature can be deduced. The sequence of events set out in *Figure 6.4* seems to account for the main properties.

The potential of the condensers applied across the electrodes is much greater than the breakdown potential of the gas (at a pressure of 0·1 mm Hg or less), which thus very rapidly becomes conducting. The current increases very rapidly and, due to the skin effect, flows

---

\* A small coil, insulated from the discharge (enclosed, for example, in a quartz tube): the potential induced gives the rate of change of the local magnetic field.

close to the wall in a thin layer which is forced inwards by the self-magnetic field, at the same time growing thicker. The magnetic pressure $(H^2/8\pi \propto I^2)$ is vastly greater than the opposing gas

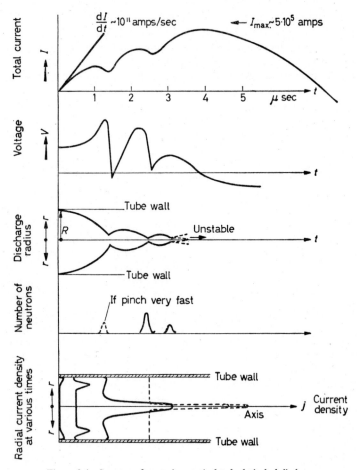

*Figure 6.4. Sequence of events in a typical pulsed pinched discharge*

pressure and therefore directed streams of fast ions and electrons converge radially on to the axis. It should be noted that, since charge neutrality is preserved, electrons and ions are driven inwards with the same speed, and hence the heavier ions possess much greater energy. Gas is carried along with these particles in the form

214

of a converging cylindrical shock front moving at about $7 \times 10^6$ cm/sec; behind it follows a wave of increasing ionization (see Chapter 2, p. 47). When all these charged particles are eventually compressed into the centre, most of the ordered motion is converted into heat: the temperature of the gas rises for a short time to a very high value (of the order of $10^6$ °K in this example). The current is now carried largely in the central channel and, assuming this to be cylindrical, it is evident that at this point the discharge has its maximum inductance, and the voltage across the electrodes is greatest.

Subsequently the reflection of the shock wave and the high gas pressure blow the plasma out towards the wall again; it is rapidly decelerated by the self-magnetic field and another contraction follows. This time, however, the gas into which the charges are accelerated is at a much lower density than at the first contraction, and also is almost fully ionized.

In the Russian work a burst of neutrons and high-energy X-rays ($h\nu \sim 300$–400 keV) was observed at the second pinch of the discharge but not at the first (it should be noted that the X-ray energy is some ten times the original potential of the condensers). These do not arise from a true thermonuclear reaction in the gas (see p. 227), but from a group of ions and electrons accelerated into a beam by an intense local longitudinal electric field created at some stage in the process. The way in which such fields arise is not yet clear, but it has been suggested that they can be produced by deformation of the discharge channel due to instabilities (see p. 222). For example, if the current channel twists into a helical shape the electric and magnetic fields are no longer perpendicular, and charged particles can be accelerated along magnetic lines of force. Alternatively, COLGATE[30] suggested that the discharge, when it develops instabilities, does not pinch uniformly along its length but, at a periodic spacing, compresses to a very narrow kink: the column then looks like a string of sausages, hence this is referred to as a sausage type instability. The inductance of this narrow region is very large and consequently a high axial electric potential develops across it. It should be noted that, in general, as the discharge pinches, the voltage $V$ across the electrodes is given by

$$V = \frac{\mathrm{d}}{\mathrm{d}t}(L . i) = L\frac{\mathrm{d}i}{\mathrm{d}t} + i\frac{\mathrm{d}L}{\mathrm{d}t} \qquad \ldots (6.25)$$

where $L$ is the inductance of the column of gas. Initially $L(\mathrm{d}i/\mathrm{d}t)$ is the important term, but when the gas rushes rapidly towards the centre, $i(\mathrm{d}L/\mathrm{d}t)$ is the dominant factor.

Most of the experiments which have been performed show this sequence of events; however, OHLIN, SIEGBAHN and their collaborators[32], in an arrangement permitting an extremely rapid rise of current (very low external inductance), have obtained neutrons during the first pinch. Subsequent pinches sometimes show rapid voltage oscillations (frequency 3 or 4 Mc/s), accompanied by an unusually large burst of neutrons. CURRAN and ALLEN[33], however, using a similar straight tube but a slower growth of current, have detected small bursts of neutrons at about the time of the third and subsequent pinches: it is possible that these were due to a genuine thermonuclear reaction in the gas. The accumulation of impurities in the gas, swept off the walls when the hot gas expands outwards, and the application of an axial magnetic field, generally reduce the number of neutrons produced. These experiments were carried out mostly in light gases ($H_2$, $D_2$) at low pressures ($10^{-3}$–$10^{-1}$ mm Hg), but transient pinched discharges have also been observed in high-current spark discharges in air at atmospheric pressure[34] (peak currents of about 300 kA).

*The Transient Pinch: Theory*

A theoretical description of the initial rapid pinching and subsequent expansion of the discharge has been given by LEONTOVICH and OSOVETS[35], and by ROSENBLUTH[36]. It is assumed that in the early stages, due to the very rapid rate of change, the current flows in a thin, almost perfectly conducting, sheet near the walls (skin effect). The inward force on the ions and electrons is assumed to be communicated by collisions to the neutral gas which is both compressed and ionized. This force is equated to the rate of change of momentum. If $\rho$ g/cm³ is the initial density of the gas, the mass $M$/cm² of the contracting surface is given by:

$$2\pi R \cdot M = \int_r^R \rho \cdot 2\pi r \, \mathrm{d}r \qquad \dots (6.26)$$

where $R$ is the radius of the tube and $r$ the minimum radius of the pinched discharge. Hence

$$M = \frac{1}{2\pi r}(R^2 - r^2) \qquad \dots (6.27)$$

The equation of motion of this mass is:

$$\frac{\mathrm{d}}{\mathrm{d}t}(Mv_{\mathrm{radial}}) = \frac{H^2}{8\pi}$$

i.e. 
$$-\frac{\mathrm{d}}{\mathrm{d}t}\left(M \cdot \frac{\mathrm{d}r}{\mathrm{d}t}\right) = \frac{1}{8\pi}\left(\frac{2I}{r}\right)^2 \quad (I \text{ in e.m.u.}) \qquad \dots (6.28)$$

Now the discharge of the condenser gives a slightly damped sinusoidal current (approximately $I_0 \sin wt$): however, in the experiments described, particularly in light gases, the speed of contraction is much faster than the natural period of the condenser discharge, and in equation (6.28) the current can be written approximately as $(I_0 wt)$. If this and equation (6.27) are inserted in equation (6.28) and the equation integrated from $R$ to $r$, a small final radius, say $\frac{1}{10}R$, the time, $\tau$, for the first pinch to develop is

$$\tau \approx 1\cdot 4R \sqrt[4]{\frac{100\pi\rho}{I_0^2\omega^2}} \quad (I_0 \text{ in amperes}) \qquad \ldots(6.29)$$

The values of $\tau$ from this equation agree well with the measured times in the American work. Leontovich, with slightly different assumptions about the initial mass distribution, includes in his equations the resistive force due to the pressure of the gas. Taking unit length of the cylinder, and assuming a mass, $m$, per unit length ($m = \rho \,.\, \pi R^2 \,.\, 1$) he writes for the equation of motion:

$$\frac{\mathrm{d}}{\mathrm{d}t}\left(\frac{1}{3}\,m\,\frac{\mathrm{d}r}{\mathrm{d}t}\right) = -\frac{H^2}{8\pi} \,.\, 2\pi r \,.\, 1 + 2\pi r \,.\, p \qquad \ldots(6.30)$$

The factor $\frac{1}{3}$ is an approximation, to allow for the fact that the mass set in motion is not all concentrated at the radius $r$ but distributed throughout the cylinder. The solution is developed in dimensionless co-ordinates $x = r/R$, $z = t/t_1$ where $t_1$ is a function of $m$ and the rate of rise of current. *Figure 6.5* shows the numerically computed change of radius with time, for various initial conditions, the parameter, $\alpha$, being essentially proportional to the initial pressure (thus the $\alpha = 0$ curves show no rebound), and $z_0$ an assumed time at which the constriction process begins. The time of maximum pinch is given in practical units by:

$$\tau = 9 \times 10^{-2} \,.\, \frac{R(p_0 M')^{\frac{1}{4}}}{\sqrt{\mathrm{d}I/\mathrm{d}t}} \qquad \ldots(6.31)$$

where $p_0$ is the initial pressure of the gas in mm Hg and $M'$ is its molecular weight. This equation, of course, shows the same dependences as equation (6.26), in particular $\tau$ varying as the fourth root of the gas density and inversely as the square root of the rate of growth of current. A fast pinch is thus obtained by using a light gas at low pressure, with a fast rise of current [provided always that the conditions justify the use of the basic equations (6.28) and

217

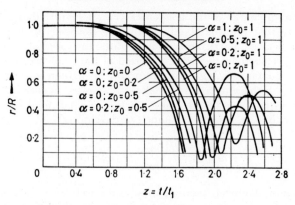

*Figure 6.5. Variation of the radius of the plasma filament with time in the pinched discharge (in dimensionless co-ordinates). $\alpha$, $z_0$ denote different initial pressures and times of the onset of constriction respectively. (From M. A. LEONTOVICH and S. M. OSOVETS[35], by courtesy of Journal of Nuclear Energy)*

(6.30)]. Equation (6.31) also gives results in accordance with experiments in various gases (see *Figure 6.6*).

A rather different, although qualitative treatment has been given by ALLEN[37], who considers the convergence and reflection of shock waves in the pinching of a plane current sheet. The time required for pinching, and the compression and temperature achieved, follow

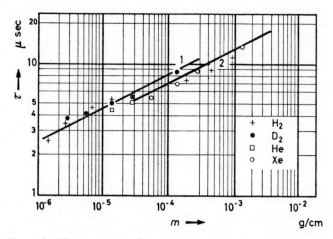

*Figure 6.6. The time, $\tau$, for the first constriction to develop in a gas of mass m g/cm length of the discharge: (1) $dI/dt = 6 \times 10^{10}$ amps/sec (for light gases); (2) $dI/dt = 7.5 \times 10^{10}$ amps/sec (for heavy gases). (From M. A. LEONTOVICH and S. M. OSOVETS[35], by courtesy of Journal of Nuclear Energy)*

218

from standard results describing the propagation of shock waves. These apply only when the gas pressure is sufficiently high that the mean free path of ions is appreciably less than the width of the vessel (i.e. $p >$ about $0.1$ mm Hg for a vessel of, say, 30 cm width). Cylindrical geometry has been treated in a similar way by JUKES[38].

## The Skin Effect

It is well known that in a solid conductor carrying a high-frequency current the resistance increases with frequency, the reason being that the current flows mainly in the outer layers near the surface; the physical explanation of this is clear from *Figure 6.7*.

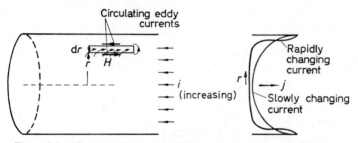

*Figure 6.7. The skin effect in a cylindrical current channel: the illustration on the right shows the radial variation of current density produced by the mechanism on the left*

A rapidly increasing current, $i$, flowing along the column produces an increasing magnetic flux ($\mu H$) through the small rectangle shown. The ensuing e.m.f. drives a current around the rectangle to oppose the change in magnetic field: this has the effect of increasing the current in the outer regions and decreasing it in the inner ones. The e.m.f. generated is proportional to $\mu \cdot \dfrac{\partial H}{\partial t}$, and hence to $\mu \cdot \dfrac{\partial}{\partial t}\left(\dfrac{2i}{r}\right)$ where $i$ is the current (in e.m.u.) enclosed in a cylinder of radius $r$. The density, $j$, of the circulating current is given by $\sigma X$ where $\sigma$ is the conductivity of the medium and $X$ is the field produced by the change of flux. Applying Maxwell's equations to any chosen region in the conductor (e.g. the rectangle in *Figure 6.7*) gives

$$\operatorname{curl} X = -\frac{\mu}{c}\frac{\partial H}{\partial t} \qquad \dots\dots (6.32)$$

$$\operatorname{curl} H = 4\pi j = \frac{4\pi\sigma}{c} X \qquad \dots\dots (6.33)$$

where $\sigma$ and $X$ are in electrostatic units and $H$ is in oersted. Taking the curl of equation (6.32), and using the identity curl curl = grad div — div grad leads to the relation, in cylindrical co-ordinates

$$\nabla^2 X = \frac{4\pi\sigma\mu}{c^2}\frac{\partial X}{\partial t} \qquad \ldots\ldots(6.34)$$

In the geometry considered here $X$ is not a function of $\theta$. The solution shows that $X$ decreases exponentially from the outer boundary; if $X$ is periodic, having a frequency $\omega/2\pi$, then it falls

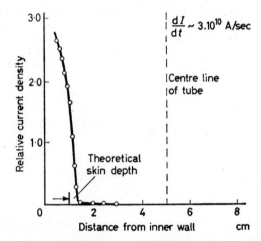

Figure 6.8. Current distribution in a 5 Mc/s discharge in a torus (krypton, $p \sim 10^{-2}$ mm Hg). (From R. CARRUTHERS[39], by courtesy of Applied Scientific Research)

to $1/e$ of its value at the edge in a distance, $d = c/\sqrt{4\pi\omega\sigma\mu}$, the so-called skin depth; the current density, equal to $\sigma X$ follows the same law. When $\omega$—or more generally $di/dt$—is large, the current flows mostly in a thin layer close to the surface. This effect is to be expected also in a gaseous conductor, and has, in fact, been found in toroidal (i.e. ring) discharges maintained at frequencies between 100 kc/s and 5 Mc/s. The radial current distribution can be deduced by inserting magnetic probes into the discharge[39]. An experimental result is shown in *Figure 6.8*: the rate of rise of total current (d$I$/d$t$) in these discharges varied up to $6 \times 10^{10}$ A/sec, a value comparable with that used in the pulsed discharges previously described, and this justifies the assumption made there that the initial current flows in a thin annular sheet.

220

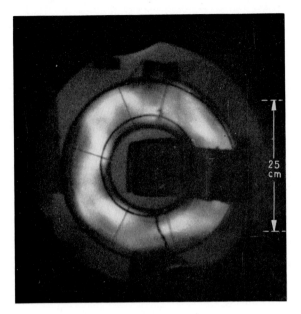

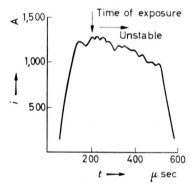

*Figure 6.9. Helical wriggle of a pinched discharge in a glass torus, photographed at the instant indicated on the current waveform.*

(From R. CARRUTHERS and P. A. DAVENPORT[40], by courtesy of the Physical Society)

*Instability of the Pinched Discharge*

Not only does the pinched discharge collapse inwardly in a series of contractions and expansions, but after these have died away the luminous current channel, as a whole, wriggles violently about in the tube, frequently striking the walls[40,41]; this occurs provided the current is sufficiently large. An example is shown in *Figure 6.9*, for a discharge in a torus together with the graph of current against time: it can be seen that the wriggling of the discharge is accompanied by fluctuations of the current. The channel shows a helical

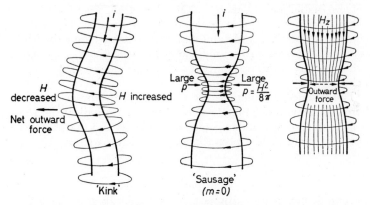

*Figure 6.10. 'Kink' and 'sausage' type instabilities of a pinched cylindrical column, and the suppression of the latter by a trapped axial magnetic field ($H_z$)*

twist, having, in this particular discharge, six complete wavelengths round the torus, which corresponds to a pitch of about twice the diameter of the tube, and an exactly similar configuration is found in discharges in straight tubes. It is a particularly dominant instability, persisting through long pulses of current.

It is clear from *Figure 6.10* that a cylindrical column is unstable when given a local deformation ('kink' type instability); the magnetic field lines crowd together on the one side causing an increased magnetic pressure ($H^2/8\pi$), whereas on the other side the field is decreased: the resultant force pushes outwards, increasing the deformation. Many other kinds of instabilities have been observed experimentally, and it is generally found that the shape and rate of growth of these irregularities is largely independent of the size and shape of the containing vessel[42]. As will be seen later, it is a matter of some practical importance to stabilize the pinched discharge for as long as possible, and two main methods have been used. Bickerton and Tuck independently suggested that an axial magnetic field, $H_z$, inside the plasma (see *Figure 6.10*) would resist the bending of the column. The magnetic lines of force exert a tension along their length, and if the column bends some of them are stretched and exert a restoring force. Furthermore, if the container has conducting walls any movement of the discharge channel causes the radial $(H_\theta)$ lines to cut the walls: the consequent change of flux causes eddy currents in the walls and a counter magnetic field opposing the wriggling of the discharge. It has been found experimentally that these methods do, in fact, make the column stable against many, although not all, fluctuations. The behaviour of plasmas in magnetic fields requires detailed and complex theoretical study and many workers have investigated the stability of such systems mainly, though not exclusively, of cylindrical columns carrying a large current with or without an axial magnetic field.

The detailed calculations are too long and complex to recount here but the two chief methods of approach are indicated. In one it is assumed that a stable configuration exists and that the surface of the plasma suffers a perturbation, $q$, which is written

$$q = q_0 e^{i(m\theta + kz) + \omega t} \qquad \dots (6.35)$$

where $q$ represents convenient parameters, such as the radius of the column or the local electric or magnetic fields, $m$ is an integer and $k$ is the wave number of the assumed undulation parallel to the axis. The factor $e^{\omega t}$ represents the rate of growth of the instability. If, now, Maxwell's equations for the plasma, the equations of continuity and the boundary conditions, are written down and the perturbed values of $X$, $H$, $j$, density and velocity inserted (e.g. $H = H_0 + H_1 e^{i(m\theta + kz) + \omega t}$, where $H_0$ is the equilibrium value) it is possible to find a solution for $\omega$ in terms of $m$ and $k$. Values of $m$ and $k$ which lead to positive real values of $\omega$ represent unstable disturbances. The actual values found depend on certain assumptions regarding the radial distribution of current, whether, for example, it flows in a thin annular sheet near the surface or is distributed through the volume. The following general results have been found: in the absence of a longitudinal magnetic field the fastest growing instabilities are those of long wavelength for which $m = 0$; these cause the column to assume the shape of a string of sausages and give rise to large potential drops along the narrow necks[43–45]. When a longitudinal magnetic field[46–50] is applied the $m = 0$ instability is suppressed and the fluctuation for which $m = 1$ is dominant, i.e. has the largest value of $\omega$, and hence the fastest growth. This is consistent with the experimental observations that the production of neutrons in a pinched discharge decreases with applied magnetic field, and with visual observations on helical motions of the luminous column. Other kinds of instability arise when plasma and magnetic lines of force change places ('interchange effects')—such instabilities are of small scale but can occur very easily since lines of magnetic field move into different positions without being bent, so that very little work has to be done on the field. In any closed system, e.g. a torus, the dangerous instabilities are those whose wavelength is an exact submultiple of the length, $L$, of the closed path. From equation (6.35) their points of maximum disturbance for $m \geqslant 1$ lie along closed helices, which fit exactly into the torus. Now the magnetic lines, resulting from the combination of the axial field and that due to the discharge current, also have a helical twist. If the current, flowing in a channel of radius $r$, is less than a critical value ($i < \pi r^2 H_z/L$, the 'Kruskal limit'[90]) no surface field line closes on itself within the length $L$. One would expect much greater stability in these conditions, and this has been found experimentally. In these theories the plasma is generally assumed to have an infinite conductivity, although some authors have considered qualitatively the damping effects of viscosity and resistance; the stabilizing effect of conducting walls has also been included.

A second, and powerful, method of investigating instabilities theoretically is by the use of a minimum energy principle[51-53]. One gives the plasma a small displacement and calculates the resulting change $\delta\varepsilon$ in the total energy of the system (plasma plus magnetic field) if a particular type of displacement, for example of the form $e^{i(m\theta + kz)}$, causes $\delta\varepsilon$ to be negative then the system is unstable against such a disturbance. This treatment, however, does not enable one to calculate the rate of growth of an instability.

These treatments enable one to derive the conditions for complete stability, or at least for marginal stability, of the pinched discharge. The earlier theories based on a thin cylindrical sheet current showed that the discharge would be most stable when the axial field, $H_z$, and the cylindrical field, $H_\theta$, are completely separated. Any $H_z$ outside the discharge channel reduces the stability. Such a situation can be achieved in practice only by passing a very large current, suddenly, through an already highly ionized (and therefore highly conducting) gas filling a tube along which an axial magnetic field is applied. As has been seen, by the skin effect, the current flows in a thin layer on the outside of the cylinder of ionized gas. As the current channel is forced inwards by its self-magnetic field, it cuts the axial lines of magnetic force and a circular current is induced whose magnetic field opposes the change of flux through this current loop. $H_z$ inside the discharge is thus increased and outside it is decreased; ideally, if the ionized gas is a perfect conductor, the change of flux is completely nullified, $H_z$ being zero outside the discharge. The lines of magnetic field may then be described as 'frozen' to the conducting medium so that the axial field remains inside and is compressed with the discharge. For a fuller discussion of 'frozen' magnetic fields and the effect in a medium of small, but not zero, resistance reference should be made to the works of ALFVÉN[9] and COWLING[22].

Clearly this condition of completely separated magnetic fields can only persist if the circulating current continues indefinitely without consuming any energy. This is not possible in a real gas of finite resistance and the magnetic field diffuses out of the conducting channel in a time, $\tau$, where

$$\tau \approx \frac{4\pi\sigma\mu}{c^2} \cdot L^2 \qquad \ldots (6.36)$$

$L$ being approximately the shortest linear dimension of the system, which here is the radius of the column. This time constant arises from the solution of the diffusion equation (6.34), since the process by which the magnetic field diffuses out is physically the same as the skin effect which is the inward diffusion of electric and magnetic fields. In practice, therefore, it is possible to stabilize a pinched discharge by an axial magnetic only for a time of the order of $\tau$, after which the $H_z$ and $H_\theta$ fields will have diffused and intermingled giving a resultant helical field, both inside and outside the discharge channel.

Recent calculations based on the minimum energy principle, and assuming a current distributed over the cross section of the column, have led to an expression which must be satisfied everywhere for stability. The combination of $H_\theta$ and the frozen-in $H_z$ leads to a system of helical fields of pitch $\mu$, defined by

$$\mu = \frac{H_\theta}{rH_z} \qquad \ldots (6.37)$$

This pitch clearly varies with radius. A necessary (but not sufficient) condition for stability is that, at every point of the plasma

$$\frac{r}{4}\left(\frac{\mathrm{d}\mu/\mathrm{d}r}{r}\right)^2 + \frac{8\pi}{H_z^2}\frac{\mathrm{d}p}{\mathrm{d}r} \geqslant 0 \qquad \ldots (6.38)$$

This can be satisfied by making $\mathrm{d}\mu/\mathrm{d}r$ large, at the surface of the

224

column, which can be achieved in practice by applying a reversed axial field when the discharge has pinched and trapped the axial field initially present. Such experiments are, of course, extremely difficult technically, because large reversed magnetic fields have to be created in times of the order of microseconds. ROSENBLUTH[85], using normal mode theory, has shown that such reversed fields can provide both necessary and sufficient conditions for stability of a column carrying current in a thin surface skin.

Theoretical treatments of stability, which are now being extensively developed, apply of course not merely to the cylindrical pinched discharge, but to the behaviour of plasmas having boundaries of general shape in magnetic fields[88-94]. One such system, in which the magnetic field increases everywhere as one moves away from the surface of the plasma is theoretically stable against all disturbances; this is to be expected on simple physical grounds since then any displacement of the plasma boundary causes it to move into a region of greater magnetic pressure, and hence greater restoring force[31].

## THERMONUCLEAR REACTIONS

A nuclear reaction can occur when two atomic nuclei approach very closely to each other, and for this to happen they must have a relative velocity at least large enough to overcome their mutual electrostatic repulsion (the 'Coulomb barrier'). In conventional nuclear experiments this is achieved by accelerating a beam of ions and bombarding a target of neutral atoms or molecules. It can also be achieved by giving the atoms large speeds by heating a gas, or gas mixture, to a very high temperature. The particles are moving about in random directions and have a distribution of velocities. Nuclear reactions can, of course, arise only from those atoms which hit with sufficiently great relative speeds, and when produced in this way are termed 'thermonuclear'.

Another distinction should be noted: when an ion beam hits a target, both kinds of nuclei are surrounded by their electron clouds, and much energy is lost in elastic collisions as these systems interpenetrate. In a very hot gas, however, the nuclei will be partially stripped of their electrons by thermal ionization—indeed the lightest elements will be completely stripped, since thermal ionization becomes appreciable at temperatures much lower than those required to produce nuclear reactions. Conditions can therefore be relatively simple, if the gas mixture consists essentially of the nuclei and electrons. The connection between thermonuclear reactions and gas discharges arises because the passage of a very large current through an ionized gas is one of the most promising methods of heating a gas to the high temperatures required.

### ENERGY BALANCE

A nucleus consists of a number of protons and neutrons held together by strong attractive forces. The work which would be necessary to completely separate the protons and neutrons is called the binding energy of that nucleus, and it is found that this is a maximum for elements of atomic number $Z$ about 24. Thus, if lighter nuclei combine together, or a heavy nucleus splits up into lighter ones, the final products in each reaction being nearer to $Z = 24$, there will be a net gain of energy, which will appear as the kinetic energy of the particles formed, or as radiation; such reactions are called fusion and fission reactions respectively. The disintegration of U235, as in a conventional nuclear reactor, is an example of a fission reaction: the combination of isotopes of hydrogen to form helium is a fusion process. There are exceptions to this general pattern, because there are minor maxima and minima in the curve of binding energy against atomic number.

In thermonuclear studies, fusion reactions are of predominant interest, because light nuclei have a small positive charge and hence their mutual repulsion may be overcome at lower temperatures. Also, the lighter elements have fewer electrons surrounding their nuclei, and are more easily completely ionized at a lower temperature. It is clearly possible to imagine conditions in which the energy released by thermonuclear reactions between light nuclei in a hot gas exceeds the energy required to heat the gas. These conditions are known to be satisfied in the sun and many stars, and thermonuclear reactions in which hydrogen isotopes combine to form helium are believed to be the source of the sun's energy[54]. The vast scale of astrophysical phenomena favours such processes, the energy being released in a very large volume of gas, whilst it is lost from the surface area. Much of the released energy is contained in the gas, thus maintaining the very high temperatures. On a laboratory scale it is impossible to achieve such a large ratio of volume to surface area, and thus it is much more difficult to maintain a controlled thermonuclear reaction. However, much research has been inspired by the prospect of releasing these sources of almost unlimited energy, some progress has been made, and several reviews of the principles and main problems of releasing energy from thermonuclear reactions are available[55–58].

### RATES OF VARIOUS REACTIONS

Assume that a fully ionized gas mixture exists, containing $n_1$ nuclei of one kind per $cm^3$ and $n_2$ of another; there will, of course, be a concentration $Z_1 n_1 + Z_2 n_2$ of electrons if $Z_1 Z_2$ are the atomic numbers of the elements, but apart from their function in preserving charge neutrality their presence will be ignored; they play no part in the nuclear reactions, which result from impacts between the nuclei. Consider nuclei of type 1 moving through the concentration $n_2$ of type 2 with velocity $v$: each impinging particle produces, on the average, $v/\lambda = v n_2 \sigma$ nuclear reactions per second, where $\lambda$ is the appropriate mean free path and $\sigma$ the nuclear cross section for a particular reaction. Thus if $n_1$ nuclei of type 1 are moving about at random among the others, also moving about at random, the total number of nuclear reactions per $cm^3$ per second (the reaction rate, $r$) is:

$$r = n_1 n_2 (\overline{\sigma v}) \qquad \qquad \dots (6.39)$$

where $v$ is the relative velocity of the two colliding particles, and the bar denotes the value of $\sigma v$ averaged over the velocity distribution. In a gas consisting of only one type of nucleus, of total density $n$ ($n_1 = n_2 = \frac{1}{2}n$) the reaction rate is:

$$r = \frac{1}{2}n^2 (\overline{\sigma v}) \qquad \qquad \dots (6.40)$$

(an additional factor 2 arises, because all collisions between like particles contribute to the reaction rate).

The reactions of especial interest are those between very light nuclei, in particular between isotopes of hydrogen, set out below. Here we write $n$ for the neutron, $p$ for the proton ($H^1$), $D$ for the deutron (the nucleus $H^2$) and $T$ for the tritium nucleus $H^3$. The energy released from the nuclear rearrangement appears as kinetic energy of the particles; the maximum cross section $\sigma_{max}$, and the relative energy, $\varepsilon_{max}$, of the colliding particles at which this occurs is also quoted.

|  | $\sigma_{max}$ | $\varepsilon_{max}$ |
|---|---|---|
| $D + D \rightarrow He^3 + n + 3 \cdot 25$ MeV | $0 \cdot 09 \times 10^{-24}$ $cm^2$ | 1 MeV |
| $D + D \rightarrow T + p + 4 \cdot 03$ MeV | $0 \cdot 08$ | 1 |
| $D + T \rightarrow He^4 + n + 17 \cdot 58$ MeV | $5 \cdot 0$ | $0 \cdot 1$ |

also of interest are

| | | |
|---|---|---|
| $D + He^3 \rightarrow He^4 + p + 18 \cdot 34$ MeV | $0 \cdot 8$ | $0 \cdot 45$ |
| $T + T \rightarrow He^4 + 2n + 11 \cdot 3$ MeV | $0 \cdot 1$ | 1 |

Clearly, $D + T$ is the most favourable reaction, having a very large cross section (by nuclear standards) at a low relative energy (i.e. a low temperature) and releasing an appreciable amount of energy in each reaction. However, in the $D - D$ reaction, tritium is one of the reaction products and if it can be prevented from escaping from the ionized gas the $D - T$ reaction is then possible. If the $He^3$ produced can also be contained, the total energy available from the $D - D$ reaction and its secondary products is then about 21 MeV, although of course the rate of release is determined by the small cross section for $D - D$ collisions. The total energy released in one reaction is distributed between charged and uncharged particles (neutrons). This is a matter of some importance since, in principle, it is hoped to contain the charged reaction products in the plasma, thus maintaining or increasing its temperature, whereas the energy of neutrons can only be used by allowing them to be absorbed by some external shield, thereby heating it. Heavy reaction products carry the smaller fraction of the energy. For example in the $D - D$ reaction the charged particles receive two thirds of the released energy (about 2 MeV), and in the $D - T$ reaction about one fifth, i.e. 3·6 MeV. Thus although this latter process gives a net gain of energy in charged particles of nearly 4 MeV per reaction its main attractiveness lies in the high probability of the reaction at low energies of impact ($\sim 100$ kev).

In order to calculate the average value of the product $\sigma v$ [equations (6.39) and (6.40)] it is necessary to know both the energy distribution of the particles (usually assumed Maxwellian) and the variation of $\sigma$ with energy. Many measurements of $\sigma$ have been made by firing beams of single energy deuterons at solid targets, mostly at energies of 20 keV and above, and the best measurements of these have been compiled within the past few years[59,60]. The values agree well with a theoretical formula due to GAMOW and CRITCHFIELD[61].

$$\sigma = \frac{A}{\varepsilon} \, e^{-B\sqrt{\varepsilon}} \qquad \qquad \dots . (6.41)$$

where $\varepsilon$ is the energy of impact and $A, B$ are constants, which depend on the nuclear charges $Z_1, Z_2$ of the two colliding particles.

The values of $\overline{(\sigma v)}$ for Maxwellian energy distributions at various temperatures have been calculated by THOMPSON[62] for pure deuterium, an equal mixture of deuterium and tritium, or deuterium and $He^3$, and several other mixtures of light elements; some of these results are shown in *Figure 6.11*. It can be seen that, at mean particle energies below 100 keV, the number of nuclear reactions per second in a mixture of tritium and deuterium is several orders of magnitude greater than in any other gas. Since the total energy released in each reaction is about 17 MeV (4 MeV of it in charged particles), and since only isotopes of hydrogen are used having nuclear charge of 1 unit ($+ e = 4 \cdot 8 \times 10^{-10}$ e.s.u.) thus giving the least possible electrostatic repulsive force, a $D - T$ mixture is,

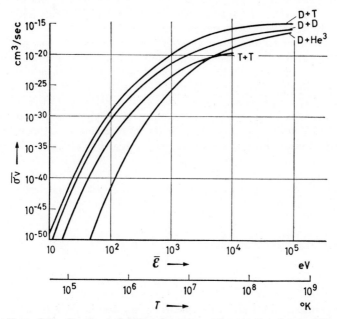

*Figure 6.11. Reaction probabilities for various nuclear reactions between light elements, as a function of mean energy, $\bar{\varepsilon}$, or temperature, $T$ ($\bar{\varepsilon} = \frac{3}{2}kT$).*
(After W. B. THOMPSON[62])

on physical grounds, the most attractive starting point for a thermo-nuclear reactor. There are disadvantages, of course, compared with, for example, the application of the $D - D$ reaction: tritium is expensive to produce, and is radioactive and so must not be allowed to escape into the air.

At any chosen temperature and particle density it is now possible, from equations (6.39) and (6.40), to calculate the power produced per unit volume. It is found that, with $n \sim 10^{12}$ particles/cm³—a typical value for ordinary gas discharges—the $D - D$ reaction produces only $10^{-5}$, and the $D - T$ reaction (assuming equal concentrations of $D$ and $T$) only $2 \times 10^{-3}$ W/cm³ at mean energies of 100 keV. To obtain appreciable power density, much higher particle densities are needed; however, an upper limit is set by the gas pressure, $p = nkT$: if $n$ is too great the pressure exerted by the

229

hot gas becomes so enormous that no container could hold it in; for example, if $n \sim 10^{20}$ (atmospheric density), and $\bar{\varepsilon} \sim 100$ keV, $p$ would be about $10^7$ atmospheres. It is not advantageous to use high densities and lower temperatures because the product $\sigma v$, and hence the reaction rate, is the most sensitive factor, and falls rapidly with decreasing temperature (see *Figure 6.11*).

Two other factors are of interest, namely the mean free path, $\lambda$, of the particles, and their mean lifetimes, $\tau$, meaning the average total path travelled and time taken by one particle before it undergoes a nuclear reaction. Within this path and time it will, of course, encounter many electrons and nuclei, but these effects merely redistribute energy and momentum. The reaction lifetime must not be long compared with the time taken for a particle to diffuse to the walls of the container, or many of the particles will lose their original kinetic energy as heat to the walls without producing any fresh energy by nuclear fusion. The number of nuclear reactions produced by each particle (say of type 1) per second is, from equation (6.39)

$$r_{\text{per particle}} = n_2(\overline{\sigma v})$$

Hence the mean lifetime is

$$\tau = \frac{1}{r} = \frac{1}{n_2(\overline{\sigma v})}$$

Taking, again, particles of mean energy 100 keV as an example, the reaction time is 1 sec for the $D - D$ reaction at a particle density of $5 \times 10^{16}$ per cm³ and for the $D - T$ reaction at $3 \times 10^{15}$ per cm³. Densities of the order of $10^{18}$ or $10^{19}$ are needed to make the reaction time a millisecond.

The mean free path of colliding particles for nuclear reactions is given by

$$\lambda = \frac{1}{n\bar{\sigma}}$$

and is of significance when compared with the dimensions of the vessel, and the method used to contain the plasma away from the walls. Here, again, assume $\bar{\varepsilon} = 100$ keV, then at a particle density of $10^{16}$ per cm³ $\lambda \approx 5 \times 10^7$ cm for a $D - T$ mixture (equal parts of each), and $10^9$ cm for $D - D$ reactions. These are enormous distances which decrease, of course, with increasing particle density and with increasing temperature. It must be remembered that the reaction products are usually released with appreciably greater energy (several MeV); the probability of their undergoing a further nuclear reaction is relatively small and the problem of containing them so that they restore some of this energy directly to the plasma is formidable. For example, a deuteron of energy 100 keV spirals with a radius of 1 cm (the 'Larmor radius') in magnetic field of 60,000 oersted; on average, it must perform $10^7$–$10^8$ gyrations before it produces a nuclear reaction. An electron of the same energy has a Larmor radius of $\frac{1}{60}$ cm. A particle such as He, emitted with an energy of 3·6 MeV would have to be subjected to a magnetic field of 700,000 oersted to perform gyrations of radius 1 cm. For a fuller account of these considerations reference should be made to the reviews by POST[55] and ALLIBONE and CHICK[95].

So far only the production of energy by thermonuclear reactions has been considered; energy is also lost from the plasma in various ways, which are now discussed briefly.

ENERGY LOSSES

Energy can be carried away from a plasma as radiation, or as kinetic energy of particles.

## Radiation

In a fully ionized plasma long-range electrostatic forces between ions and electrons replace the short-range forces which give rise to 'collisions' as they are understood in classical discharges. An electron approaching the vicinity of an ion is attracted towards it and bent from its original path and, due to the acceleration, a pulse of radiation is emitted. On a quantum view the electron is regarded as having been displaced from one energy level to another, both in the continuum—a so-called free-free transition—the frequency of the pulse of radiation being given as usual by $h\nu = \Delta\varepsilon$. Thus in a plasma, where electrons move at random, energy is radiated continuously over a wide band of frequencies: this is Bremsstrahlung. In the plasma under consideration this radiation escapes immediately—the probability of its being absorbed and re-emitted within the plasma is very small—or, in other words, the mean free path of the photons is much larger than the size of the plasma. It does not, therefore, radiate like a black body at the same temperature, but at a very much smaller rate. The energy $\varepsilon_\nu d\nu$ radiated per sec in a frequency interval $\nu$, $\nu + d\nu$ is related to the electron temperature by:

$$\varepsilon_\nu d\nu = C \cdot \frac{n_e n_i \mathcal{Z}^2}{\sqrt{T_e}} e^{-h\nu/kT_e} d\nu \qquad \ldots (6.42)$$

$n_e$, $n_i$ being the electron and ion densities and $\mathcal{Z}$ the atomic number of the ions. This expression, given by Cillié[63], leads to a total radiated power per cm³ from a neutral plasma:

$$P_{\text{Bremsstrahlung}} = 1.7 \times 10^{-34} Z^2 n_e^2 \sqrt{T_e} \text{ W/cm}^3 \quad \ldots (6.43)$$

The loss increases slowly with temperature ($\propto \sqrt{T_e}$) but it is very sensitive to $Z$. In a hydrogen or deuterium plasma $Z = 1$ and the loss is relatively small, but small quantities of heavy impurities, for example residual oxygen or nitrogen remaining in the system after being pumped out ($Z = 7, 8$) or, worse still, silicon ($Z = 14$) or metal vapours (Cu, $Z = 29$) released from the walls or electrodes by hot gases, would cause the energy radiated to increase at an alarming rate. To give a numerical example, if a system is filled with deuterium at a pressure of $10^{-2}$ mm Hg, which it is intended to heat to thermonuclear temperatures, one must ensure that, before filling, it is evacuated to $10^{-5}$ mm Hg so that the remaining oxygen and nitrogen atoms shall not increase the Bremsstrahlung loss by more than 10 per cent.

A second source of radiated energy comes from the gyration of electrons around the lines of magnetic force; this motion creates electric and magnetic fields fluctuating with a frequency, $f = eH/2\pi mc$, which transmit energy out of the plasma. Until recently it was thought that this represented a trivial loss of energy, but it has now been realized that electrons of 10–100 keV energy, moving with relativistic speed, have a gyro frequency depending on their velocity. Not only is energy thus emitted in a band of frequencies about $f$, but in the harmonics as well, up to the plasma frequency (this is the frequency with which electrons will oscillate if slightly displaced from their neutralizing ions: electric fields of frequencies greater than this do not penetrate, and so the energy does not escape—see Chapter 5, p. 176). The total loss can be appreciable, and has been considered in some detail[64].

*Particle Losses*

*Diffusion*—At the temperatures envisaged it is clear that no material walls can contain plasma. Since the plasma consists, ideally, only of charged particles it can, in principle, be contained by electric or magnetic fields; actually only magnetic confinement is practicable, first because the spiralling of positive and negative charges around the field lines does not cause any separation of charge, and secondly on numerical grounds. When electric and magnetic pressures, $X^2/8\pi$ and $H^2/8\pi$ are compared, $X$ being in e.s.u. (= 300 V/cm), and $H$ in oersted, it is found that quite modest magnetic fields are as effective as very large electric fields.

One of the main sources of loss will therefore be due to diffusion of electrons and ions across the magnetic field. In classical discharges, having low density of ionization and small particle energies, it is known that the coefficient of diffusion across a magnetic field is reduced according to

$$D_H = \frac{D}{1 + \omega_H^2 \tau^2} \approx \frac{\frac{1}{3}\lambda \bar{v}_r}{\omega_H^2 \tau^2} \propto \frac{1}{H^2} \qquad \dots\dots (6.44)$$

Theory shows that in a fully ionized and energetic plasma the diffusion coefficient follows the same $1/H^2$ law[65]; the classical mean free path must be replaced by a mean free path for electron–ion collisions, as it can be shown that only encounters between unlike particles result in a net drift of particles across the field*. The cross section, $\sigma$, for these distant encounters (resulting in deflections described by the Rutherford scattering formula), is inversely proportional to $v_r^2$ (i.e. to the energy of the particle). If, in the above formula, $\lambda = 1/n\sigma$, $\tau = v_r/\lambda$, are substituted it can easily be shown from the usual definition of the diffusion coefficient that the drift velocity, $v_{\text{drift}}$, of particles across the lines of magnetic force is:

$$v_{\text{drift}} \propto \frac{1}{H^2 v_r} \operatorname{grad} n \propto \frac{1}{H^2 \sqrt{T}} \operatorname{grad} n \propto \frac{1}{H^2 T^{3/2}} \operatorname{grad} p \quad \dots\dots (6.45)$$

This derivation, being an extrapolation from lightly ionized discharges, in which charged particles collide mainly with neutral molecules (not with each other), is of course not rigorous, but it leads to the correct dependence on $H$ and $T$. A proper treatment has been given by CHANDRASEKAR[65,66] (see also SPITZER[8]). At first sight it seems odd that the diffusion across the field should decrease as the temperature increases; the reason is that the drift occurs only because of collisions, without which the particles would merely gyrate about the field lines and return to their original positions. In a highly ionized gas the faster the particles move, the less they are deflected by the fields of neighbouring particles, or in other words the fewer 'collisions' they make, a collision now being regarded as an encounter resulting in an appreciable deflection of the paths of the particles.

There is controversy about the correctness of this result, however: some experimental work[67] has shown excellent agreement with

---

* It is doubtful whether the concept of a mean free path is applicable to fully ionized gases, where one needs to compute rigorously the total effect of many small deviations produced by long-range electrostatic forces.

equation (6.44), whilst other measurements[68,69] tend to show a drift velocity varying sometimes as $1/H$. It has been suggested that diffusion can be caused by turbulent bodily movements of bunches of plasma, as distinct from single particle encounters, a process akin to plasma oscillations and resulting in more rapid drift, but more experimental work is needed before this is fully understood.

It is interesting to compare diffusion of particles across magnetic fields with the reverse effect, diffusion of magnetic field into a conducting gas (the skin effect—see pp. 219, 220), and the relation

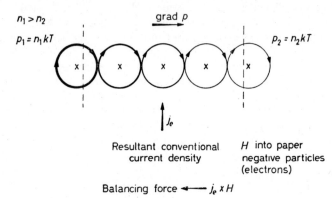

*Figure 6.12. Particle diffusion across a magnetic field*

of both to the electrical conductivity, $\sigma$, of the medium. Consider the conditions illustrated in *Figure 6.12*: the particles of the plasma, distributed with a density (and hence pressure) gradient, spiral about stationary lines of magnetic force. There are more particles spiralling on the left- (blacker lines) than on the right-hand side, the circles representing particles of only one sign, e.g. electrons. Macroscopically there is a force $dp_e/dx$ (generally grad $p_e$) per unit volume acting on the electrons to the right; in any chosen volume (which does not, in general, enclose an integral number of circles) the density gradient causes a net current, as shown, and a balancing force $j_e \times H$ per unit volume which keeps the system in equilibrium. Hence

$$\mathrm{grad}\, p_e = j_e \times H \qquad \ldots . (6.46)$$

The positive ions undergo a similar motion, gyrating in the opposite sense. Thus

$$\mathrm{grad}\, p_{\mathrm{ions}} = j_{\mathrm{ions}} \times H \qquad \ldots . (6.47)$$

Addition gives the general equation

$$\text{grad } p = j \times H \qquad \ldots (6.48)$$

where $p, j$ are the total pressure and current density.

This picture ignores the effect of collisions, which deflect particles from their circular paths and lead to a diffusion velocity, $v_{\text{drift}}$, down the density gradient. This motion is against the restoring force $j \times H$, so that work $(j \times H) . v_{\text{drift}}$ is done per cm$^3$ per sec. Since there is no directed acceleration of the particles, it follows that this work is dissipated as heat in the gas; if $r$ is the resistivity the energy dissipated is $j^2 r = j^2/\sigma$ where $\sigma$ is the conductivity. This gives, with all quantities in e.m.u.

$$\text{energy dissipated/cm}^3/\text{sec} = (j \times H)v_{\text{drift}} = j^2/\sigma \quad \ldots (6.49)$$

which, combined with equation (6.48), gives

$$v_{\text{drift}} = \frac{1}{\sigma H^2} \text{grad } p \approx \frac{1}{\sigma H^2} \frac{p}{L} \qquad \ldots (6.50)$$

where $L$ is the linear dimension of the plasma perpendicular to $H$. This leads to a 'diffusion time' $\tau = L/v_{\text{drift}}$, therefore

$$\tau_{\text{particle flow}} = \frac{\sigma H^2 L^2}{p} \qquad \ldots (6.51)$$

Comparing this with equation (6.34), which describes the diffusion of an external magnetic field into a conductor, gives a time of $4\pi\sigma\mu L^2$; for a gaseous plasma $\mu = 1$, hence

$$\tau_{\text{field penetration}} = 4\pi\sigma L^2 \qquad \ldots (6.52)$$

Hence

$$\frac{\tau_{\text{field penetration}}}{\tau_{\text{particle flow}}} \approx \frac{p}{H^2/4\pi} \approx \frac{1}{2}\beta \qquad \ldots (6.53)$$

where $\beta = \dfrac{p}{H^2/8\pi}$ is the ratio of particle energy density to magnetic energy density, a factor of some importance in the design of a thermonuclear reactor. The physical reason for the above result is that, when a magnetic field diffuses inwards the velocity is determined by the rate at which the magnetic energy density is destroyed by resistive heating; when ions and electrons diffuse out the particle energy density $p$ is degraded by the same process. The factor $\frac{1}{2}$ is not significant because the actual value of $L$ used, and the detailed description of the inward flow of $H$, depend on the geometry of the system.

*Charge transfer*—The presence of any neutral gas results in appreciable cooling of the plasma, first because the atoms can be excited to a number of different levels and, in returning to the ground state, radiate energy, and secondly—which is important here since particle losses are being considered—they can exchange charges with a fast ion. In such collisions, a fast ion hits a slow neutral atom, resulting in a slow ion (i.e. nucleus) and a fast neutral atom which flies to the walls of the vessel and gives up its energy. Cross sections for charge transfer lie in the gas-kinetic range ($10^{-18}$–$10^{-16}$ cm$^2$) whereas those for 'collision' between electrons and ions in a fully ionized gas are several orders of magnitude less and nuclear reaction cross sections are about $10^{-24}$ cm$^2$. Thus a very high degree of ionization is necessary to avoid very large amounts of energy being carried away by neutral atoms.

*Formation of beams*—Particles which are accelerated along an electric field can sometimes gain energy without sharing it effectively by collisions with other particles. In such circumstances the plasma is traversed by a fast beam, which has gained its energy at the expense of the thermal energy of the remainder of the plasma. These fast beams are more difficult to contain than the particles moving at random with lower average speeds, and they are frequently observed to strike the walls of the apparatus emitting bursts of neutrons or X-rays. Beams of ions can arise from the instability mechanism discussed on pp. 221–225, a constriction in a pinched discharge causing a transient high potential to be developed. Beams of electrons can be produced in this way, and also even in the absence of instabilities by the fact that their collision cross section decreases with increasing energy, so that, having gained an energy exceeding that at which the cross section is a maximum, they have an ever-increasing probability of gaining more energy; these are called 'runaway' electrons (see Chapter 2), and constitute a serious source of loss in straight and toroidal discharges[70,71].

*Gross instabilities*—Finally, and most obvious, instabilities of the entire plasma which causes it either to break up or wriggle violently and uncontrollably result in the entire energy being wasted when the plasma hits the wall (these motions are described on p. 221). Instabilities are not confined, of course, to pinched discharges, but must be considered whenever a plasma is bounded by a magnetic field.

#### TEMPERATURE, PARTICLE DENSITY AND CONTAINMENT TIME: CRITERIA FOR A REACTOR

Thermonuclear reactions in a plasma can, in principle, be made self-sustaining when the rate of energy release is equal to the losses. If all losses, with the exception of Bremsstrahlung, are neglected then, by equating the product of reaction rate (*Figure 6.11*) and energy released per reaction with the relation for radiation loss [equation (6.43)], a critical temperature may be derived, below which the reactions are certainly not self-sustaining. For the $D - D$ reaction this is about $1.5 \times 10^8$ °K (assuming that the tritium formed is also used up) and for the $T - D$ reaction $3 \times 10^7$ °K. Here it is assumed that all the reaction products are retained. A particular example, the equilibrium of a stable pinched discharge cooled by Bremsstrahlung, has been worked out in detail by PEASE[72], and related to the discharge current.

Of more practical interest are the critical conditions for a reactor in which the reaction products escape. In an idealized system, treated by LAWSON[73], a plasma is instantaneously heated and maintained at a temperature $T$ for $t$ sec, then allowed to cool; in a system not pulsed $t$ would represent the lifetime of the reacting particles. Again only radiation loss is considered, and it is assumed that the energy used to heat the gas and supply losses can be regained. The ratio, $R$, of energy released in reactions to the energy supplied is

$$R = \frac{t \cdot P_{\text{reactions}}}{t \cdot P_{\text{Bremsstrahlung}} + 3nkT} = \frac{P_r / 3n^2kT}{P_B / 3n^2kT + \dfrac{1}{nt}} \quad \dots (6.54)$$

where the $P$'s are the power produced and radiated per unit volume respectively. The gas is assumed to consist of $n$ nuclei and $n$ electrons per cm³, hence $3nkT$ rather than $\frac{3}{2}nkT$. Since $P_{\text{reaction}}$ and $P_{\text{Bremsstrahlung}}$ are both proportional to $n^2$, $R$ is a function of $T$ and the product $nt$.

Now the energy released escapes to heat up the walls of the apparatus and must be recovered by some electrical, chemical or thermal process, having an efficiency $E$, for example. Then, for a net gain of energy,

$$E(R + 1) > 1 \qquad \dots (6.55)$$

and, since the maximum value of $E$ is about $\frac{1}{3}$, this reduces to $R > 2$.

*Figure 6.13* illustrates this result in a logarithmic plot of $R$ against $T$, a reactor being possible in principle when the curves lie above the dotted line $R = 2$. The curves for the $D - D$ reaction lie rather lower and the conditions are more severe; for $D - T$ reactions, $nt$ must exceed $10^{14}$ (sec × particles/cm³), and for $D - D$ reactions, $nt$ must exceed $10^{16}$. The density of unused fuel (i.e. $D$ and $T$ nuclei which have not undergone reactions) is assumed to be maintained somehow, and the fraction used up in time $t$ negligible ($\sim 1$ per cent).

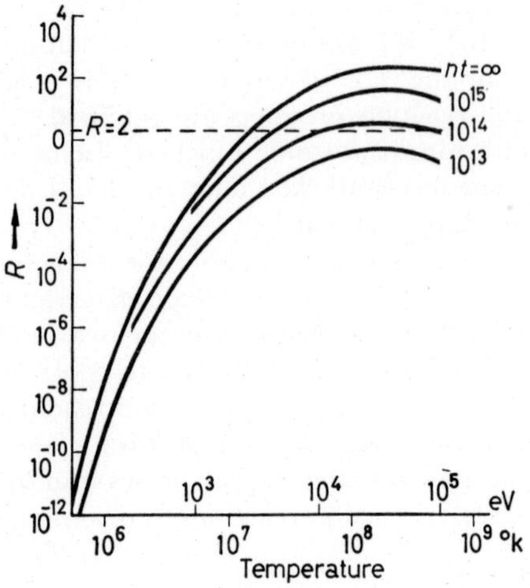

Figure 6.13. Ratio, R, of energy released in reactions to energy supplied in heating gas, as a function of temperature, for the $D-T$ reaction. (After J. D. Lawson[73])

## SOME EXPERIMENTAL DEVICES

In any device designed to produce thermonuclear reactions, three things must be achieved: (a) the creation of a fully ionized plasma of sufficient density; (b) heating of the plasma to a sufficiently high temperature ($10^8$–$10^9$ °K); (c) containment of the hot plasma for an appreciable time—but not necessarily in that order. For example, in the pinched discharge all three processes take place almost simultaneously, by the application of a large electric field which makes the gas conducting and causes a very large current to pass. In other systems a plasma may first be produced, for example, by shock waves, and a magnetic field then applied to compress it and confine it away from the walls of the vessel; alternatively, a static magnetic field may first be produced and plasma, or the individual positive and negative particles, fired into it. All methods rely on magnetic containment, as previously explained, but different methods of heating the plasma are employed.

### Joule Heating

By passing a current through the plasma driven by an electric field, the heat produced is $i^2R$, if $R$ is some effective resistance of the plasma—physically the energy of directed drift motion in the field is converted into random motion. In this class comes so-called 'diffusion heating', in systems having separated magnetic fields; an example is the pinched discharge with a trapped axial magnetic field and current flowing in a thin cylindrical sheet at the surface. In addition to the axially directed current $i_z$, there is a circular current around the sheet $i_\theta$ which prevents the trapped axial field escaping. As these currents dissipate their energy, the two magnetic fields interdiffuse, giving a final state of lower magnetic energy; this loss has appeared as heat in the plasma due to the Joule effect of the sheet currents.

*Magnetic Compression*

If an externally applied magnetic field containing the plasma is rapidly increased, the lines of force move inward and carry the charged particles with them. The plasma is thus compressed, work is carried out on it and its temperature rises. If the compression takes place in a time which is long compared with the collision time of the particles, the inward directed motion rapidly becomes random and the plasma obeys the usual gas law for adiabatic expansion, $pV^\gamma = $ constant. If the compression is very rapid an inward moving shock wave develops, the mechanism of which has been discussed by ALLEN and ADLAM[74].

A variant on this method is magnetic pumping, by which one attempts to heat the ions selectively; it must be remembered here that nuclear reactions arise from fast ions, and that, provided the electron temperature is sufficiently high to give good electrical conductivity, it is an advantage to have a high ion temperature and relatively low $T_e$. The principle is to accelerate the ions in resonance with their period of gyration around the magnetic field, by changing the applied field at this frequency[75] (compare the resonance of electrons in high-frequency discharges, Chapter 4). This can be regarded either as an oscillatory motion of the guiding centre of the particle's orbit, or as acceleration in the alternating electric field produced by the changing magnetic flux.

Magnetic pumping at other frequencies is also theoretically effective in heating a plasma, for example when the period of the applied oscillation in the field is comparable with the collision time of the particles, or their transit time across the confining region, or the time taken by a sound wave to cross the region. Pumping by a 'magnetic piston' on a perfect adiabatic medium will, of course, do no work: there must be a phase lag between the change of the field and the response of the plasma. These have been fully discussed by SPITZER and his colleagues[76].

*Acceleration and Mixing of Beams*

In this method the plasma is built up of its component particles by firing into an evacuated space surrounded by strong, suitably shaped, magnetic fields, energetic beams of electrons and ions. This of itself does not, of course, result in a neutral plasma, since the energies, although large (say 10 keV) are in directed motion and the beams must be compelled to mix and assume random motion before thermonuclear effects can be expected. Two other points should be noted: first a particle which has sufficient energy to be

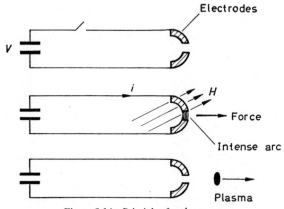

*Figure 6.14. Principle of a plasma gun*

fired across a confining magnetic field (so-called 'magnetic bottle') will, unless it loses some energy, also emerge again, hence one must either cause the ratio $e/M$ to be changed whilst it is inside or ensure that it moves into regions of stronger magnetic field until it exchanges energy by collision with other particles. Secondly, even the highest obtainable vacua leave about $10^7$ neutral gas atoms per $cm^3$ in the space, and so intense charged particle beams must be used to obtain a fully ionized plasma. However, the method offers, in principle, a means of operating a thermonuclear reactor continuously.

It is worth noting an interesting device, the plasma gun, which produces a beam of neutral plasma[79], the principle of which is shown in *Figure 6.14*. Condensers charged to some suitably high potential are connected across a pair of electrodes. The gas breaks down and forms a very high-current arc, the magnetic field of the current in the loop formed by condensers, electrodes and arc, accelerates the plasma outwards and it finally breaks away from the electrodes and shoots outwards at high speed ($v \sim 10^7$ cm/sec has been measured).

240

The behaviour of these bunches of plasma ('plasmoids') in magnetic fields has been studied[79,80].

These principal methods do not exhaust the possibilities of heating and containing a plasma, and many other ingenious ideas have been suggested, mostly in papers presented at the 1958 Geneva Conference. A brief description is now given of a few of the devices based on these principles; further details can be found in the original papers, and the review by BICKERTON[81]. BRAGINSKY and SHAFRANOV[87] have summarized the principles of toroidal systems of various kinds.

### Toroidal Pinch Machine (ZETA)[82,86]

This is illustrated in *Figure 6.15*: a bank of condensers discharged through a primary winding linked with an iron core produces a large change of flux through the centre of the torus. The gas in the bore is weakly pre-ionized by a radio frequency discharge, and the induced e.m.f. causes a very large current to flow. The current channel contracts inwards by the pinch effect trapping a previously applied axial magnetic field which, together with eddy currents in the conducting walls, helps to stabilize the channel for several milliseconds and temperatures of about $10^6$ °K have been achieved. Several smaller machines have also been built, which, making due allowance for the scaling laws[83], give comparable results. The Bennett relation, extended to include the trapped axial field, becomes $\beta I^2 = 4NkT$; the highest possible temperature for a given current would be expected at a low line density, $N$, but beams of runaway electrons then grow very rapidly. The methods of measurement, which are as difficult as the production of the plasma, have been reviewed by HARDING and his colleagues[84]. Such a system which depends on a change of flux in the centre is suitable only for pulsed operation; also, in toroidal geometry, the magnetic pressure is greater nearer the centre of the system, and so the current channel as a whole must drift outwards towards the walls.

### Joule Heating and Magnetic Compression Machine ('Stellarator')[76]

In this apparatus the gas is contained in a toroidal-shaped vessel, a steady axial magnetic field being applied by means of external windings. A current is induced in the gas (as in the toroidal pinch) by a change of magnetic flux through the core, but its value is restricted so that the self-magnetic field is not important, heating of the gas being due only to the ohmic resistance of the plasma, without inward compression by the pinch effect; the current is also below the limiting value at which instabilities set in. The outward

241

drift of the plasma, common to all toroidal systems is compensated by twisting the magnetic field so that each line of force describes a complete surface instead of a closed circle. This is done either by an additional external helical winding, which actually rotates the field lines, or by connecting two toruses in a figure of eight, effectively twisting the surface of the vessel. The result is that the separation of charges in the plasma, which results from the radial gradient of magnetic field, can be cancelled by charges flowing along the field lines. This artifice is known as the 'rotational transform' and has proved successful in reducing the net outward drift, although of course it does not affect general diffusion of plasma across $H$. The initial ohmic heating is followed either by adiabatic magnetic compression (produced by an increase in applied magnetic field), or by applying an oscillatory field of suitably chosen frequency along a selected part of the torus (i.e. magnetic pumping); the effectiveness of this latter method is not yet proved, however. The apparatus suffers from some of the disadvantages of the toroidal pinch: it has to be pulsed to produce the gas current, and the induced axial electric field produces beams of runaway electrons. A general view is shown in *Figure 6.16*.

### The Mirror Machine[77],[78]

A magnetic mirror is a field configuration produced by currents flowing in the same direction in two parallel coils (*Figure 6.17*), the field being large at the ends and smaller in the middle. The curvature of the lines of force is not large, first because the proper functioning of the mirror requires that $H$ shall not change appreciably over the Larmor radius of a particle, and secondly for stability when the mirror is filled with plasma.

The principle of the mirror is as follows: suppose a particle of charge $e$ has a total velocity $v$ (energy $\frac{1}{2}mv^2$), the component $v_\perp$ being perpendicular to the field $H$, at some point. The equation of circular motion gives:

$$\frac{mv_\perp^2}{r} = \frac{Hev_\perp}{c}$$

therefore

$$\frac{\frac{1}{2}mv_\perp^2}{H} = \frac{e}{2mc}(mv_\perp r) = \text{constant}$$

since $mv_\perp r$, the angular momentum of the particle about the centre of its orbit, is constant, there being no couple acting*. If, due to

---

\* This is true provided that the curvature of $H$ is not severe, so that the orbit of the particle is, to a high degree of approximation, a plane.

242

*Figure 6.15. General view of ZETA. The bands wound closely around the torus casing are coils to provide the stabilizing axial magnetic field. The torus threads through a large iron core. (By courtesy of the United Kingdom Atomic Energy Authority)*

*Figure 6.16. A model of the figure-eight Stellarator. The loops are windings to provide a very large magnetic field.*
*(By courtesy of the United States Information Service)*

the component of velocity along $H$, the particle moves along lines to a region of more intense field, $\frac{1}{2}mv_{\perp}^2$ must increase: there is, however, an upper limit since $\frac{1}{2}mv_{\perp}^2$ can never exceed $\frac{1}{2}mv^2$, the initial energy. When a particle reaches a region of this field strength

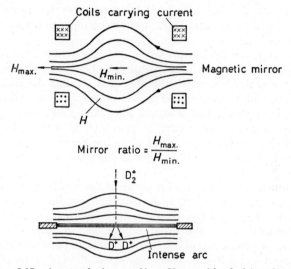

Figure 6.17. A proposed mirror machine. Here particles fired into the mirror are contained due to the change in $e/M$. In other systems particles of energy just sufficient to penetrate the magnetic field are injected and are contained if they lose a little energy by encountering other particles. Alternatively, beams of neutral atoms may be injected, which become ionized by collisions inside the mirror

it is reflected back along the line of force again; clearly, if its initial velocity has a small component of velocity across $H$ and a large component along $H$ very large fields are required to reflect it, and if such fields are not available the particle will escape through the ends of the mirror. If all the particles are imagined to have the same velocity (equal to the average), those directed at a sufficiently small angle to the axis (within the so-called 'loss cone') will escape. The remainder would remain permanently imprisoned unless their motion is altered by collisions which deflect some into the loss cone: in this sense the losses are similar to those by diffusion, and decrease with increasing temperature; even so, end losses are severe.

*Figure 6.17* shows a proposed method of filling a mirror: a beam of $D_2^+$ ions is fired across the field lines into an intense arc (maintained along the axis) which dissociates the ions into $D^+$. Since $e/M$ is now twice that of the original particle, and the velocity is

243

also reduced (energy shared between two masses) the Larmor radius is appreciably reduced and the particles remain confined within the mirror.

The most attractive feature of the mirror machine is the possibility of continuous operation, and the exclusion of runaway effects. Losses by charge exchange, and by escape through the ends are very large, however, and high operating temperatures are needed to offset them.

In general, the devices proposed and partly tested fall into two main groups, those with magnetic field lines which form closed surfaces, and those in which the lines pass through the walls of the apparatus. The former need to be pulsed (at least when joule heating is applied), but if stable have low losses and need low temperatures; the latter can, in principle, be operated continuously but have greater losses, and also when considered in detail are found to be less economic in magnetic fields (i.e. give a lower value of $\beta$).

Not much thought has been given to the problem of extracting the surplus energy which these devices might produce, for the simple reason that there has not yet been any surplus energy. However, fusion reactors have the great advantage, in principle, that a considerable proportion of the energy produced (that which appears in charged particles) can be converted directly into electrical energy. The reason is that these energetic particles, which we assume to be contained, build up a large plasma pressure, pushing the magnetic field outwards and inducing currents in external conductors. The thermodynamics of this process has been worked out by BICKERTON and JUKES[96]. Neutrons are not, of course, contained by the field and their energy can be converted into useful form only via a thermal cycle.

### REFERENCES

[1] VON ENGEL, A., *Ionized Gases*; Oxford: Clarendon Press, 1955

[2] MEEK, J. M. and CRAGGS, J. D., *Electrical Breakdown in Gases*; Oxford: Clarendon Press, 1953

[3] LOEB, L. B., *Fundamental Processes of Electrical Discharge in Gases*; New York: John Wiley, 1939

[4] VON ENGEL, A. and STEENBECK, M., *Elecktrische Gasentladungen*; Berlin: Springer, 1932–4

[5] FINKELNBURG, W. and MAECKER, H. in *Handbuch der Physik*, Vol. 22; Heidelberg: Springer, 1956

[6] LOCHTE-HOLTGREVEN, W., *Rep. Progr. Phys.*, **21** (1958) 312

[7] DRUYVESTEYN ,M. J. and PENNING, F. M., *Rev. mod. Phys.*, **12** (1940) 87

[8] SPITZER, L., *Physics of Fully Ionized Gases*; New York: Interscience, 1956

[9] ALFVÉN, H., *Cosmical Electrodynamics*; Oxford: Clarendon Press, 1950

[10] BENNETT, W. H., *Phys. Rev.*, **45** (1934) 890

[11] LAWSON, J. D., *J. Electron. Cont.*, **3** (1957) 587

[12] TONKS, L., *Phys. Rev.*, **56** (1939) 360; *Trans. Electrochem. Soc.*, **72** (1937) 167; see also FETZ, H., *Ann. Phys.*, **40** (1941) 579

[13] BLACKMAN, M., *Proc. phys. Soc. Lond.*, **B64** (1951) 1039

[14] THONEMANN, P. C. and COWHIG, W. T., *Nature, Lond.*, **166** (1950) 903; *Proc. phys. Soc., Lond.*, **B64** (1951) 345

[15] TONKS, L. and ALLIS, W. P., *Phys. Rev.*, **52** (1937) 710

[16] SCHLÜTER, A., *Z. Naturf.*, **6A** (1951) 73

[17] ALLEN, J. E., *Proc. phys. Soc. Lond.*, **B64** (1951) 587

[18] DAVYDOV, B., *Phys. Z. Sowjet.*, **12** (1937) 269

[19] THOMPSON, W. B., *A.E.R.E. Rep.* T/R 997 (1952); T/R 1050 (1952)

[20] THOMPSON, W. B. and BURLEY, B., *A.E.R.E. Rep.* T/R 1066 (1952)

[21] ROBERTS, S. J., *A.E.R.E. Rep.* T/R 1344 (1954)

[22] COWLING, T. G., *Magnetohydrodynamics*; New York: Interscience, 1957

[23] LANDSHOFF, R. K. M. (Ed.), *Magnetohydrodynamics*; Stanford: The University Press, 1957

[24] WARE, A. A., *Phil. Trans.*, **A243** (1953) 197

[25] COUSINS, S. W. and WARE, A. A., *Proc. phys. Soc. Lond.*, **B64** (1951) 159

[26] KURCHATOV, I. V., *J. nucl. Energy*, **4** (1957) 193

[27] ARTSIMOVICH, L. A. *et al.*, *ibid.*, **4** (1957) 203, 213

[28] LUKYANOV, S. Y. and SINITSYN, V. I., *ibid.*, **4** (1957) 216

[29] LUKYANOV, S. Y. and PODGORNY, I. M., *ibid.*, **4** (1957) 224

[30] COLGATE, S. *et al.*, *Proceedings of the Third International Conference on Ionization Phenomena in Gases*, Venice, 1957

[31] BERKOWITZ, J. *et al.*, *Proceedings of the Second United Nations Conference on the Peaceful Uses of Atomic Energy*, Geneva, 1958, Vol. 31, p. 171

[32] BERGLUND, S. *et al.*, *Nucl. Instrum.*, **1** (1957) 233; also *Proceedings of the Third International Conference on Ionization Phenomena in Gases*, Venice, 1957

[33] ALLEN, K. W., BODIN, H. A., CURRAN, S. C. and FITCH, R. A., *ibid.*

[34] ALLEN, J. E. and CRAGGS, J. D., *Brit. J. appl. Phys.*, **5** (1954) 446

[35] LEONTOVICH, M. A. and OSOVETS, S. M., *J. nucl. Energy*, **4** (1957) 209

[36] ROSENBLUTH, M. N. *et al.*, *Los Alamos Rep.* LA–1850 (1954)

[37] ALLEN, J. E., *Proc. phys. Soc. Lond.*, **B70** (1957) 24

[38] JUKES, J. D., *A.E.R.E. Rep.* GP/R 2293 (1958); see also *J. fluid Mech.*, **3** (1957) 275

[39] CARRUTHERS, R., *Appl. sci. Res. Hague*, **B5** (1955) 135

[40] CARRUTHERS, R. and DAVENPORT, P. A., *Proc. phys. Soc. Lond.*, **B70** (1957) 49

[41] TIMOFEEVA, G. G. and GRANOVSKII, V. L., *J. exp. theor. Phys.*, **30** (1956) 477

[42] ALLEN, T. K., *Proceedings of the Third International Conference on Ionization Phenomena in Gases*, Venice, 1957

[43] KRUSKAL, M. and SCHWARZSCHILD, M., *Proc. roy. Soc.*, **A223** (1954) 348

[44] ROBERTS, S. J., et al., A.E.R.E. Rep. T/R 1792 (1955)

[45] TAYLER, R. J., Proc. phys. Soc. Lond., **B70** (1957) 31

[46] SHAFRANOV, V. D., J. nucl. Energy, **5** (1957) 86

[47] TAYLER, R. J., Proc. phys. Soc. Lond., **B70** (1957) 1049; also Proceedings of the Third International Conference on Ionization Phenomena in Gases, Venice, 1957

[48] KRUSKAL, M. and TUCK, J. L., Los Alamos Rep. LA–1716 (1953); Proc. roy. Soc., **245** (1958) 222

[49] LEVINE, M. A., Bull. Amer. phys. Soc., **2** (1958) 39

[50] ROSENBLUTH, M. N., Proceedings of the Third International Conference on Ionization Phenomena in Gases, Venice, 1957

[51] BERNSTEIN, I. B. et al., Proc. roy. Soc., **A244** (1958) 17

[52] SUYDAM, B. R., Proceedings of the Second United Nations Conference on the Peaceful Uses of Atomic Energy, Geneva, 1958, Vol. 31, p. 157

[53] TAYLER, R. J., ibid., Vol. 31, p. 160

[54] ATKINSON, R. D'E. and HOUTERMANS, F. G., Z. Phys., **54** (1929) 656

[55] POST, R. F., Rev. mod. Phys., **28** (1956) 338; also Proc. Instn Radio Engrs, N.Y., **45** (1957) 134

[56] TELLER, E., Nucl. Sci. & Engng, **1** (1956) 313

[57] WARE, A. A., Engineering, Lond., **184** (1957) 610

[58] THIRRING, H., Nucleonics, No. 11 (1955) 62

[59] ARNOLD, W. R. et al., Phys. Rev., **93** (1956) 483

[60] HIRST, F., A.E.R.E. Rep. N/M 64 (1953)

[61] GAMOW, G. and CRITCHFIELD, C. L., Theory of Atomic Nucleus and Nuclear Energy Sources; London: Oxford University Press, 1949

[62] THOMPSON, W. B., Proc. phys. Soc. Lond., **B70** (1957) 1

[63] CILLIÉ, G., Mon. Not. R. astr. Soc., **92** (1932) 820

[64] TRUBNIKOV, B. A. et al., Proceedings of the Second United Nations Conference on the Peaceful Uses of Atomic Energy, Geneva, 1958, Vol. 31, p. 93

[65] CHANDRASEKHAR, S., Principles of Stellar Dynamics; Chicago: The University Press, 1942

[66] CHANDRASEKHAR, S., Astrophys. J., **97** (1943) 255

[67] SIMON, A., Proceedings of the Second United Nations Conference on the Peaceful Uses of Atomic Energy, Geneva, 1958, Vol. 32, p. 343; Phys. Rev., **98** (1955) 317; **100** (1955) 1557; also BICKERTON, R. J., Proc. phys. Soc. Lond., **B70** (1957) 305

[68] BOHM, D. in The Characteristics of Electrical Discharges in Magnetic Fields (Ed. by GUTHRIE and WAKERLIN); New York: McGraw-Hill Book Co., 1949

[69] LEHNERT, B., Proceedings of the Second United Nations Conference on the Peaceful Uses of Atomic Energy, Geneva, 1958, Vol. 32, p. 349

[70] GIBSON, A., Proceedings of the Third International Conference on Ionization Phenomena in Gases, Venice, 1957; Nature, Lond., **183** (1959) 101

[71] DREICER, H. and TUCK, J. L., Proceedings of the Second United Nations Conference on the Peaceful Uses of Atomic Energy, Geneva, 1958, Vol. 31, p. 57

[72] PEASE, R. S., Proc. phys. Soc. Lond., **B70** (1957) 11

[73] LAWSON, J. D., ibid., **B70** (1957) 6

BIBLIOGRAPHY

[74] ALLEN, J. E. and ADLAM, J. H., *Proceedings of the Second United Nations Conference on the Peaceful Uses of Atomic Energy*, Geneva, 1958, Vol. 31, p. 221; *Phil. Mag.*, **3** (1958) 448; see also ROSENBLUTH, M. in *Magnetohydrodynamics* (Ed. by R. K. M. LANDSHOFF); Stanford: The University Press, 1957

[75] STIX, T. H. and PALLADINO, R. W., *Proceedings of the Second United Nations Conference on the Peaceful Uses of Atomic Energy*, Geneva, 1958, Vol. 31, p. 282; see also *Phys. Fluids*, **1** (1958) 308; *Phys. Rev.*, **106** (1957) 1146

[76] SPITZER, L., *Phys. Fluids*, **1** (1958) 253

[77] POST, R. F., *Proceedings of the Second United Nations Conference on the Peaceful Uses of Atomic Energy*, Geneva, 1958, Vol. 32, p. 245

[78] BARNETT, C. F. *et al.*, *ibid.*, Vol. 31, p. 298

[79] BOSTICK, W. H., *Phys. Rev.*, **104** (1956) 292; *Proceedings of the Second United Nations Conference on the Peaceful Uses of Atomic Energy*, Geneva, 1958, Vol. 32, p. 427; see also ALFVÉN, H., *ibid.*, Vol. 31, p. 3

[80] FINKELSTEIN, D., SAWYER, G. A. and STRATTON, T. F., *Phys. Fluids*, **1** (1958) 188

[81] BICKERTON, R. J., *Engineering*, **186** (1958) 824; *Proc. Instn elect. Engrs*, **106A** (1959); see also WARE, A. A., *Engineering*, **186** (1958) 796

[82] THONEMANN, P. C. *et al.*, *Nature, Lond.*, **181** (1958) 217

[83] BICKERTON, R. J. and LONDON, H., *Proc. phys. Soc. Lond.*, **72** (1958) 116

[84] HARDING, G. N. *et al.*, *Proceedings of the Second United Nations Conference on the Peaceful Uses of Atomic Energy*, Geneva, 1958, Vol. 32, p. 365

[85] ROSENBLUTH, M. N., *ibid.*, Vol. 31, p. 85

[86] BUTT, E. P. *et al.*, *ibid.*, Vol. 32, p. 42

[87] BRAGINSKY, S. and SHAFRANOV, D., *ibid.*, Vol. 31, p. 43

[88] HUBBARD, J., *A.E.R.E. Rep.* T/R 2668 (1958)

[89] LAING, E. W., *ibid.*, T/M 161 (1958)

[90] KRUSKAL, M. D. *et al.*, *Phys. Fluids*, **1** (1958) 421

[91] KANEKO, S., *J. phys. Soc. Japan*, **13** (1958) 947

[92] KÖRPER, K., *Z. Naturf.* **12a** (1957) 815

[93] TAYLER, R. J., *A.E.R.E. Rep.* T/R 2786, T/R 2787 (1959)

[94] BOON, M. H. *et al.*, *ibid.*, T/R 2503 (1958)

[95] ALLIBONE, T. E. and CHICK, D. R., *Proc. Instn elect. Engrs*, **106A** (1959)

[96] JUKES, J. D., *ibid.*


BIBLIOGRAPHY

BISHOP, A. S., *Project Sherwood*; New York: Addison Wesley, 1958

SIMON, A., *Introduction to Thermonuclear Research*; London: Pergamon Press, 1959

LANDSHOFF, R. K. M. (Ed.), *The Plasma in a Magnetic Field*; Stanford: The University Press, 1958

# 7

# PLASMA OSCILLATIONS AND WAVES

A PLASMA has previously been considered as a substance held in static or dynamic equilibrium by combinations of electric and magnetic fields. On a macroscopic scale it can be thought of as two intermixed compressible fluids of opposite sign, having densities $\rho^+$ and $\rho^-$; if a current flows, they stream in opposite directions with velocities $V^+$ and $V^-$ respectively. Its motion is then described by the usual hydrodynamic equations of force and continuity for a charged fluid streaming in electric and magnetic fields[1-3], with the neutral gas providing a continuous frictional force. Microscopically, the plasma is treated, by the usual gas-kinetic laws, as an assembly of small particles of three kinds—positive, negative and neutral—moving at random and colliding with each other. In all except very high-current discharges there are many more neutral than charged particles, and the equilibrium of the groups of charged particles is maintained by collisions with the neutral particles rather than with each other. In electric fields a relatively small drift velocity is superimposed upon the random velocities of the charges; they gain energy from the field and a new equilibrium is set up at a higher average energy, so that it becomes possible for the three groups to exist in equilibrium at three different temperatures.

Neither of these descriptions is fully adequate, since each assumes complete equilibrium everywhere (or transient changes which are rapidly and steadily restored to equilibrium), and ignores local departures from equilibrium conditions by assemblies of particles on a scale which is large compared with atomic distances but is small compared with the plasma as a whole. For example, a momentary separation of charges in a small volume of the plasma might arise; the mutual electric field of the charges in the displaced volumes produces a restoring force which could lead to consequent oscillatory motion of the charges.

The first observation that periodic fluctuations could occur in an apparently completely stable plasma was made in 1923 by APPLETON and WEBB[4] and shortly afterwards by PENNING[5] (in argon), CLAY[6], and WEBB and PARDUE[7]. They found that the current through a d.c. glow discharge had, superimposed upon it, a small a.c.

component, whose frequency, depending upon discharge conditions, could vary from $10^3$ to more than $10^8$ c/s. These signals could also be picked by metal foil sheets stuck externally on the walls of the discharge tube, acting as the condenser of a resonant circuit. The oscillatory signals were often found to be associated with striations in the discharge, when their frequency was usually about $10^5$ c/s, not of pure sine wave form, but also showing components of other frequencies.

In some recent careful work on moving striations in all the rare gases, Hg, $H_2$ and air, DONAHUE and DIEKE[8] have used a photomultiplier and oscilloscope to examine, simultaneously, fluctuations in the discharge current, voltage and light intensity. With suitable timing it was possible to measure the frequency, velocity and decay of the fluctuations along the tube. Two kinds of moving periodic disturbances were found, one moving towards the anode with speeds from $3 \times 10^3$ to $3 \times 10^4$ cm/sec (these are the striations usually observed by eye), and another moving in the opposite direction at about $10^5$ cm/sec and associated with relatively small fluctuations in light intensity. Their work has shown also that such oscillations are often found in plasma which, to the eye, appear to be completely stable. It thus appears that periodic disturbances propagating through a plasma may be a very common feature of ionized regions; they have been detected and studied also by Emeleus and his colleagues using Langmuir probe methods in a variety of discharges. The experimental work can be found in several recent reviews[9,10]. GABOR[11] has written a general account of plasma oscillations.

## THEORY OF SIMPLE OSCILLATIONS

The first simple treatment of plasma oscillations was given by TONKS and LANGMUIR[12], who considered an idealized plasma with no thermal motion of the ions and electrons, in which two types of oscillation are basically possible: first, electron oscillations which are so fast that the ions can be regarded as stationary, and secondly, ion oscillations which are so slow that the electrons at all times adjust their energy and density so as to remain in equilibrium and satisfy the Boltzmann distribution. The disturbed regions are presumed to contain a large number of particles and to have large dimensions compared with the distances between atoms.

### Electron Oscillations

Imagine, for simplicity, a region of uniform density, $n$ electrons and ions bounded by two imaginary planes perpendicular to the $x$ axis. Let each electron be displaced a small distance $\xi$ in the $x$

direction only, $\xi$ being zero at both boundary planes. The change in density $\delta n$ at some point $x$ is then:

$$\delta n = n \cdot \frac{d\xi}{dx} \qquad \ldots (7.1)$$

Poisson's equation gives, for the field $X$

$$\frac{dX}{dx} = 4\pi ne \frac{d\xi}{dx}$$
$$X = 4\pi ne\xi \qquad \ldots (7.2)$$

(the arbitrary constant, which would represent a steady applied field, is ignored, since $X$ is the electric field arising only from the displacement). Since the force on each electron is $- eX = m\ddot{\xi}$ the following equation of simple harmonic motion is obtained:

$$m\ddot{\xi} + 4\pi ne^2\xi = 0 \qquad \ldots (7.3)$$

The electrons oscillate about a mean position with an angular frequency $\omega_0 = (2\pi f_0)$ where

$$\omega_0^2 = \frac{4\pi ne^2}{m}$$

$$f_0 = \sqrt{\frac{ne^2}{\pi m}} = 8{,}980\sqrt{n} \text{ c/s} \qquad \ldots (7.4)$$

$\omega_0$ is called the 'plasma frequency', and is an important quantity which occurs in the theory of wave propagation (see Chapters 4 and 5) as the critical frequency below which incident waves are reflected from the plasma. In fact it was known as a critical frequency by Rayleigh in the theory of wave propagation long before the treatment described here. $\omega_0$ is now often called quite generally the 'plasma frequency' even when no plasma is present, for example in a charged particle beam.

This derivation, although greatly restricted by simplifying assumptions, shows clearly that the oscillations are longitudinal and stationary, i.e. they do not progress as waves. Neighbouring regions may oscillate in like manner and in some fixed phase relationship, but their motions are quite independent; there is no propagation of the disturbance.

The frequency can, however, be derived quite generally, independently of these assumptions. Following Tonks and Langmuir, two of Maxwell's equations (for free space and with free charges) may be written:

$$\operatorname{curl} X = -\frac{1}{c}\frac{\partial H}{\partial t}; \quad \operatorname{curl} H = \frac{4\pi j}{c} \qquad \ldots(7.5)$$

together with the equations of current flow and force

$$\left.\begin{array}{l} j = \dfrac{1}{4\pi}\dfrac{\partial X}{\partial t} - nev \\[2mm] -m\dfrac{d\mathbf{v}}{dt} = eX + \dfrac{e}{c}.\mathbf{v}\times H \end{array}\right\} \qquad \ldots(7.6)$$

For small oscillations $\mathbf{v}\times H$ can be ignored and for oscillations of electric charges $\partial H/\partial t$ can similarly be ignored. Solution of the remaining equations gives

$$\ddot{X} + \frac{4\pi ne^2}{m}.X = 0 \qquad \ldots(7.5a)$$

which gives the same frequency, but without any restrictions of symmetry. It can be shown that even when magnetic effects occur (i.e. $\partial H/\partial t \neq 0$) a similar equation results. However, if div. $X = 0$ is added to the equations listed, the result is

$$\ddot{X} + \frac{4\pi ne^2}{m}.X = c^2\nabla^2 X \qquad \ldots(7.6a)$$

a solution of which is a plane wave motion which has the relation between frequency, $f$, and wavelength, $\lambda$ (i.e. the dispersion relation)

$$f^2 = \frac{ne^2}{\pi m} + \frac{c^2}{\lambda^2} \qquad \ldots(7.7)$$

For very long wavelengths this also reduces to the plasma frequency.

For ordinary discharges $n \sim 10^{10}$ is a common value, giving $f_0 \sim 10^9$ c/s—a frequency in the microwave region. For plasma in thermonuclear application $n \sim 10^{14}$ or more, giving $f_0 \sim 10^{11}$ c/s.

The reason that electron oscillations do not propagate, according to this simple theory, is the neglect of their thermal motion (see p. 259). Physically it may be seen that slow electrons remain in a given region and, by their contribution to the average space charge, sustain the oscillation; fast electrons, however, contribute nothing to the local space charge but, in traversing the region of disturbance, are accelerated or retarded by the instantaneous electric field thus gaining or losing energy which they can transmit to neighbouring regions.

*Ion Oscillations and Waves*

It is assumed that, as in the case of electrons, ions have a displacement $\xi$:

$$\delta n^+ = n\,\frac{\partial \xi}{\partial x} \qquad \ldots (7.8)$$

Electrons, adjusting themselves to equilibrium, obey Boltzmann's law, and the increase in electron density is:

$$\delta n_e = n[e^{eV/kT_e} - 1] \qquad \ldots (7.9)$$

Poisson's equation gives

$$\frac{\partial X}{\partial x} = -4\pi e(n^+ - n_e) \qquad \ldots (7.10)$$

and the equation of motion of ions, of mass $M$, is:

$$eX = M\,.\,\ddot{\xi} \qquad \ldots (7.11)$$

The solution, expanding and assuming $eV/kT_e \ll 1$, is

$$\frac{\partial^2}{\partial x^2}\left(\ddot{\xi} + \frac{4\pi ne^2}{M}\,\xi\right) - \frac{4\pi ne^2}{kT_e}\,\ddot{\xi} = 0 \qquad \ldots (7.12)$$

One solution capable of simple physical interpretation is a train of plane parallel waves having displacements $\xi = A\cos\left(2\pi ft - \dfrac{2\pi x}{\lambda}\right)$ where:

$$f^2 = \frac{ne^2}{\pi M + ne^2 M\,\dfrac{\lambda^2}{kT_e}} \qquad \ldots (7.13)$$

or

$$f^2 = \frac{f_i^2}{1 + f_i^2\,\dfrac{M\lambda^2}{kT_e}} \qquad \ldots (7.13a)$$

where

$$f_i = \sqrt{\frac{ne^2}{\pi M}}$$

The actual frequency thus depends on the wavelength. When $\lambda$ is small, so that the first term in the denominator is greatest, the ion plasma oscillations are analogous to those of electrons, having a frequency $f_i = \sqrt{\dfrac{ne^2}{\pi M}}$; if $\lambda$ is large and the second term predominates, the oscillations become analogous to sound waves, having

252

the same phase and group velocity $V$, which rapidly approaches the limiting value:

$$V \ (= f\lambda) = \sqrt{kT_e/M} \qquad \ldots\ldots(7.14)$$

It should be noted here that the consideration of random thermal motion has resulted in a progressive wave as distinct from a stationary oscillation. Both the ion and electron oscillations discussed so far are pure electrostatic effects, the field and current fluctuations being in the direction of propagation and not perpendicular as in electromagnetic waves.

The transition from stationary ion oscillations to progressive ion waves occurs at wavelengths which satisfy

$$\pi M \sim \frac{ne^2 M\lambda^2}{kT_e} \qquad \ldots\ldots(7.15)$$

or

$$\lambda \sim \sqrt{\frac{\pi kT_e}{ne^2}} \quad \text{i.e.} \ \sim 2 \cdot \sqrt{2}\pi\lambda_D \qquad \ldots\ldots(7.15a)$$

where $\lambda_D$ is the Debye screening distance.

### Debye Screening

An isolated positive charge placed in space (for example, on a small sphere) gives rise to an electric field $q/r^2$, and a potential $q/r$. If the charge is placed in a neutral ionized medium, however, charge separation takes place to a limited extent and modifies the field. An exact solution is mathematically complicated, and was first solved for a charge immersed in an electrolyte, by DEBYE and HÜCKEL[13]. Following their treatment, a single particle (charge $q$) is studied at some point in the neutral plasma, and an examination made of the way in which the field, due to it, is modified by the ionized medium (the particle is a constituent ion or electron of the plasma itself). Let the potential in a small volume element at a distance, $r$, from $q$ be $V$; this arises from the combined effects of the field due to the charge, $q$, and the charge separation in the plasma which reduces this field. If $q$ is positive then, clearly, the volume element will have a surplus of negative charges and a deficiency of positive ones. It is assumed that the concentrations are given by the Boltzmann distribution law, namely

$$n^+ = n\varepsilon^{-eV/kT}$$

$$n_e = n\varepsilon^{-\left(\frac{-eV}{kT}\right)} = n\varepsilon^{+eV/kT} \qquad \ldots\ldots(7.16)$$

Poisson's equation gives

$$\nabla^2 V = - 4\pi(n^+ - n_e)e$$

$$= 4\pi ne \cdot (\varepsilon^{eV/kT} - \varepsilon^{-eV/kT})$$

$$\approx 4\pi ne \left(\frac{2eV}{kT}\right) \qquad \dots (7.17)$$

$$\approx \frac{8\pi ne^2}{kT} \cdot V = \frac{1}{\lambda_D^2} \cdot V$$

provided that $eV \ll kT$, i.e. that the potential energy of charges due to their separation is small compared with their thermal energy. The factor $8\pi ne^2/kT$ has the dimensions of $1/(\text{length})^2$. In spherical co-ordinates the general solution is:

$$V = A \cdot \frac{\varepsilon^{-r/\lambda_D}}{r} + B \frac{\varepsilon^{r/\lambda_D}}{r} \qquad \dots (7.18)$$

and for physical reasons $B = 0$, since $V$ cannot go to infinity.

Thus the potential in the region surrounding any chosen ion or electron drops as $(q/r) \cdot e^{-r/\lambda_D}$ instead of as $q/r$ in free space. In an approximate fashion the field of the chosen ion can be regarded as being effectively screened off at distances beyond $\lambda_D$, since for $r > \lambda_D$ the potential drops very rapidly in a short distance.

$$\lambda_D = \sqrt{\frac{kT}{8\pi ne^2}} \qquad \dots (7.19)$$

is called the Debye screening distance.

Referring again to the Tonks–Langmuir equation (7.13), it may now be understood that disturbances which show a pattern in space, periodic in distances less than $\lambda_D$, will be chiefly determined by simple electrostatic attractions, whilst those periodic over much longer distances must have arisen by the mass motion and inertia of the vibrating elements of the plasma, i.e. they must be like sound waves.

*Thomson's Theory*

Very similar results for ion waves in plasma were found by THOMSON[14], who used the equation of continuity:

$$\frac{dn}{dt} = \text{div.} \, (nv) \qquad \dots (7.20)$$

254

for each type of particle, and the equations of transference:

$$\frac{\mathrm{d}}{\mathrm{d}t}\,(n_e\bar{v}_e) + \frac{\mathrm{d}}{\mathrm{d}x}\,(n_e\overline{v_e^2}) = -\frac{Xen_e}{m} + \frac{P}{m}\ \text{for electrons}$$

$$....(7.21)$$

$$\frac{\mathrm{d}}{\mathrm{d}t}\,(n_+\bar{v}_+) + \frac{\mathrm{d}}{\mathrm{d}x}\,(n_+\overline{v_+^2}) = \frac{Xen_+}{M} - \frac{P}{M}\ \text{for ions}$$

Here $P$ is the momentum transferred per second to the electrons in unit volume by impacts of positive ions, and is of the form $n_e n_+(v_e - v_+)$. The $v$'s are the random velocities in one direction only, and $n_e$, $n_+$ are the instantaneous local values of electron and ion density, slightly perturbed from their normal equilibrium values which are equal $(= n)$. These, combined with Poisson's equation, lead to two equations for the electron and ion oscillations very similar to those of Langmuir and Tonks but with the addition of terms giving the random energy of electrons and ions:

$$f_e^2 = \frac{\kappa T_e}{\lambda^2 m} + \frac{ne^2}{\pi m}\ \text{for electrons}\qquad ....(7.22)$$

[or $\omega^2 = \omega_0^2 + \kappa T_e m \,.\, k^2$ where $k$ is the propagation constant $(= 2\pi/\lambda)$].

$$f_+^2 = \frac{\kappa T_+}{\lambda^2 M} + \frac{f_i^2}{1 + f_i^2 \dfrac{\lambda^2 M}{\kappa T_e}}\ \text{for ions}\qquad ....(7.23)$$

where $f_i = \sqrt{\dfrac{ne^2}{\pi M}}$ as before.

Here, again, the inclusion of the random motion has resulted in a progressing electron wave. Its phase velocity must exceed $\sqrt{\overline{v_e^2}}$ $\left(= \sqrt{\dfrac{\kappa T_e}{m}}\ \text{in one dimension}\right)$, but only waves of frequency greater than $\sqrt{\dfrac{ne^2}{\pi m}}$, the critical frequency, are transmitted. Ion waves are of the same form as equation (7.13) except for the small additional random term.

### MORE GENERAL THEORIES

The treatments just described are much simplified, giving, in particular, no indication how the oscillations arise, and the thermal motion of the particles is included only by their average velocity or temperature. Furthermore, no prediction of the amplitudes of oscillations at different frequencies can be made; this is, of course, a consequence of simplifying the equations to linear form, i.e. neglecting all squares and higher powers of the perturbed quantities [e.g. in Thomson's theory, assuming $(n_e - n)^2$ to be negligible]. However, the non-linear equations are so difficult that few attempts have been made, even in the most sophisticated theories, to treat them.

The first step towards a more rigorous treatment is to consider what effect an arbitrary perturbation (i.e. change of particle densities at some point, resulting in a net charge or a displacement of certain particles) will have on the distribution, both in energy and space, of the charged particles. The earliest attempts were due to VLASOV[15,16], who used the Boltzmann transfer equation*, but neglected the term describing the rate of change of the distribution due to collisions and replaced it by one depending on the mutual electrostatic forces between elementary volumes containing numbers of charges ('collective' or 'co-operative' effects). It should be mentioned here that all the theories to be described proceed on the Hartree self-consistent field approximation, that is to say the behaviour of one electron is considered as a particle, whilst the effect of all the surrounding particles is replaced by their resultant field smoothed out in space and averaged in time. The physical justification is that, since electrostatic forces have such long range, any one electron suffers, simultaneously, small forces from a very large number of surrounding charged particles, as well as relatively large forces from its nearest neighbours. (The validity of this approach has recently been discussed by ECKER[17].)

In this method of solution Vlasov assumed disturbances of the form $e^{i(\omega t + \mathbf{k} \cdot \mathbf{r})}$, $\omega$ being the angular frequency and $\mathbf{k}$ the propagation constant $(2\pi/\lambda)$, and found a number of discrete values (eigenvalues) of $\omega$ and $\mathbf{k}$ which satisfied the equations. From this he concluded that a plasma assumes, spontaneously, a crystal-like structure periodic in space. However, certain mathematical errors in his treatment were pointed out by LANDAU[18], who showed that disturbances need not be of the form $e^{i(\omega t + \mathbf{k} \cdot \mathbf{r})}$ but can be of arbitrary initial form expressed as the sum of a Fourier series. The basic equations are set up as follows, assuming that the frequency of the vibrations is so rapid that collisions between ions and electrons may be neglected compared with the electrostatic effects, which are, of course, continuous. Let $F$ represent the distribution in space,

---

* Compare the use of this equation in rigorous theories of high-frequency discharges, superseding simpler theories in which averaged values are used in the initial equations.

velocity and time of the electrons which are perturbed from their equilibrium Maxwellian distribution $f_0(v)$ which is uniform in space. Then

$$F = f_0(v) + f(\mathbf{v}, \mathbf{r}, t) \qquad \dots (7.24)$$

$f$ being a perturbation, small compared with $f_0$. The transfer equation, neglecting collisions, is

$$\frac{\partial f}{\partial t} + \mathbf{v} \operatorname{grad} f + \frac{eX}{m} \frac{\partial f_0}{\partial \mathbf{v}} = 0 \qquad \dots (7.25)$$

Poisson's equation:

$$\operatorname{grad} X = -4\pi e \int f \cdot d\tau \qquad \dots (7.26)$$

where $d\tau = dv_x \, dv_y \, dv_z$, completes the set of equations. $X$, here, is the field set up by the arbitrary separation of charge; the equilibrium component, $e \int f_0 \, d\tau$, is cancelled by the similar integral for positive ions.

Landau now assumes an initial arbitrary distribution, which can be expanded into Fourier integrals (integrated in space, i.e. with respect to $x, y, z$), and since the last two equations are linear and do not contain $x, y, z$ explicitly, they can be written separately for each Fourier component. It is thus sufficient to consider solutions of the form:

$$f_k(\mathbf{v}, t) \cdot e^{i\mathbf{k}\mathbf{r}} \qquad \dots (7.27)$$

The actual details of the solution will not be given here. The method avoids the difficulties of Vlasov's treatment, and shows that, in fact, there are no discrete states of vibration of the electrons. For any given value of $k$, arbitrary values of $\omega$ are generally possible; it is also shown that all electronic vibrations are damped. For long waves $(k \to 0)$ the damping is small, the wave amplitude decreasing as $e^{-\gamma t}$ where

$$\gamma = \omega_0 \sqrt{\frac{\pi}{8}} \cdot \frac{1}{(\lambda_D k)^3} \cdot e^{-\left(\frac{\lambda_D k}{2}\right)^2} \qquad \dots (7.28)$$

where $\lambda_D$ is the Debye screening distance. At the opposite limit, very short waves, the damping is very much greater. In these limiting conditions $(\lambda \to \infty$ and $\lambda \to 0)$ Landau also derives dispersion relations, i.e. dependences of $\omega$ on $k$.

A somewhat different, and rather more complicated, general theory has been developed by Twiss[19], who treats the propagation of electromagnetic waves in electron–ion streams, and extends the solution to a continuous velocity distribution.

In criticism of Vlasov's treatment, Landau points out that since the Boltzmann equation is six-dimensional, an explicit dispersion formula could only result if some restrictions were imposed, and that these restrictions were inherent in the type of solution assumed. The physical reason for this can be found by considering the theory of BOHM and GROSS[20].

These authors assume solutions for the potential distribution $\phi$ varying as $\phi_0 \cos(kx - \omega t)$, noting that any small disturbances, for which the plasma acts as a refracting medium, can be represented as the sum of such wave functions, provided that $\omega$ and $k$ satisfy a certain dispersion relation (which is to be found). The problem

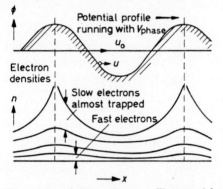

*Figure 7.1. The trapping of electrons by a travelling potential wave, and the consequent distribution of density.* (From D. GABOR[11], by courtesy of British Journal of Applied Physics)

can be simplified by choosing a co-ordinate system in which the wave is at rest, i.e. one moving in the direction of the wave with the phase velocity $v_{\text{phase}} = \omega/k$. The potential is then represented by $\phi = \phi_0 \cos kx$, and the electrons which have a thermal velocity, $v$, stream past it at a mean relative speed $u_0 = v - v_{\text{phase}}$ (here $v$ is the $x$ component of the random velocity). An important physical consequence can now be seen: particles having random velocities very different from the wave velocity stream past suffering only small periodic changes, whereas those close to the wave velocity may not have enough kinetic energy to surmount the potential crests of the wave. These latter are carried forward with the wave at the phase velocity, oscillating slightly in the potential troughs; they are termed trapped electrons. To avoid trapping (see *Figure 7.1*)

$$\tfrac{1}{2}mu^2 \geqslant \tfrac{1}{2}mu_0^2 + e\phi_0 \qquad \ldots\ldots(7.29)$$

For long waves (i.e. small $k = 2\pi/\lambda$) with phase velocities very much larger than the random thermal velocities, the number of trapped electrons will be very small and their presence can be neglected in a first approximation. The contribution to the total space charge of each group of electrons, $dn = f(v) \, dv$, in the velocity distribution (assumed Maxwellian) can be found since each group has an effect inversely proportional to its relative velocity. The total density within the wave structure is:

$$n_e = n_0 \int \frac{u_0}{u} f(v) \, dv = n_0 \int_{-\infty}^{\infty} \frac{f(v) \, dv}{\sqrt{1 + \dfrac{2e\phi}{mu_0^2}}} \quad \ldots (7.30)$$

The positive ion density is, of course, assumed to remain constant at the unperturbed value $n_0$, and so when Poisson's equation is applied, the resulting potential distribution in the wave is:

$$-\nabla^2\phi = 4\pi n_0 e \left\{ 1 - \int_{-\infty}^{\infty} \frac{f(v)(v - v_{\text{phase}}) \, dv}{\sqrt{(v - v_{\text{phase}})^2 + \dfrac{2e\phi}{m}}} \right\} \quad \ldots (7.31)$$

which must equal $k^2\phi$ to give the potential originally assumed, and make the treatment self-consistent; this is not, of course, the most general solution. Bohm and Gross solve this with certain approximations and restrictions: in particular they assume that the relative energy $\frac{1}{2}mu^2$ of the electrons to be much greater than $e\phi_0$, so that they suffer only minor fluctuations as the wave passes. The equation reduces to:

$$k^2\phi = \frac{4\pi n_0 e^2}{m} \, \phi \int \frac{f(v) \, dv}{(v - v_{\text{phase}})^2} \quad \ldots (7.32)$$

Here it is essential that when $v = v_{\text{phase}}$, $f(v) = 0$, otherwise the integration cannot be performed, since the expression has an infinity at this point. Physically, this means that it must be assumed there are no electrons moving with the phase velocity. In fact, to obtain an explicit solution all electrons of velocities greater than $v_{\text{phase}}$ are neglected, finally giving

$$\left( \frac{k}{\omega_0} \right)^2 = \int \frac{f(v) \, dv}{(v - \omega/k)^2} \quad \ldots (7.33)$$

which reduces approximately (neglecting all $v > \omega/k$) to:

$$\omega^2 = \omega_v^2 + \overline{v^2} k^2$$
$$= \omega_0^2 + \left( \frac{3\kappa T}{m} \right) k^2 \quad \ldots (7.34)$$

259

This may be compared with Thomson's solution [equation (7.22)], although physical conditions are quite different (see p. 265).

Quite apart from its own merits this presentation sheds light on previous results. It shows that an important group of electrons can exist trapped in the potential wave and travelling with the phase velocity, and that the restrictions implicit in Vlasov's treatment (criticized by Landau on mathematical grounds) amount in fact to their being neglected.

A physical picture of Landau damping, i.e. without collisions, now emerges. Electrons having velocity components close to the phase velocity are trapped and carried along with the wave; finally, they all move with a mean velocity, $v_{\text{phase}}$, those originally moving slower having been accelerated, and vice versa. Assuming $v_{\text{phase}} \gg \sqrt{\overline{v^2}}$, and a Maxwellian type distribution, it follows that there were originally more slower electrons trapped than faster, hence the trapped group has, in total, gained kinetic energy from the electric field of the wave, which is therefore damped (waves with $v_{\text{phase}} \lesssim \sqrt{\overline{v^2}}$ can be ignored, because if $\omega/k \sim \omega_0/k \lesssim \sqrt{\overline{v^2}}$ then $\lambda \lesssim \lambda_D$; such waves are damped by thermal motion). Any distribution function decreasing towards higher velocities must lead to damped waves; conversely, functions which increase at higher velocities (provided $v \gg \sqrt{\overline{v^2}}$) can lead to amplified waves (electrostatic instabilities). Rigorous analysis confirms this (see pp. 263, 270).

When the effect of these trapped electrons is included then it can be shown that almost any combination of $k$ and $\omega$ can be obtained, depending on the initial conditions. The results of several authors are summarized in *Table 7.1*.

*Table 7.1*

| Assumptions | Results |
| --- | --- |
| TONKS and LANGMUIR[12]<br>All fluctuating quantities vary as $e^{i(kx - \omega t)}$: electrons have no thermal motion. | One frequency of oscillation<br>$$\omega = \omega_0 = \sqrt{\frac{4\pi n e^2}{m}},$$<br>with any wavelength. |
| VLASOV[15,16], BOHM and GROSS[20]<br>All fluctuating quantities vary as $e^{i(kx - \omega t)}$: electrons have thermal motion. | Continuous frequency spectrum for $\omega \geqslant \omega_0$. Undamped waves<br>$$\omega^2 \approx \omega_0^2 + 3k^2\overline{v^2}$$ |
| LANDAU[18]<br>Electrons have thermal motion. Arbitrary initial conditions are imposed. | Continuous frequency spectrum for $\omega \geqslant \omega_0$. Damped waves (i.e. $k$ complex) $\omega^2 \approx \omega_0^2 + 3(\mathscr{R}k)^2\overline{v^2}$ |

The discrepancies between these results have been largely explained and clarified by the work of BERZ[21], who uses the Boltzmann equation and Poisson's equation, but assumes only that the fluctuating component of the electric field varies as $e^{i(kx-\omega t)}$. The fluctuating component of the distribution function is not assumed to vary in this fashion but remains to be determined.

Let $f_0(v, x, t)$ be the distribution function in the steady state, where $v$ is the electron velocity in the $x$ direction: $f_0 + \tilde{f}$ is the actual value in the presence of oscillations and $\tilde{X}$ is the oscillating electric field. Collisions are neglected as also are products of fluctuating variables, i.e. the plasma frequency is assumed to be much greater than the collision frequency and the oscillating components are regarded as small.

The essential new feature of Berz' results is that, by standard methods of solution (with $k$ real), $\tilde{f}$ can be derived:

$$\tilde{f} = f(v, t)\, e^{ikx} \qquad \ldots (7.35)$$

where

$$f(v, t) = -\, i\, \frac{eX}{m}\, \frac{f'(v)}{kv - \omega}\, e^{-i\omega t} - i\, \frac{e}{m}\, C(v)\, e^{-ikvt} \quad \ldots (7.36)$$

where $C(v)$ is a completely arbitrary function. Any function $C(v)$ satisfies the equations (i.e. Boltzmann and Poisson), and the value to be assigned to it depends entirely on the initial conditions. If, now, one takes any value of $\omega$ having a small negative imaginary component $\mathscr{I}\omega < 0$ (i.e. damped waves) the result becomes

$$\tilde{f}(v, x, t) = -\, i\, \frac{eX}{m} \cdot \frac{f_0'}{kv - \omega} \cdot e^{i(kx - \omega t)} + i\, \frac{eX}{m} \cdot \frac{C_0 k}{kv - \omega} \cdot e^{ik(x - vt)}$$
$$\ldots (7.37)$$

where $C_0$ is a constant. The dispersion relation for these damped waves is

$$\left(\frac{k}{\omega_0}\right)^2 = \int_{-\infty}^{\infty} \frac{f_0'(v)}{v - \omega/k}\, dv + 2\pi i k C_0 \qquad \ldots (7.38)$$

Thus for any real value of $k$, i.e. any wavelength, any value of $\omega$, i.e. any frequency (provided it has a negative imaginary component) is possible for these damped waves, the only condition being that $C_0$, which depends on the initial conditions, is suitably chosen.

Now if it is assumed that $\tilde{f}$ varies like $\tilde{X}$ in space and time it follows, from equation (7.37), that $C_0 = 0$. This is the condition imposed in the treatments of Vlasov and Bohm and Gross; in equation (7.38) only the first term on the right-hand side remains and this, when integrated by parts, reduces to equation (7.33).

Referring to equation (7.37), the second term represents an addition of the form

$$\frac{C_0 X}{v - \omega/k} \cdot \cos k(x - vt) \qquad \dots (7.39)$$

to the distribution assumed by previous authors. This expression represents a velocity distribution which is carried along with the electron velocity $v$, and is therefore dispersed in space; the electron density waves do not keep together but flow apart. This represents a source of damping.

If a value of $\omega$ is now chosen having a positive imaginary component ($\mathscr{I}\omega > 0$, corresponding to amplified waves), then it can

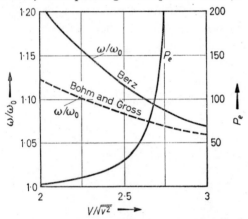

*Figure 7.2. Damping of plasma waves (without collisions) after Berz. $P_e$ is the number of periods in which the intensity of the waves falls by a factor $e$.*
(From D. GABOR, in: Electromagnetic Wave Theory Symposium)

be shown that the additional term is zero, and that the dispersion relation is, again, that found by Bohm and Gross [equation (7.38) with $C_0 = 0$]. Hence only that component of $\tilde{f}$ which varies as the electric field, i.e. as $e^{i(kx - \omega t)}$, plays any part in the sustaining of amplified plasma waves, but such waves are entirely determined by the equilibrium properties of the plasma, independently of the initial conditions. However, the general dispersion relation for amplified waves,

$$\left(\frac{k}{\omega_0}\right)^2 = \int_{-\infty}^{\infty} \frac{f_0'(v)}{v - \omega/k} \, dv \qquad \dots (7.40)$$

has no solution, and hence no amplified waves arise, except for

262

certain restricted kinds of velocity distribution, $f_0$. Isotropic distributions of a Maxwellian type do not fulfil these requirements and always lead to damped waves, except for the particular solution $\omega = \omega_0$, $k = 0$ (i.e. the simple Langmuir–Tonks equation which describes oscillations, but not waves). In general, damped waves always exist; amplified or undamped waves either do not exist at all, or are finite in number.

Here it should be noted that these particular results refer to damping in time, since $k$ has been assumed real, and describe what happens at some subsequent time, $t$, to a disturbance initially periodic in space. By assuming $\omega$ real and $k$ complex one can deduce, with similar results, the propagation in space of a disturbance which is constantly generated in time at $x = 0$ (see p. 270). Some of these results are illustrated in *Figure 7.2*.

SUMMARY OF DISPERSION RELATIONS

A concise account and correlation of the results of many authors has been given by VAN KAMPEN[22]. We begin fundamentally with the Boltzmann transfer equation in its full form, and Poisson's equation:

$$\frac{\partial f}{\partial t} + \mathbf{v}\,\frac{\partial f}{\partial \mathbf{r}} + \frac{e}{m}\cdot X\cdot\frac{\partial f}{\partial \mathbf{v}} = \left(\frac{\partial f}{\partial t}\right)_{\text{collisions}} \quad \ldots(7.41)$$

$$\text{div. } X = 4\pi e \int [f(\mathbf{r}, \mathbf{v}, t) - f_0(\mathbf{v})]\,\mathrm{d}\mathbf{v} = 4\pi e(n - n_0) \quad \ldots(7.42)$$

where $f_0$, $n_0$ represent the equilibrium distribution and density; $f$ is related to the instantaneous particle density $n(\mathbf{r}, t)$ by

$$\int_{-\infty}^{\infty} f(\mathbf{r}, \mathbf{v}, t)\,\mathrm{d}\mathbf{v} = n \quad \ldots(7.43)$$

The right-hand term $\left(\dfrac{\partial f}{\partial t}\right)_{\text{collisions}}$ incorporates effects due to collisions with heavy ions or uncharged particles, all short-range forces and the effects on an electron due to rapid fluctuations in the local value of $X$ caused by movements of its near neighbours.

Two limiting conditions arise: first, when collisions are very frequent and rapidly establish local equilibrium, so that the velocity distribution has its equilibrium form everywhere and at all times (for example, Maxwellian). The behaviour of the plasma is then described by macroscopic hydrodynamic equations, using average values, which can be derived from the Boltzmann equation. For example, in one dimension only, integration of equation (7.41) leads to the equation of continuity:

$$\frac{\partial n}{\partial t} + \frac{\partial}{\partial x}(n\bar{v}) = 0 \quad \ldots(7.44)$$

since collisions do not alter $n$ (integration of the right-hand side gives zero). Conservation of momentum and energy give respectively

$$\frac{\partial}{\partial t}(n\bar{v}) + \frac{\partial}{\partial t}(n\overline{v^2}) - \frac{e}{m}Xn = 0 \qquad \ldots\ldots(7.45)$$

$$\frac{\partial}{\partial t}(n\overline{v^2}) + \frac{\partial}{\partial t}(n\overline{v^3}) - \frac{e}{m}Xn\bar{v} = 0 \qquad \ldots\ldots(7.46)$$

These are Maxwell's transport equations[23]. If a Maxwellian energy distribution of mean velocity, $u$, is assumed everywhere:

$$f(x, v, t) = n\sqrt{\frac{2\pi kT}{m}}\,e^{-\frac{1}{2}m(v-u)^2/\kappa T} \qquad \ldots\ldots(7.47)$$

there are enough equations to solve the unknown quantities $n$, $u$ and $T$. All the averages of $v$ depend only on $u$ and $T$, in particular

$$\bar{v} = u;\quad \overline{v^2} = u^2 + \frac{\kappa T}{m};\quad \overline{v^3} = u^3 + 3u\frac{\kappa T}{m} \quad \ldots\ldots(7.48)$$

To solve these equations in the form of plane waves put $n = n_0 + \tilde{n}$; $T = T_0 + \tilde{T}$, and ignore all except first powers of the small perturbations $\tilde{n}$, $\tilde{T}$, of the equilibrium values $n_0$, $T_0$. This is essentially the procedure adopted by Thomson and in a more general and complicated theory by BAILEY[24] who includes the effects of static electric and magnetic fields. However, these authors assume $\tilde{T} = 0$, and thus do not invoke the conservation of energy equation. van Kampen has shown that this assumption leads to an inconsistency in the equations, since by the gas laws, fluctuations in density and temperature are connected. This approximation is equivalent to assuming that local compressions and rarefactions are isothermal, not adiabatic, and leads to the incorrect result

$$\omega^2 = \omega_0^2 + \frac{\kappa T}{m} \cdot k^2 \qquad \ldots\ldots(7.49)$$

whereas a full solution leads, for plane waves, to

$$\omega^2 = \omega_0^2 + 3\frac{\kappa T}{m} \cdot k^2 \qquad \ldots\ldots(7.50)$$

and in a proper three-dimensional treatment, to

$$\omega^2 = \omega_0^2 + \frac{5}{3}\frac{\kappa T}{m} \cdot k^2 \qquad \ldots\ldots(7.51)$$

It must be emphasized that this treatment is not an alternative to the rigorous methods used by Landau, Berz and others, but is applicable to completely different physical conditions, namely many collisions per oscillation $(\nu \gg \omega)$. The resemblance between equation (7.50) and the results of Vlasov, Bohm and Gross is therefore accidental.

It is interesting to note that PIDDINGTON[25], by a method similar to Bailey but ignoring his drift currents (using Maxwell's electromagnetic equations and his transport equation), shows that four types of waves can be propagated in an ionized medium (his resulting equation is of the fourth degree in $\omega^2$). Two of these reduce to the ordinary and extraordinary rays of the usual magnetoionic theory (see Chapter 5), the third to the Tonks–Langmuir electrostatic waves and the fourth, which arises from the motion of positive ions, are magnetohydrodynamic sound waves.

The second limiting condition arises when collisions are so infrequent that the fluctuations are due entirely to long-range electrostatic forces. Here the term $(\partial f/\partial t)_{\text{collisions}}$ may be neglected entirely, and the local variations in the velocity distribution are the dominating factor in the growth of the waves. The detailed solutions of Boltzmann's and Poisson's equations were discussed on pp. 256–261; they lead rigorously to no specific dispersion relation, but describe damped, undamped and amplified waves depending on initial conditions and the particular form of velocity distribution of the electrons. In some approximate treatments it has been necessary to postulate a 'cut-off' velocity distribution, i.e. one which has no electrons with speeds above $v_{\text{max.}}$ and theory shows here that for any wavelength $\lambda$ it is possible to have any arbitrary frequency $f$ provided that the phase velocity $f\lambda$ ($= \omega/k$) is less than $v_{\text{max.}}$. This is to be expected on physical grounds, since any given disturbance (e.g. a fluctuation in spatial density) could be propagated with a chosen phase velocity by imposing it on particles which have just that velocity in the desired direction, so that it is carried along bodily. In practice this is not possible, except in carefully defined beams; the fluctuation is impressed upon electrons of many different velocities, and each velocity group propagates its own component, with the result that the disturbance is spread out in space. This normally results in damped waves and, in exceptional circumstances when the velocity distribution is such that the phases of these advancing fluctuations are favourable, in amplified waves. However, as van Kampen points out, the only solutions which can be physically observed are those which exhibit steady periodic behaviour for a sufficiently long time, and these obey the dispersion relation of equation (7.50), as found by Vlasov, Bohm and Gross.

Many experimental observations are consistent with these results. Plasma waves have been detected in a narrow band[5],[26] close to $\omega_0$; it must be remembered that the term $3 \dfrac{\kappa T}{m} \cdot k^2$ is small compared with $\omega_0^2$ so that wide variations of wavelength make little difference to the observed frequency, and also that frequencies much different from $\omega_0$ are heavily damped. Fluctuations have also been detected covering a broad frequency band from about $\omega_i = \sqrt{\dfrac{4\pi n e^2}{M}}$ downwards[8],[27],[28], although it is not certain whether these are the ion waves derived from the linear (and hence small amplitude) theory, since they are often associated with positive striations which have potential maxima and minima comparable with the ionization potential of the gas[10].

AMPLITUDE OF PLASMA OSCILLATIONS: NON-LINEAR THEORY

Inclusion of any terms other than linear in the small quantities (e.g. $\tilde{f}$, $\tilde{X}$, $\tilde{n}$) representing the departure from equilibrium state, generally makes the resulting equations intractable. However, there have been several attempts to treat the non-linear equations, although they have mostly been restricted only to plasma oscillations, not propagating waves. A straightforward derivation is given by AMER[29]; taking a surplus or deficiency of electrons per cm³ $\rho = n - n_0$ (i.e. $= \tilde{n}$), occurring in a region of constant uniform positive charge density $n_0$, he uses the equation of continuity, Poisson's equation and the equation of motion of an electron in the local electric field, to give the exact equation:

$$\ddot{\rho} - \frac{\dot{\rho}^2}{n_0 + \rho} + \omega_0^2 \rho \left(1 + \frac{\rho}{n_0}\right) = 0 \qquad \ldots (7.52)$$

If non-linear terms are neglected this reduces to the Langmuir–Tonks equation. A quantity $a_0$, related to the amplitude of oscillations, is now introduced, defined by:

$$\dot{\rho}_{t=0} = a_0 \omega_0 \qquad \ldots (7.53)$$

An exact first integration shows that the oscillations are asymmetrical:

$$\rho_{\text{max.}} = a_0 + \frac{a_0^2}{3n_0}; \quad \rho_{\text{min.}} = -a_0 + \frac{a_0^2}{3n_0} \qquad \ldots (7.54)$$

Further approximate integrations lead to the explicit form

$$\rho = \frac{a_0 \sin \omega t - a_0^2/2n_0}{1 - \dfrac{1}{n_0} \cdot a_0 \sin \omega t} \qquad \ldots(7.55)$$

and the relation between frequency and amplitude

$$\frac{\omega}{\omega_0} = \sqrt{1 - \left(\frac{a_0}{n_0}\right)^2} \qquad \ldots(7.56)$$

A somewhat more approximate treatment of spherical oscillations is also given.

GOLD[30] tackles a similar problem for a plasma, through which a current flows, of density:

$$j = j_e + j_+ \approx j_e = nev \qquad \ldots(7.57)$$

$v$ being the velocity of the electrons. For stationary oscillations the variation of the local electric field $X$ in space and time are related by

$$\frac{dX}{dx} = \frac{dX}{dt} \cdot \frac{dt}{dx} = \frac{1}{v} \frac{dX}{dt} \qquad \ldots(7.58)$$

When these are combined with Poisson's equation and the equation of motion of the electron, there results a second order equation for the velocity of the electrons. Insertion in equation (7.58) above, gives $X$ as a function of time and hence the intensity, $I$, of the waves ($\propto X^2$). This leads to:

$$I \propto \left(v_0 - \frac{j}{n_+}\right)^2 \cdot \frac{4\pi n_+ m}{e} \qquad \ldots(7.59)$$

where $v_0$ is the electron velocity at $t = 0$ and $n_+$ is the equilibrium ion density. No assumption is made here about the neutrality of the plasma. Further treatment, including the effects of collisions, shows that dense plasma favours strong oscillations, provided the collision frequency is not too great. The behaviour in a superimposed magnetic field is also treated, and it is shown that when small currents flow in the plasma, an increasing magnetic field increases the amplitude of oscillations to a saturation value. If large currents flow, however, strong magnetic fields reduce the amplitude of oscillation, this effect being pronounced as the Larmor frequency approaches and exceeds the plasma frequency ($\omega_H \gtrsim \omega_0$). In passing, it may be noted that if electrons move with relativistic speeds their change of mass with velocity leads to a

267

dependence of amplitude upon frequency[31]. The simplest equation of motion is:

$$\ddot{p} + \frac{\omega_0^2}{\sqrt{1 + p^2/mc^2}} \cdot p = 0 \qquad \dots (7.60)$$

where $p$ is the momentum of the electron. More general accounts of non-linear effects have been given by Russian workers[32,33], and by STURROCK[55] and DAWSON[56]. The latter consider the fine scale mixing which occurs when the amplitude of motion of the electrons becomes comparable with the wavelength.

### OSCILLATIONS IN ELECTRON BEAMS: BEAMS IN PLASMA

The first clear indication that a simple electron beam could give oscillations within its own structure was provided by the experiments of MERRILL and WEBB[34], who showed by probe measurements that the electrons from the cathode of an arc were scattered within a narrow region only a fraction of a millimetre long. They found, on the far side of this region, electrons having a Maxwellian energy distribution (mean energy $\sim 4$ eV) superimposed on a stream of fast electrons from the cathode. A crystal detector showed the presence of strong stable plasma oscillations (of frequency about $\omega_0$) in this region (similar velocity scattering of initially homogeneous beams had earlier been noticed by LANGMUIR and MOTT-SMITH[35] and DITTMER[36]). Here it should be noted that the scattering is mainly a modulation of the velocity of the electrons in their original direction, due to potential fluctuations along the beam, and not a scattering in direction due to collisions. These results have been confirmed by later experiments[37-40]. Some electrons on the anode side of the scattering region frequently have more energy than on the cathode side, although their mean energy on the average is unchanged. Clearly, space-charge oscillations, with their associated potential wave form, are being sustained by the kinetic energy of the incident electrons.

The theory of these waves was developed independently by HAEFF[41] and PIERCE[42], the former considering only electron beams and the latter the effect of positive ions. Since we are concerned only with fluctuations in space charge, this makes no difference to the result. Haeff considers first two electron streams of densities $n_1$ and $n_2$, velocities $v_1$ and $v_2$ and current densities $j_1$ and $j_2$ respectively. The total densities $\rho$ and $j$ are the sum of the two components. The fundamental equations (in one co-ordinate) are:

(a) Poisson's:

$$\frac{d^2V}{dx^2} = 4\pi ne \qquad \dots (7.61)$$

(b) Conservation of electric charge:

$$\frac{\partial j}{\partial x} = \frac{\partial \rho}{\partial t} = \frac{\partial}{\partial t} (ne) \qquad \ldots (7.62)$$

and the force on an electron

$$e \cdot \operatorname{grad} V = m \frac{dv}{dt} = m \left( \frac{\partial v}{\partial t} + v \cdot \frac{\partial v}{\partial x} \right) \qquad \ldots (7.63)$$

These are applied separately to the two beams, and one looks for mutually consistent periodic solutions of the form

$$V = V_0 e^{i(kx - \omega t)} \qquad \ldots (7.64)$$

There results the dispersion law:

$$\frac{\omega_1^2}{(\omega - v_1 k)^2} + \frac{\omega_2^2}{(\omega - v_2 k)^2} = 1 \qquad \ldots (7.65)$$

where $\omega_1$ and $\omega_2$ are the plasma frequencies of the two beams given by

$$\omega_{1,2}^2 = \frac{4\pi e^2 n_{1,2}}{m} \qquad \ldots (7.66)$$

This result can be made quite general for any number of parallel beams of different velocities.

It can be shown that, within certain limits, the solution of equation (7.65) for real values of $\omega$, leads to complex values of $k$. Some of these have a negative imaginary part which, from equation (7.64), implies a travelling wave whose amplitude increases exponentially in the $x$ direction. It is known that small signals of appropriate frequency are amplified along electron beams and there is good agreement between the experimentally observed gain of such beam devices and the analysis given here. However some caution is necessary in applying these theoretical results because, as Twiss[19] has pointed out, insertion of a real $k$ would give complex solutions for $\omega$ indicating that a given periodicity in space could increase rapidly in time (i.e. be unstable), and it is known that this does not happen. The proper solution, describing what is physically possible, is obtained only when the boundary conditions are added to equation (7.65), but little work on this has been carried out.

The oscillations found in such beams are termed slipping stream oscillations, and they arise because the kinetic energy of groups of electrons is periodically converted into potential energy of the electric fields associated with the fluctuations in space charge, the electrons themselves being alternately accelerated and retarded.

It is natural to think of this mechanism as one means whereby oscillations in a normal neutral plasma might be excited, especially since the ions provide a stationary background to the rapidly moving electrons, selected groups of which might be regarded instantaneously as parallel beams. Several workers have investigated, theoretically, what happens when a beam of particles (usually electrons) is fired into a region containing particles of opposite sign, or into a neutral plasma. BUNEMAN[43] has treated the first condition, regarding it as a particular example of two-stream oscillations, one being the electrons, the other the ions. He deduces that a very turbulent plasma results, oscillations being sustained with an energy corresponding to the average d.c. electron velocity, and a consequent lower electrical conductivity and higher loss of energy by Bremsstrahlung (due to coherence) than would be expected from ordinary elastic collision theory. On the other hand AUER[44], extending the results of Landau and Berz to fully ionized plasma, shows that any velocity distribution having a single peak, and regardless of symmetry, is stable in the sense that only damped waves result. He shows that a plasma carrying a directed current of density $j$ is certainly stable in this way, provided

$$j \leqslant n_0 e \cdot f\left(\frac{M}{m}\right) \cdot \sqrt{\frac{2\kappa T}{M_+}} \qquad \ldots (7.67)$$

$M$ being the mass of the ion and $n_0$ the equilibrium density; $f(M/m)$ is a function of order unity. Rearrangement of this formula shows that, to ensure stability, the drift velocity of electrons must be less than the random velocity of ions. Similar treatments show that any electron velocity distribution having a double peak with an intervening minimum may, but do not necessarily, lead to electrostatic instabilities. Our simple physical picture of Landau damping (p. 260) suggests that waves having phase velocities in the range of the rising part of the distribution curve should be amplified. Whether this leads to an instability depends to what extent the amplification proceeds before encountering non-linear effects or boundary conditions. Here, again, distinction must be drawn between amplification in time (complex $\omega$) and amplification in space (complex $k$), the implications of which have been fully discussed by Sturrock[45].

An analysis of these problems is clearly of great importance in thermonuclear plasma, especially in the presence of beams of fast electrons (runaways), and the possible effects of oscillations upon the diffusion of particles across magnetic fields.

Another treatment of oscillations in plasma carrying large currents is due to LUCHINA[46], who finds that if $v_{\text{drift}} > v_{\text{random}}$ of the electrons, spatial periodicity of potential, electron density, etc., arise only if the mean free path of electrons exceeds the Debye screening distance $(\lambda_e > \lambda_D)$.

At the moment there is little correlation between these theories and experimental results. Plasma oscillations have certainly been produced in ordinary low-pressure discharges by the passage of electron beams[47-50], but some results indicate that they are generated as the beam passes through a boundary layer sheath, not, as theory would predict, in the 'infinite' plasma itself. Other workers find that a sheath is not necessary[48]. The oscillations grow when a beam of electrons moves down a concentration gradient, and vice versa. In highly ionized plasmas the presence of these oscillations has been shown to extract energy from a beam very rapidly indeed[51]. This is presumably due to bunching of the beam into packets of, say, $N$ electrons; the energy loss is proportional to $(Ne)^2$, and is thus $N$ times greater for each particle than in a uniform beam.

### MAGNETOHYDRODYNAMIC WAVES

Another type of wave motion exists, which is neither the ordinary electromagnetic nor the longitudinal electrostatic kind discussed earlier in this chapter. It arises when an ionized medium is permeated by a static magnetic field. The charged particles, by virtue of their tight spiral motions about the field lines, can be regarded as tied to them, whilst the lines themselves have a tension $T$ along their length of $\mu H^2/4\pi$. The lines are analogous to stretched strings loaded with a mass $\rho = nM$ per unit length ($M$, here, being the mass of the ions, since that of the electrons can be neglected). Thus there is the possibility that transverse waves could exist, propagated with the phase velocity

$$v_A = \sqrt{\frac{\mu H^2}{4\pi n M}} \text{ (Alfvén velocity)} \qquad \ldots(7.68)$$

The conception of such waves is due to ALFVÉN[3], and the rigorous theory has been developed by WALÉN[52]. They have been shown to exist in liquid metals, and recently their speed and damping have been measured in highly ionized gases, confirming the theory[53,54].

### PLASMA OSCILLATIONS IN MAGNETIC FIELDS

In the presence of an applied magnetic field a great variety of wave motions is possible, due to the combination of space-charge effects and the electrodynamic forces between the local oscillatory currents and the applied field. In addition, the gyration of charged particles about the magnetic lines of force leads to characteristic resonant frequencies.

Mathematical treatments have been given by a number of authors, some using hydrodynamic approximations or the transport equations[2,24,25,64–68], others using the Boltzmann equation for the distribution function, with the full force term $\dfrac{e}{m}\left(X + \dfrac{\mathbf{v} \times H}{c}\right)$ and neglecting collisions[57–63]. The general solutions are complicated but reduce to simpler forms in certain ranges of frequency, plasma density and magnetic field. These ranges may be defined in terms of certain characteristic frequencies and lengths; the angular frequencies are:

Plasma frequency $\qquad\qquad\qquad \omega_0 = \sqrt{\pi n e^2 / m}$

'Ion plasma frequency' $\qquad\qquad \omega_i = \sqrt{4\pi n e^2 / M}$

Electron gyro or cyclotron frequency (or Larmor frequency) $\qquad\qquad \omega_{ce} = \dfrac{eH_0}{mc}$

Ion gyro or cyclotron frequency $\quad \omega_{ci} = \dfrac{eH_0}{Mc}$

$$\left.\vphantom{\begin{array}{c}a\\a\\a\\a\\a\\a\end{array}}\right\} \ \dots\,(7.69)$$

where $H_0$ is the static applied magnetic field. These are to be compared with $\omega$, the angular frequency of the plasma wave, which will be of the form $e^{i(\mathbf{k}\cdot\mathbf{r}-\omega t)}$ (in this section we use the notation which has recently become most common in this field, although unfortunately there is no standard usage. Thus $\omega_0$ is identical with $\omega_p$ as used by some authors, and $\omega_{ce}$ with $\omega_H$ as used in Chapters 4 and 5). It will be seen later that certain hybrid frequencies, like $\omega_1 = \sqrt{\omega_{ce}\omega_{ci}}$ are also significant. Important lengths are:

Debye shielding distance

$$\lambda_D = \sqrt{\frac{\kappa T}{8\pi n e^2}} \approx \sqrt{\frac{\kappa T}{m\omega_0^2}}$$

Electron radius of gyration

$$\rho_e = v\,\frac{mc}{eH_0} \approx \sqrt{\frac{\kappa T_e}{m\omega_{ce}^2}}$$

Ion radius of gyration

$$\rho_i = v_i\,\frac{Mc}{eH_0} \approx \sqrt{\frac{\kappa T_i}{M\omega_{ci}^2}}$$

$$\left.\vphantom{\begin{array}{c}a\\a\\a\\a\\a\\a\end{array}}\right\} \ \dots\,(7.70)$$

These are to be compared with the wavelength, $\lambda$, of the plasma wave, $\lambda = 2\pi/k$, where $k$ is the wave vector. One must also distinguish between longitudinal and transverse waves, in which the electric field is along or perpendicular to the direction of propagation, respectively. Longitudinal motions lead to electron plasma oscillations or waves at high frequency, and at low frequency to ion sound waves (magneto-acoustic waves), or to ion waves propagating with the Alfvén velocity, depending whether the kinetic pressure of neighbouring particles or the magnetic pressure provides the main restoring force. Transverse motions include simple gyrations about the magnetic field, electromagnetic waves propagated by electrons, and magnetohydrodynamic (Alfvén) waves due to the heavy ions. In all theories it is assumed that the applied magnetic field does not change within these lengths, and the results of most authors apply to a uniform neutral plasma consisting of $n$ ions and electrons per cm³, in a homogeneous field.

Some of the simpler dispersion formulae derived by various authors are given below; it can be shown that many of their results, although expressed in different forms and deduced via different methods and approximations, are in agreement. We consider first high-frequency oscillations, in which the motion of the positive ions can be neglected. $\theta$ is the angle between the direction of propagation and $H_0$.

*No Thermal Motion: Longitudinal Oscillations*

The full equation is

$$\omega^2 = \tfrac{1}{2}(\omega_0^2 + \omega_{ce}^2) \pm \sqrt{(\omega_0^2 + \omega_{ce}^2)^2 - 4\omega_0^2\omega_{ce}^2 \cos^2\theta} \quad \ldots (7.71)$$

Since there is no dependence on the wave number $k$ there is no group velocity $d\omega/dk$ and hence no propagation. The equation describes only oscillations, not waves.

(*i*) If $\theta = 0$ the result reduces to

and

$$\left.\begin{array}{c} \omega = \omega_0 \\[2mm] \omega = \omega_{ce} \end{array}\right\} \qquad \ldots (7.72)$$

The first represents, of course, Langmuir–Tonks plasma oscillations; since the oscillatory electron current is parallel to $H_0$ the motion is unaffected by the magnetic field. The second value is simply the gyration of the electrons around the lines of force, and it is physically obvious that the two motions are independent.

(*ii*) When $\theta = \pi/2$ equation (7.71) gives

$$\omega^2 = \omega_0^2 + \omega_{ce}^2 \qquad \ldots (7.73)$$

273

Here, the linear and the circular motions are in the same plane and coupled together, since the restoring force is produced by electrostatic field due to charge separation plus the electromagnetic effect, $j \times H_0$. The electron cloud moves in an ellipse, perpendicular to $H_0$.

For any arbitrary direction $\theta$, equation (7.71) leads to simple limiting results.

(*iii*) If $\omega_0 \gg \omega_{ce}$, i.e. dense plasmas and/or weak magnetic fields.

and
$$\left. \begin{array}{l} \omega^2 = \omega_0^2 + \omega_{ce}^2 \sin^2 \theta \\[3mm] \omega^2 = \omega_{ce}^2 \cos^2 \theta \left( 1 - \dfrac{\omega_{ce}^2}{\omega_0^2} \right) \approx \omega_{ce}^2 \cos^2 \theta \end{array} \right\} \quad \ldots . (7.74)$$

(*iv*) If $\omega_{ce} \gg \omega_0$, i.e. plasmas of low density and/or strong magnetic field.

and
$$\left. \begin{array}{l} \omega^2 = \omega_{ce}^2 + \omega_0^2 \sin^2 \theta \\[3mm] \omega^2 = \omega_0^2 \cos^2 \theta \left( 1 - \dfrac{\omega_0^2}{\omega_{ce}^2} \right) \approx \omega_0^2 \cos^2 \theta \end{array} \right\} \quad \ldots . (7.75)$$

Equations (7.74) represent the dominance of the electric field, due to charge separation, over the electromagnetic force. The electric field causes the electrons to oscillate rapidly along some assumed direction of propagation—a line $k$ inclined at $\theta$ to $H_0$—and determines almost entirely the velocity, $v$, of the electrons in both magnitude and direction. The magnetic force, $\mathbf{v} \times H_0$ is thus $vH_0 \sin \theta$, and hence the electrons gyrate as though influenced only by the field $H_0 \sin \theta$. The motion in a plane containing $k$ and perpendicular to the plane defined by $k$ and $H_0$ is an ellipse, with a frequency $\sqrt{(\omega_0^2 + \omega_{ce}^2 \sin^2 \theta)}$. In a plane perpendicular to $k$ the frequency of motion is very nearly $\omega_{ce}^2 \cos^2 \theta$, independent of $\omega_0$. Thus the two frequencies apply to longitudinal and transverse motions.

Equations (7.75) show that the electrostatic forces have little influence. The first equation represents the transverse gyration of the electrons around the lines of force; the second represents the longitudinal oscillations of the plasma. Here the $\cos \theta$ term indicates that the particles are tied to lines of force; a displacement $\xi$ of charge along $k$ results in the separation of two slanted layers and a restoring electric field which, in the absence of a magnetic field, would be produced by a displacement of only $\xi \cos \theta$.

*Small Thermal Motion (Low Temperature): Longitudinal Waves*

(*i*) Provided that $\omega^2 \gg \omega_{ce}^2$, $\omega^2 \gg \dfrac{\kappa T}{m} k^2$, i.e. that the electro-static effects are predominant, and the phase velocity $\omega/k$ of the wave much greater than the random thermal motion of the ions, then

$$\omega^2 = \omega_0^2 + \omega_{ce}^2 \sin^2 \theta + 3 \frac{\kappa T}{m} k^2 \qquad \ldots (7.76)$$

This reduces to equation (7.74) when $T = 0$, but it should be noted that since the restraint $\omega^2 \gg \dfrac{\kappa T}{m} k^2$ was imposed in order to obtain the above solution, it applies only to small $k$, i.e. to long wavelengths. When the magnetic field tends to zero this equation reduces to equation (7.34).

(*ii*) If, now, the plasma is in a strong magnetic field, such that the Debye length greatly exceeds the Larmor radius of electrons, then for wavelengths much greater than both of these (i.e. $k^2 \rho_e^2 \ll k^2 \lambda_D^2 \ll 1$, consequently $\omega_{ce} \gg \omega_0$), the dispersion relation is:

$$\left.\begin{aligned} \omega^2 &= \omega_0^2 \cos^2 \theta \left( 1 - \frac{\rho_e^2}{\lambda_D^2} + 3k^2 \lambda_D^2 \right) \\ &\approx \omega_0^2 \cos^2 \theta \left( 1 - \frac{\omega_0^2}{\omega_{ce}^2} \right) + 3 \frac{\kappa T}{m} k^2 \cos \theta \end{aligned}\right\} \quad \ldots (7.77)$$

Here, again, when $T = 0$ this reduces to equation (7.75), and if the magnetic field is parallel to the wave vector $(\theta = 0)$ the longitudinal motion is almost the same as in the absence of a magnetic field. This is physically reasonable since the electrons gyrate in many tight spirals during each oscillation along the direction of the magnetic field.

(*iii*) For propagation perpendicular to the magnetic field it is possible to solve the dispersion relation completely in terms of tabulated functions. In the form given by Bernstein the solution is:

$$1 + k^2 \lambda_D^2 = \frac{\displaystyle\int_0^{2\pi} e^{\left[ -i \frac{\omega}{\omega_{ce}} y - k^2 \rho_e^2 (1 - \cos y) \right]} \cdot dy}{1 - e^{-i2\pi\omega/\omega_{ce}}} \quad \ldots (7.78)$$

The interesting point is that when $\omega/\omega_{ce}$ is an integer the denominator becomes zero. When the dispersion curve is plotted, $k = f(\omega)$, the curve has vertical branches at the frequencies $\omega_{ce}$, $2\omega_{ce}$, $3\omega_{ce}$, etc. It follows that $d\omega/dk$ is zero, there is no group velocity and the wave does not propagate. In cold plasmas ($T = 0$) this occurs only at exact multiples of $\omega_{ce}$; with thermal motion present there are small finite gaps (width $\propto \kappa T$) in the frequency spectrum, such that longitudinal electron waves of these frequencies will not propagate perpendicular to $H_0$.

## General Motions of Electrons and Ions

The general dispersion relation, including thermal effects and the combined motion of electrons and ions, can be expressed in manageable form only in matrix notation, because the properties of the plasma are not isotropic in the presence of a magnetic field. Some limiting conditions are given by:

(i) $\theta = 0$, $T = 0$, i.e. propagation along the magnetic field, when the organized velocity greatly exceeds random motion. The dispersion equation is

$$\left[ c^2 k^2 - \omega^2 + \frac{\omega \omega_i^2}{\omega + \omega_{ci}} + \frac{\omega \omega_0^2}{\omega - \omega_{ce}} \right]$$
$$\times \left[ c^2 k^2 - \omega^2 + \frac{\omega \omega_i^2}{\omega - \omega_{ci}} + \frac{\omega \omega_0^2}{\omega + \omega_{ce}} \right] [\omega_0^2 + \omega_i^2 - \omega^2] = 0$$
$$\ldots (7.79)$$

One solution of this is

$$\omega^2 = \omega_0^2 + \omega_i^2 \qquad \ldots (7.80)$$

These are the normal plasma oscillations, with the motion of the ions included. The remaining solution can be divided into two limiting groups, waves having phase velocities close to $c$ ($\omega/k \sim c$, i.e. $\omega^2 \sim c^2 k^2$), and those which are very much slower ($\omega^2 \ll c^2 k^2$, also $\omega^2 \ll \omega_{ci}^2$). The former group are not influenced by ion motion, and the first two factors in equation (7.79) can be combined in the equation:

$$\omega^2 = c^2 k^2 + \frac{\omega \omega_0^2}{\omega \pm \omega_{ce}} \qquad \ldots (7.81)$$

This represents two electromagnetic waves, circularly polarized in opposite senses; the minus sign signifies the extraordinary wave, when the electrons and the electric field vector rotate in the same sense.

The low-frequency solution can be derived from either of the first two factors in equation (7.79), for example

$$\omega^2 = c^2 k^2 + \frac{\omega \omega_i^2}{\omega_{ci}} \left( 1 - \frac{\omega}{\omega_{ci}} + \ldots \right) + \frac{\omega \omega_0^2}{\omega_{ce}} \left( 1 + \frac{\omega}{\omega_{ce}} + \ldots \right)$$
$$\ldots (7.82)$$

Noting that $\dfrac{\omega_i^2}{\omega_{ci}} = \dfrac{\omega_0^2}{\omega_{ce}}$, and neglecting small terms, we derive

$$\omega^2 \left(1 + \frac{\omega_i^2}{\omega_{ci}^2}\right) - 2\omega \frac{\omega_i^2}{\omega_{ci}} = c^2 k^2 \qquad \dots (7.83)$$

Since the solution $\omega \ll ck$ is sought, the first term is dominant, hence

$$v_{\text{phase}} = \frac{\omega}{k} = \frac{c}{\sqrt{1 + \dfrac{4\pi n M c^2}{H_0^2}}} \approx \frac{H_0}{\sqrt{4\pi n M}} \qquad \dots (7.84)$$

This is an Alfvén wave, and the derivation shows that it is analogous to an electromagnetic wave passing through a medium whose dielectric constant has been changed from 1 to $1 + \omega_i^2/\omega_{ci}^2$ due to the oscillation of the ions [cf. equation (5.3)]. Note that the factor $\omega_0^2/\omega_{ci}\omega_{ce}$, which appears as a parameter in several theories, is equal to $c^2/v_A^2$, the square of the ratio of the velocity of an electromagnetic wave, in free space, to that of an Alfvén wave.

(ii) $\theta = \pi/2$, $T = 0$, i.e. propagation perpendicular to the magnetic field.

Here the total dispersion relation, although straightforward, is lengthy to write down.

The low-frequency solutions lead again to Alfvén waves. For high-frequency motion (ion motion being neglected), the general expression reduces to:

$$\omega^2 = \omega_0^2 + \tfrac{1}{2}(\omega_{ce}^2 + c^2 k^2) \pm \tfrac{1}{2}\sqrt{(\omega_{ce}^2 - c^2 k^2)^2 + 4\omega_{ce}^2 \omega_0^2} \quad \dots (7.85)$$

Two sets of solutions are easily separable, waves with phase velocities $\omega/k \sim c$, others at much lower frequencies $\omega \sim \omega_0$. The first are electromagnetic waves:

$$\omega^2 \approx c^2 k^2 + \omega_0^2 + \frac{\omega_0^2 \omega_{ce}^2}{c^2 k^2} \qquad \dots (7.86)$$

The second type are plasma oscillations

$$\omega^2 \approx \omega_0^2 + \omega_{ce}^2 \qquad \dots (7.87)$$

(iii) $\theta = \pi/2$, $T = 0$, *intermediate frequencies*—For frequencies which lie in the range $\omega_{ci}$ to $\omega_{ce}$ the full dispersion relation is complicated, but it has been shown[67] that the dispersion curve has singularities at the hybrid frequency $\omega_1 = \sqrt{\omega_{ce}\omega_{ci}}$. The reason, pointed out by Gabor, is that an electric field in this range drives an electron below its resonant gyro frequency and an ion above its gyro frequency, so that both rotate in phase. At the frequency $\sqrt{\omega_{ce}\omega_{ci}}$ they have the same amplitude, charge separation does not occur and so the amplitude of oscillation can grow very large. Waves of this frequency do not propagate.

(iv) *Longitudinal ion oscillations*—These can be deduced from theory only when thermal motion is included, in particular the thermal motion of the electrons which rapidly set themselves in equilibrium in the electric field created by the motion of the ions. The restoring forces are then due to the stretching of the lines of magnetic force by the motion of the particles and to the kinetic pressure of neighbouring ions. The hydrodynamic approximation[2] gives:

$$v_{\text{phase}}^2 = v_A^2 + 2\gamma \frac{\kappa T}{M}\left(1 - \frac{v_A^2}{c^2}\right) \qquad \dots \dots (7.88)$$

In strong magnetic fields these are like magnetohydrodynamic waves, while in weak fields or at high temperatures they are like sound waves, except that $T$ here refers to the electron temperature [see equation (7.23)].

A review of the many possible modes of high-frequency wave propagation in an ionized gas in magnetic fields has recently been given by BROWN[69].

### REFERENCES

[1] COWLING, T. G., *Magnetohydrodynamics*; New York: Interscience, 1957
[2] SPITZER, L., *Physics of Fully Ionized Gases*; New York: Interscience, 1956
[3] ALFVÉN, H., *Cosmical Electrodynamics*; Oxford: Clarendon Press, 1950
[4] APPLETON, E. V. and WEBB, A. G. D., *Phil. Mag.*, **45** (1923) 879
[5] PENNING, F. M., *Nature, Lond.*, **118** (1926) 301; *Physica*, **6** (1926) 241
[6] CLAY, R. E., *Phil. Mag.*, **50** (1925) 985
[7] WEBB, J. S. and PARDUE, L. A., *Phys. Rev.*, **31** (1928) 1122; **32** (1928) 946
[8] DONAHUE, T. and DIEKE, G. H., *ibid.*, **81** (1951) 248
[9] EMELEUS, K. G., *Nuovo Cim.* (Supplt.), **3** (1956) 490
[10] FRANCIS, G. in *Handbuch der Physik*, Vol. 22; Heidelberg: Springer, 1956
[11] GABOR, D., *Brit. J. appl. Phys.*, **2** (1951) 209
[12] TONKS, L. and LANGMUIR, I., *Phys. Rev.*, **33** (1929) 195
[13] DEBYE, P. and HÜCKEL, E., *Phys. Z.*, **24** (1923) 185, 305
[14] THOMSON, J. J. and THOMSON, G. P., *Conduction of Electricity through Gases* Vol. 2, 2nd edn; London: Cambridge University Press, 1933
[15] VLASOV, A., *J. exp. theor. Phys.*, **8** (1938) 291
[16] VLASOV, A., *J. Phys., Moscow*, **9** (1945) 25
[17] ECKER, G., *Z. Phys.*, **140** (1955) 274, 293; **141** (1955) 294

## REFERENCES

18 LANDAU, L., *J. Phys.*, *Moscow*, **10** (1946) 25
19 TWISS, R. Q., *Phys. Rev.*, **88** (1952) 1392
20 BOHM, D. and GROSS, E. P., *ibid.*, **75** (1949) 1851, 1864
21 BERZ, F., *Proc. phys. Soc. Lond.*, **B69** (1956) 939
22 VAN KAMPEN, N. G., *Physica*, **23** (1957) 641; **21** (1955) 949; see also CASE, K. M., *Ann. Phys.*, **7** (1959) 349
23 JEANS, J. H., *Dynamical Theory of Gases*; London: Cambridge University Press, 1925
24 BAILEY, V. A., *Phys. Rev.*, **78** (1950) 428
25 PIDDINGTON, J. H., *Phil. Mag.*, **46** (1955) 1037
26 ARMSTRONG, E. B. and EMELEUS, K. G., *Proc. Instn elect. Engrs*, **96** (Pt. 3) (1949) 390
27 COBINE, J. D. and GALLAHER, C. J., *J. appl. Phys.*, **18** (1947) 110
28 MARTIN, H. and WOODS, H. A., *Proc. phys. Soc. Lond.*, **B65** (1952) 281
29 AMER, S., *J. Electron. Control*, **5** (1958) 105
30 GOLD, L., *ibid.*, **4** (1958) 219
31 AKHIEZER, A. I. and POLOVIN, R. V., *Dokl. obsch. Sobr. Ak. Nauk S.S.S.R.*, **80** (1951) 193
32 POLOVIN, R. V., *J. exp. theor. Phys.*, **4** (1957) 290
33 AKHIEZER, A. I. and POLOVIN, R. V., *ibid.*, **3** (1956/7) 696
34 MERRILL, H. J. and WEBB, H. W., *Phys. Rev.*, **55** (1939) 1191
35 LANGMUIR, I. and MOTT-SMITH, H., *Gen. Elect. Rev.*, **27** (1924) 449, 538, 616, 762, 810
36 DITTMER, A. F., *Phys. Rev.*, **28** (1926) 507
37 EMELEUS, K. G., *Appl. sci. Res.*, *Hague*, **B5** (1955) 66
38 ALLEN, T. K., BAILEY, R. A. and EMELEUS, K. G., *Brit. J. appl. Phys.*, **6** (1955) 320
39 ALLEN, T. K., *Proc. phys. Soc. Lond.*, **A68** (1955) 696
40 BAILEY, R. A. and EMELEUS, K. G., *Proc. R. Irish Acad.*, **57** (1955) 53
41 HAEFF, A. V., *Phys. Rev.*, **74** (1948) 1532; *Proc. Inst. Radio Engrs*, *N.Y.*, **37** (1949) 1
42 PIERCE, J. R., *Theory and Design of Electron Beams*; New York: van Nostrand, 1950; *J. appl. Phys.*, **19** (1948) 231; **20** (1949) 1060
43 BUNEMAN, O., *Phys. Rev. Lett.*, **1** (1958) 8
44 AUER, P. L., *ibid.*, **1** (1958) 412
45 STURROCK, P. A., *Phys. Rev.*, **112** (1958) 1488
46 LUCHINA, A. A., *J. exp. theor. Phys.*, **1** (1955) 12, 21
47 LOONEY, D. H. and BROWN, S. C., *Phys. Rev.*, **93** (1954) 965
48 KOJIMA, S., KATO, K. and HAGIWARA, S., *J. phys. Soc. Japan*, **12** (1957) 1276
49 MAHAFFEY, D. W., McCULLAGH, G. and EMELEUS, K. G., *Phys. Rev.*, **112** (1958) 1052
50 MAHAFFEY, D. W., *J. Electron. Control*, **6** (1959) 193
51 FEINBERG, Y. B. *et al.*, *Proceedings of the Fourth International Conference on Ionization Phenomena in Gases*, Uppsala, 1959
52 WALÉN, C., *Ark. Mat. Astr. Fys.*, **30A** (1944) No. 15; **33A** (1946) No. 18

279

[53] JEPHCOTT, D. F., *Nature, Lond.*, **183** (1959) 1652; *Proceedings of the Fourth International Conference on Ionization Phenomena in Gases*, Uppsala, 1959

[54] ALLEN, T. K., BAKER, W. R., PYLE, R. V. and WILCOX, J. M., *Phys. Rev. Lett.*, **2** (1959) 383

[55] STURROCK, P. A., *Proc. roy. Soc.*, **A242** (1957) 277

[56] DAWSON, J. M., *Phys. Rev.*, **113** (1959) 383

[57] GORDEEV, G. V., *J. exp. theor. Phys.*, **23** (1952) 660

[58] GROSS, E. P., *Phys. Rev.*, **82** (1951) 232

[59] SEN, H. K., *ibid.*, **88** (1952) 816

[60] AKHIEZER, A. I. *et al.*, *Proceedings of the Second United Nations Conference on the Peaceful Uses of Atomic Energy*, Geneva, 1958, Vol. 31, p. 99

[61] BERNSTEIN, I. B., *Phys. Rev.*, **109** (1958) 10

[62] STEPANOV, K., *J. exp. theor. Phys.*, **7** (1958) 892; **8** (1959) 808

[63] HARRIS, E. G., *Phys. Rev. Lett.*, **2** (1959) 34

[64] ÅSTRÖM, E., *Ark. Fys.*, **2** (1950) 443

[65] BRAGINSKY, S. I., *Dokl. obsch. Sobr. Ak. Nauk S.S.S.R.*, **4** (1957) 345

[66] GOLD, L., *J. Electron. Control*, **4** (1958) 409

[67] AUER, P. L., HURWITZ, H. and MILLER, R. D., *Phys. Fluids*, **1** (1958) 501

[68] SCHUMANN, W. O., *Z. angew. Phys.*, **10** (1958) 428

[69] BROWN, S. C., *Proceedings of the Fourth International Conference on Ionization Phenomena in Gases*, Uppsala, 1959

BIBLIOGRAPHY

RATCLIFFE, J. A., *The Magneto-ionic Theory;* London: Cambridge University Press, 1959

BECK, A. H. W., *Space Charge Waves*; London: Pergamon Press, 1958

APPENDICES

| Period | Inner Electron Core | Group | | | | | | |
|---|---|---|---|---|---|---|---|---|
| | | Ia | IIa | IIIa | IVa | Va | VIa | VIIa |
| 1 | | ¹ H ¹ $1s^1$ | | | | | | |
| 2 | $1s^2$ | ³ Li ⁷ $2s^1$ | ⁴ Be ⁹ $2s^2$ | | | | | |
| 3 | Neon configuration $1s^2, 2s^2\,2p^6$ | ¹¹ Na ²³ $3s^1$ | ¹² Mg ²⁴ $3s^1$ | Transition Elements | | | | |
| 4 | Argon configuration $1s^2, 2s^2\,2p^6$ $3s^2\,3p^6$ | ¹⁹ K ³⁹ $4s^{1*}$ | ²⁰ Ca ⁴⁰ $4s^2$ $(4s^2$ plus →$)$ | ²¹ Sc ⁴⁵ $3d^1$ | ²² Ti ⁴⁸ $3d^2$ | ²³ V ⁵¹ $3d^3$ | ²⁴ Cr ⁵² $3d^4$ | ²⁵ Mn $3d^5$ |
| 5 | Krypton configuration $1s^2, 2s^2\,2p^6$ $3s^2\,3p^6\,3d^{10}$ $4s^2\,4p^6$ | ³⁷ Rb ⁸⁵ $5s^{1*}$ | ³⁸ Sr ⁸⁸ $5s^2$ | ³⁹ Y ⁸⁹ $5s^2\,4d^1$ | ⁴⁰ Zr ⁹⁰ $5s^2\,4d^2$ | ⁴¹ Nb† ⁹⁴ $5s^1\,4d^4$ | ⁴² Mo ⁹⁶ $5s^1\,4d^5$ | ⁴³ Tc $5s^1\,4d$● |
| 6 | Xenon configuration $1s^2, 2s^2\,2p^6$ $3s^2\,3p^6\,3d^{10}$ $4s^2\,4p^6\,4d^{10}$ $5s^2\,5p^6$ | ⁵⁵ Cs ¹³³ $6s^{1*}$ | ⁵⁶ Ba ¹³⁷ $6s^2$ $4f^{14}$ | ⁵⁷ to 71 La Series plus → | ⁷² Hf ¹⁷⁹ $6s^2\,5d^2$ | ⁷³ Ta ¹⁸² $6s^2\,5d^3$ | ⁷⁴ W ¹⁸⁴ $6s^2\,5d^4$ | ⁷⁵ Re ● $6s^2\,5d$● |
| 7 | Radon configuration $1s^2, 2s^2\,2p^6$ $3s^2\,3p^6\,3d^{10}$ $4s^2\,4p^6\,4d^{10}\,4f^{14}$ $5s^2\,5p^6\,5d^{10}$ $6s^2\,6p^6$ | ⁸⁷ Fr ²²³ $7s^{1*}$ | ⁸⁸ Ra ²²⁶ $7s^2$ | Ac Series | | | | |

### Inner Transition Elements

Lanthanum series: Xenon core, plus

| ⁵⁷ La ¹³⁹ $6s^2\,5d^1$ | ⁵⁸ Ce ¹⁴⁰ | ⁵⁹ Pr ¹⁴¹ | ⁶⁰ Nd ¹⁴⁴ | ⁶¹ ● |
|---|---|---|---|---|

Xenon core plus $6s^2$ plus →

| | $5d^1\,4f^1$ | $5d^1\,4f^2$ | $5d^1\,4f^3$ | $5d$● |
|---|---|---|---|---|

Actinium series: Radon core, plus

| ⁸⁹ Ac ²²⁷ $7s^2\,6d^1$ | ⁹⁰ Th ²³² $7s^2\,6d^2$ | ⁹¹ Pa† ²³¹ $5f^2\,6d^1\,7s^2$ | ⁹² U ²³⁸ $5f^3\,6d^1\,7s^2$ | ⁹³ N● $5f^5$ |
|---|---|---|---|---|

*Atomic number and weight.* The number in the top left-hand corner of each square is the atomic number of the element—the number of protons in the nucleus. In the top right-hand corner is the atomic weight (to the nearest whole number) of the most common isotope, this being the total number of protons ● neutrons. The number of neutrons is $A - Z$.

*Electron configuration* (see Chapter 1). The electrons are designated by type, called $s, p, d, f \ldots$ accord● as $l = 0, 1, 2, 3 \ldots$ . The preceding number denotes the shell (value of $n$) in which the electron is pla●● and the superscript the number of electrons of a particular type.

Thus, for example, chromium ($Z = 24$) has 24 external electrons. In the shell $n = 1$ there are 2 elect●● having $l = 0$ ($1s^2$); in the shell $n = 2$ there are 2 electrons having $l = 0$ and 6 having $l = 1$ ($2s^2\,2p^6$);

| | Group | | | | | | | | |
|---|---|---|---|---|---|---|---|---|---|
| VIII | | | Ib | IIb | IIIb | IVb | Vb | VIb | VIIb | 0 |

| VIII | | | Ib | IIb | IIIb | IVb | Vb | VIb | VIIb | 0 |
|---|---|---|---|---|---|---|---|---|---|---|
| | | | | | | | | | | 2 He 4 $1s^2$ |
| | | | $2s^2$ plus → | | 5 B 11 $2p^1$ | 6 C 12 $2p^2$ | 7 N 14 $2p^3$ | 8 O 16 $2p^4$ | 9 F 19 $2p^5$ | 10 Ne 20 $2p^6$ |
| Transition Elements | | | $3s^2$ plus → | | 13 Al 27 $3p^1$ | 14 Si 28 $3p^2$ | 15 P 31 $3p^3$ | 16 S 32 $3p^4$ | 17 Cl 35 $3p^5$ | 18 A 40 $3p^6$ |
| Fe 56 $3d^6$ | 27 Co 59 $3d^7$ | 28 Ni 59 $3d^8$ † | 29 Cu 64 $4s^1 3d^{10}$ | 30 Zn 65 $4s^2 3d^{10}$ ($4s^2 3d^{10}$ plus →) | 31 Ga 69 $4p^1$ | 32 Ge 73 $4p^2$ | 33 As 75 $4p^3$ | 34 Se 79 $4p^4$ | 35 Br 80 $4p^5$ | 36 Kr 83 $4p^6$ |
| Ru 102 $5s^1 4d^7$ | 45 Rh 103 $5s^1 4d^8$ | 46 Pd 104 $4d^{10}$ † | 47 Ag 108 ($4d^{10}$ plus →) $5s^1$ | 48 Cd 112 $5s^2$ ($4d^{10} 5s^2$ plus →) | 49 In 115 $5p^1$ | 50 Sn 119 $5p^2$ | 51 Sb 122 $5p^3$ | 52 Te 128 $5p^4$ | 53 I 127 $5p^5$ | 54 Xe 130 $5p^6$ |
| Os 191 $6s^2 5d^6$ | 77 Ir 193 $6s^2 5d^7$ | 78 Pt† 195 $6s^1 5d^9$ | 79 Au 197 $6s^1 5d^{10}$ | 80 Hg 201 $6s^2 5d^{10}$ | 81 Tl 204 ($6s^2 5d^{10} 4f^{14}$ plus →) $6p^1$ | 82 Pb 207 $6p^2$ | 83 Bi 209 $6p^3$ | 84 Po 210 $6p^4$ | 85 At 211 $6p^5$ | 86 Rn 222 $6p^6$ |

Key:

$$\boxed{\begin{array}{cc} Z & A \\ \multicolumn{2}{c}{\text{Element}} \\ \multicolumn{2}{c}{\text{Number and type}} \\ \multicolumn{2}{c}{\text{of outer electrons}} \end{array}}$$

| 150 | 63 Eu 152 | 64 Gd 157 | 65 Tb 159 | 66 Dy 162 | 67 Ho 164 | 68 Er 167 | 69 Tm† 169 | 70 Yb 173 | 71 Lu† 175 |
|---|---|---|---|---|---|---|---|---|---|
| $f^5$ | $5d^1 4f^6$ | $5d^1 4f^7$ | $5d^1 4f^8$ | $5d^1 4f^9$ | $5d^1 4f^{10}$ | $5d^1 4f^{11}$ | $4f^{13}$ | $4f^{14}$ | $5d^1 4f^{14}$ |
| 242 | 95 Am 243 | 96 Cm 245 | 97 Bk 249 | 98 Cf† 249 | 99 E 254 | 100 Fm 252 | 101 Mv 256 | | |
| $s^2$ | $5f^7 7s^2$ | $5f^7 6d^1 7s^2$ | $5f^8 6d^1 7s^2$ | $5f^{10} 7s^2$ | $5f^{11} 7s^2$ | $5f^{12} 7s^2$ | $5f^{13} 7s^2$ | | |

...l $n = 3$ there are 2 electrons having $l = 0$, 6 having $l = 1$, and 4 having $l = 2$ ($3s^2 3p^6 3d^4$), in the outer-st shell $n = 4$, there are 2 electrons having $l = 0$ ($4s^2$).
n the first two periods of the table, elements follow consecutively by the addition of electrons to the outer-st shell. In the third and subsequent series the two $s$ electrons are first added to the next outer shell, then inner shells are filled, before $p$ electrons are added to the outer shell (e.g. Ca → Sc, Sr → Y). In a few ces rearrangement occurs by an electron already in the atom changing shells when another is added (e.g. ...r → 41Nb; 45Rh → 46Pd, 77Ir → 78Pt).

\* Electrons added to outer shell before inner shells filled.   † Rearrangement.

APPENDIX II. CRITICAL POTENTIALS OF ATOMS. METASTABLE POTENTIALS, $V_m$, RESONANCE POTENTIALS, $V_r$, AND IONIZATION POTENTIALS, $V_i$ I, $V_i$ II . . . FOR THE REMOVAL OF 1, 2 . . . ELECTRONS* (ALL IN VOLTS).

| | Element | $V_m$ | $V_r$ | $V_i$ I | $V_i$ II | $V_i$ III | $V_i$ IV |
|---|---|---|---|---|---|---|---|
| 1 | H | | 10·20 | 13·60 | | | |
| 2 | He | 19·80 | 21·21 | 24·58 | 54·40 | | |
| 3 | Li | | 1·85 | 5·39 | 75·62 | 122·42 | |
| 4 | Be | | 5·28 | 9·32 | 18·21 | 153·85 | 217·66 |
| 5 | B | | 4·96 | 8·30 | 25·15 | 37·92 | 259·30 |
| 6 | C | 1·26 | 7·48 | 11·26 | 24·38 | 47·86 | 64·48 |
| 7 | N | 2·38 | 10·3 | 14·54 | 29·60 | 47·43 | 77·45 |
| 8 | O | 1·97 | 9·15 | 13·61 | 35·15 | 54·93 | 77·39 |
| 9 | F | | 12·7 | 17·42 | 34·98 | 62·65 | 87·23 |
| 10 | Ne | 16·62 | 16·85 | 21·56 | 41·07 | 63·5 | 97·16 |
| 11 | Na | | 2·1 | 5·14 | 47·29 | 71·8 | 98·88 |
| 12 | Mg | 2·71 | 2·71 | 7·64 | 15·03 | 78·2 | 109·3 |
| 13 | Al | | 3·14 | 5·98 | 18·82 | 28·44 | 119·96 |
| 14 | Si | 0·78 | 4·93 | 8·15 | 16·34 | 33·46 | 45·13 |
| 15 | P | 0·91 | 6·95 | 10·55 | 19·65 | 30·16 | 51·35 |
| 16 | S | | 6·52 | 10·36 | 23·4 | 34·8 | 47·29 |
| 17 | Cl | | 8·92 | 13·01 | 23·80 | 39·9 | 53·3 |
| 18 | A | 11·55 | 11·61 | 15·76 | 27·6 | 40·90 | 59·79 |
| 19 | K | | 1·61 | 4·34 | 31·81 | 45·9 | 61·1 |
| 20 | Ca | 1·88 | 1·89 | 6·11 | 11·87 | 51·21 | 67·3 |
| 21 | Sc | 1·61 | 1·98 | 6·56 | 12·89 | 24·75 | 73·9 |
| 22 | Ti | 0·81 | 1·97 | 6·83 | 13·57 | 28·14 | 43·24 |
| 23 | V | 0·26 | 2·03 | 6·74 | 14·2 | 29·7 | 48·0 |
| 24 | Cr | 0·94 | 2·89 | 6·76 | 16·49 | 31 | |
| 25 | Mn | 2·11 | 2·28 | 7·43 | 15·64 | 33·69 | |
| 26 | Fe | 0·85 | 2·40 | 7·90 | 16·18 | 30·64 | |
| 27 | Co | 0·43 | 2·92 | 7·86 | 17·05 | 33·49 | |
| 28 | Ni | 0·42 | 3·31 | 7·63 | 18·15 | 36·16 | |
| 29 | Cu | 1·38 | 3·78 | 7·72 | 20·29 | 36·83 | |
| 30 | Zn | 4·00 | 4·03 | 9·39 | 17·96 | 39·70 | |
| 31 | Ga | | 3·07 | 6·00 | 20·51 | 30·70 | 64·2 |
| 32 | Ge | 0·88 | 4·65 | 7·88 | 15·93 | 34·21 | 45·7 |
| 33 | As | 1·31 | 6·28 | 9·81 | 18·7 | 28·3 | 50·1 |
| 34 | Se | | 6·10 | 9·75 | 21·5 | 32·0 | 42·9 |
| 35 | Br | | 7·86 | 11·84 | 21·6 | 35·9 | 47·3 |
| 36 | Kr | 9·91 | 10·02 | 14·00 | 24·56 | 36·9 | 52·5 |
| 37 | Rb | | 1·56 | 4·18 | 27·56 | 40 | 52·6 |
| 38 | Sr | 1·77 | 1·80 | 5·69 | 11·03 | 43·6 | 57·1 |
| 39 | Y | | 1·31 | 6·38 | 12·23 | 20·5 | 61·8 |
| 40 | Zr | 0·52 | 1·83 | 6·84 | 12·92 | 24·8 | 33·97 |
| 41 | Nb | | 2·97 | 6·88 | 13·90 | 28·1 | 38·3 |
| 42 | Mo | 1·34 | 3·18 | 7·13 | 15·72 | 29·6 | 46·4 |
| 43 | Tc | | | 7·23 | 14·87 | 31·9 | |
| 44 | Ru | 0·81 | 3·16 | 7·36 | 16·60 | 30·3 | |
| 45 | Rh | 0·41 | 3·36 | 7·46 | 15·92 | 32·8 | |

* More detailed and comprehensive values of $V_i$, together with estimated errors, can be found in: Finkelnberg, W. and Humbach, W., *Naturwissenschaften*, **42** (1955), 35.

| | Element | $V_m$ | $V_r$ | $V_i$ I | $V_i$ II | $V_i$ III | $V_i$ IV |
|---|---|---|---|---|---|---|---|
| 46 | Pd | 0·81 | 4·48 | 8·33 | 19·42 | | |
| 47 | Ag | | 3·57 | 7·57 | 21·48 | 36·10 | |
| 48 | Cd | 3·73 | 3·80 | 8·99 | 16·90 | 44·5 | |
| 49 | In | | 3·02 | 5·79 | 18·86 | 28·0 | 58·0 |
| 50 | Sn | 1·07 | 4·33 | 7·33 | 14·6 | 30·7 | 46·4 |
| 51 | Sb | 1·05 | 5·35 | 8·64 | 16·7 | 24·8 | 44·1 |
| 52 | Te | 1·31 | 5·49 | 9·01 | 18·8 | 31 | 38 |
| 53 | I | | | 10·44 | 19·0 | 33 | |
| 54 | Xe | 8·32 | 8·45 | 12·13 | 21·2 | 32·1 | |
| 55 | Cs | | 1·39 | 3·89 | 25·1 | 34·6 | |
| 56 | Ba | 1·13 | 1·57 | 5·81 | 10·00 | 37 | |
| 57 | La | 0·37 | 1·84 | 5·61 | 11·43 | 19·17 | |
| 58 | Ce | | | 6·91 | 12·3 | 19·5 | 36·7 |
| 59 | Pr | | | 5·76 | | | |
| 60 | Nd | | | 6·31 | | | |
| 61 | Pm | | | | | | |
| 62 | Sm | | | 5·6 | 11·2 | | |
| 63 | Eu | | | 5·67 | 11·24 | | |
| 64 | Gd | | | 6·16 | 12 | | |
| 65 | Tb | | | 6·74 | | | |
| 66 | Dy | | | 6·82 | | | |
| 67 | Ho | | | | | | |
| 68 | Er | | | | | | |
| 69 | Tm | | | | | | |
| 70 | Yb | | | 6·2 | 12·10 | | |
| 71 | Lu | | | 6·15 | 14·7 | | |
| 72 | Hf | | 2·19 | 5·5 | 14·9 | | |
| 73 | Ta | | | 7·7 | 16·2 | | |
| 74 | W | 0·37 | 2·3 | 7·98 | 17·7 | | |
| 75 | Re | | 2·35 | 7·87 | 16·6 | | |
| 76 | Os | | | 8·7 | 17 | | |
| 77 | Ir | | | 9·2 | 17·0 | | |
| 78 | Pt | 0·10 | 3·74 | 8·96 | 18·54 | | |
| 79 | Au | 1·14 | 4·63 | 9·22 | 20·5 | | |
| 80 | Hg | 4·67 | 4·89 | 10·43 | 18·75 | 34·2 | |
| 81 | Tl | | 3·28 | 6·11 | 20·42 | 29·8 | 50·0 |
| 82 | Pb | 2·66 | 4·38 | 7·42 | 15·03 | 31·93 | 39·0 |
| 83 | Bi | 1·42 | 4·04 | 7·29 | 19·3 | 25·6 | 45·3 |
| 84 | Po | | | 8·2 | 19·4 | 27·3 | |
| 85 | At | | | 9·2 | 20·1 | 29·3 | |
| 86 | Rn | 6·77 | 8·41 | 10·75 | 21·4 | 29·4 | |
| 87 | Fr | | | 3·98 | 22·5 | 33·5 | |
| 88 | Ra | | | 5·28 | 10·14 | | |
| 89 | Ac | | | 6·89 | 11·5 | | |
| 90 | Th | | | | 11·5 | 20·0 | 28·7 |
| 91 | Pa | | | | | | |
| 92 | U | | | 4 | | | |

(By courtesy of Massachusetts Institute of Technology and
John Wiley and Sons, Inc.)

APPENDIX III. CRITICAL POTENTIALS OF COMMON MOLECULES (IN VOLTS). DISSOCIATION POTENTIAL, $V_d$, RESONANCE POTENTIAL, $V_r$, AND IONIZATION POTENTIAL, $V_i$, FOR THE REMOVAL OF A SINGLE ELECTRON (GIVING IONS OF THE TYPE $M_2{}^+$ or $AB^+$)

| Molecule | $V_d$ | $V_r$ | $V_i$ |
|---|---|---|---|
| $H_2$ | 4·5 | 11·5 | 15·6 |
| $N_2$ | 9·8 | 6·1 | 15·5 |
| $O_2$ | 5·1 | 7·9 | 12·5 |
| $O_3$ | 6·2 | | |
| $F_2$ | | | 17·8 |
| $Cl_2$ | 2·5 | | 13·2 |
| $Br_2$ | 2·0 | | 12·8 |
| $CO$ | 11·1 | 6·0 | 14·1 |
| $CO_2$ | 16·6 | 10·0 | 14·4 |
| $H_2O$ | 9·5 | 7·6 | 12·6 |
| $NO$ | 6·5 | 5·4 | 9·5 |
| $NO_2$ | | | 11·0 |
| $N_2O$ | | | 12·9 |

## Appendix IV. Physical Constants

| | |
|---|---|
| $e$ | Charge on the electron, $e = 4\cdot80 \times 10^{-10}$ e.s.u. $= 1\cdot60 \times 10^{-20}$ e.m.u. $= 1\cdot60 \times 10^{-19}$ Coulombs. |
| $m_0$ | Rest mass of the electron, $m_0 = 9\cdot11 \times 10^{-28}$ g ($= 8\cdot19 \times 10^{-7}$ erg $= 0\cdot51$ MeV, from Einstein's relation, $\varepsilon = mc^2$). |
| $e/m_0$ | Specific electronic charge, $e/m_0 = 5\cdot27 \times 10^{17}$ e.s.u./g $= 1\cdot76 \times 10^7$ e.m.u./g $= 1\cdot76 \times 10^8$ Coulombs/g. |
| $M_{\text{proton}}$ | Mass of proton $= 1\cdot672 \times 10^{-24}$ g $= 1\cdot00759$ atomic mass units (on physical scale, taking $O^{16} = 16\cdot000$). |
| $M_{\text{neutron}}$ | Mass of neutron $= 1\cdot675 \times 10^{-24}$ g $= 1\cdot00898$ a.m.u. |
| $M_{\text{proton}}/m_0$ | Mass ratio, proton to electron $M/m_0 = 1{,}837$. |
| $c$ | Velocity of light in vacuum, $c = 2\cdot998 \times 10^{10}$ cm/sec. |
| $h$ | Planck's constant, $h = 6\cdot625 \times 10^{-27}$ erg sec. |
| $R_\infty$ | Rydberg constant, for nucleus of infinite mass, $R_\infty = \dfrac{2\pi m_0 e^4}{h^3 c} = 1\cdot097 \times 10^5$ cm$^{-1}$. |
| $a_0$ | Radius, $a_0$, of the first Bohr orbit $= 0\cdot53 \times 10^{-8}$ cm. |
| $\pi a_0{}^2$ | Area, $\pi a_0{}^2$ of the first Bohr orbit $= 8\cdot8 \times 10^{-17}$ cm$^2$. |
| $N$ | Avogadro's number, $N = 6\cdot025 \times 10^{23}$ mol./g mol. |
| $L$ | Loschmidt's number, $L = 2\cdot69 \times 10^{19}$ mol./cm$^3$ at 0°C, 760 mm Hg (N.T.P.). |
| $R$ | Gas constant, $R(= Nk) = 8\cdot32 \times 10^7$ erg/°K/g mol. |
| $k$ | Boltzmann's constant, $k = 1\cdot38 \times 10^{-16}$ erg/°K. |
| $F$ | Faraday, $F (= Ne) = 2\cdot89 \times 10^{14}$ e.s.u./g mol. $= 9652\cdot2$ e.m.u./g mol. $= 96{,}522$ Coulombs/g mol. |
| eV | Electron-volt: 1 eV $= 1\cdot6 \times 10^{-12}$ erg. |

Let a gas consist of $n$ particles per cm³, of which a number $dn$ lie at any instant, $t$, within a volume element $x$, $x + dx$; $y$, $y + dy$; $z$, $z + dz$, and have velocity components between $u$, $u + du$; $v$, $v + dv$; $w$, $w + dw$ in the $x, y, z$ directions, respectively. The distribution of particles in these volume and velocity elements is described by a function, $f$:

$$\frac{dn}{n} = f(x, y, z, u, v, w, t) \, dx \, dy \, dz \, du \, dv \, dw \qquad \ldots.(1)$$

$[= f(\mathbf{r}, \mathbf{v}t) \, d\mathbf{r} \, d\mathbf{v}$ in vector notation]

Since both the positions and velocities of each group of particles is known it is possible to follow their motions through the subsequent interval of time, $dt$, and by subsequently considering the history of all the groups to deduce the new distribution law at time $t + dt$. Thus the distribution is completely determined if it is known at one instant, and must satisfy an equation such that $\frac{d}{dt}(nf)$ depends only on $nf$.

[In a steady state $f$ is determined from this equation by putting $\frac{d}{dt} \cdot (nf)$ to zero.] Considering the transient state, following Boltzmann we assume that the particles suffer forces $X$, $Y$, $Z$ per unit mass in the $x, y, z$ directions, respectively, so that

$$\frac{du}{dt} = X, \qquad \frac{dv}{dt} = Y, \qquad \frac{dw}{dt} = Z \qquad \ldots.(2)$$

After a time, $dt$, the original group of particles defined by equation (1) will have moved to a volume element at co-ordinates $x + u \, dt$, $y + v \, dt$, $z + w \, dt$, with velocities increased to $u + X \, dt$, $v + Y \, dt$, $w + Z \, dt$ (the change in the size of the volume and velocity elements is a second order effect). This, of course, assumes that the particles have continued on their previous paths uninterrupted by collisions. It follows that, in the new situation

$$\frac{dn}{n} = f(x + u \, dt, y + v \, dt, z + w \, dt, u + X \, dt, v + Y \, dt,$$
$$w + Z \, dt \; t + dt) \, dx \, dy \, dz \, du \, dv \, dw \quad \ldots.(3)$$

which, in the steady state, must be identical with the original distribution (equation (1)).

* See: Jeans, J. H., *Dynamical Theory of Gases*; London, Cambridge University Press, 1925.

If, now, equation (3) is expanded by Taylor's theorem to first order terms and equated to equation (1) we get:

$$\frac{\partial}{\partial t}(nf) = -\left[u\frac{\partial}{\partial x} + v\frac{\partial}{\partial y} + w\frac{\partial}{\partial z} + X\frac{\partial}{\partial u} + Y\frac{\partial}{\partial v} + Z\frac{\partial}{\partial w}\right](nf) \quad \ldots(4)$$

This equation describes how $nf$ (the number of particles in a particular volume and velocity element) changes, due only to the motion of the particles and the steady forces on them. If, also, collisions occur, an additional term $+\left[\dfrac{\partial}{\partial t}(nf)\right]_{\text{collisions}}$ must be added to the right-hand side of equation (4). In general, the form of this term is not known, and, in any case, requires separate calculation depending on the types of particles and collisions. In the steady state $\dfrac{\partial}{\partial t}(nf)$ is zero, and the equation reduces, in vector form, to:

$$\left(\mathbf{v}\cdot\frac{\partial}{\partial \mathbf{r}} + F\cdot\frac{\partial}{\partial \mathbf{v}}\right)nf = \left[\frac{\partial}{\partial t}(nf)\right]_{\text{collisions}} \quad \ldots(5)$$

where $F$ is the vector force per unit mass. Frequently $n$, the particle density, is a constant, and disappears from the equation.

# APPENDIX VI. RECENT SPECIAL REFERENCES
## (1955–59 APPROX.)

*Scattering*

GILARDINI, A., *Proceedings of the Third International Conference on Ionization Phenomena in Gases*, Venice, 1957 (review of microwave methods)

GILARDINI, A. and BROWN, S. C., *Phys. Rev.*, **105** (1957) 25, 31

BOYD, R. L. F., *Proceedings of the Third International Conference on Ionization Phenomena in Gases*, Venice, 1957

HASTED, J. B., *ibid.*

KELLY, D. C. and MARGENAU, H., *ibid.* (microwave methods)

CRAMER, W. H., *J. chem. Phys.*, **28** (1958) 688 (slow ions in rare gases)

McDOWELL, M. R. C., *Proc. phys. Soc. Lond.*, **72** (1958) 1087 (slow ions in parent gases, calculated)

BEDERSON, B., MALAMUD, H. and HAMMER, J. M., *U.S. Atom. En. Comm. Rep. No.* NP 6572 (1957) (with many references to theoretical cross sections for elastic scattering)

BRACKMANN, R. T., FITE, W. L. and NEYNABER, R. N., *Phys. Rev.*, **112** (1958) 1157 (electrons in H)

MITTLEMAN, M. H. and WATSON, K. M., *ibid.*, **113** (1959) 198 (theoretical)

*Excitation and Ionization*

FOX, R. E., HICKAM, W. M. and KJELDAAS, T., *Phys. Rev.*, **89** (1953) 555

FOX, R. E., HICKAM, W. M., KJELDAAS, T. and GROVE, D. J., *Rev. sci. Instrum.*, **26** (1955) 1101

CLARKE, E. M., *Canad. J. Phys.*, **32** (1954) 764

FROST, D. C. and McDOWELL, C. A., *Proc. roy. Soc.*, **A232** (1955) 227

CHAUDHRI, R. M., ASLAM, C. M. and HASAN, S. V., *Nature, Lond.*, **173** (1954) 1186

HUTCHINSON, D. A., *J. chem. Phys.*, **24** (1956) 628

KUIPER, J. and VAN ZOONEN, D., *Appl. sci. Res. Hague*, **B4** (1954) 235

JESSE, W. P. and SADAUSKI, J., *Phys. Rev.*, **97** (1955) 1668; **100** (1955) 1755; **102** (1956) 389

MOYAL, J. E., *Nuclear Phys.*, **1** (1956) 180

CROWE, R. W., BRAGG, J. K. and DEVINS, J. C., *J. appl. Phys.*, **26** (1955) 1121

FINKELNBURG, W. and HUMBACH, W., *Naturwissenschaften*, **42** (1955) 35 (table of critical energies)

CURRAN, S. C. and VALENTINE, J. M., *Rep. Progr. Phys.*, **21** (1958) 1 (review—energy per ion pair)

BATES, D. R. and GRIFFIN, G. W., *Proc. phys. Soc. Lond.*, **A68** (1955) 90, 173

BATES, D. R. and MASSEY, H. S. W., *Phil. Mag.*, **45** (1954) 111 (theoretical)

VARNEY, R. N., *Proceedings of the Third International Conference on Ionization Phenomena in Gases, Venice* 1957 (ionization by ions)

CRAGGS, J. D. and McDOWELL, C. A., *Rep. Progr. Phys.*, **18** (1955) 374 (review—complex molecules)

FITE, W. L. and BRACKMANN, R. T., *Phys. Rev.*, **112** (1958) 1141, 1151; **113** (1959) 815 (ionization and excitation of H and O by electrons)

SEATON, M. J., *ibid.*, **113** (1959) 814 (theory of measurements quoted above)

LOWRY, R. A. and MILLER, G. H., *ibid.*, **109** (1958) 826 (ionization by $H^+$ in $N_2$, A)

JONES, P. R., ZIEMBA, F. P., MOSES, H. A. and EVERHART, E., *ibid.*, **113** (1959) 182 (multiple ionization in atomic collisions)

JONES, E. and LLEWELLYN JONES, F., *Proc. phys. Soc. Lond.*, **72** (1958) 363 (Townsend's $\alpha$ at low pressure)

AUER, P. L., *Phys. Rev.*, **111** (1958) 671 (transient Townsend discharge)

MOE, D. E. and PETSCH, O. H., *ibid.*, **110** (1958) 1358 (energies of electrons ejected from atoms ionized by ions)

*Charge Transfer*

STEDEFORD, J. B. and HASTED, J. B., *Proc. roy. Soc.*, **A227** (1955) 446

BATES, D. R., *Proc. phys. Soc. Lond.*, **A68** (1955) 344

POTTER, R. F., *J. chem. Phys.*, **33** (1955) 2462

STIER, P. M. and BARNETT, C. F., *Phys. Rev.*, **103** (1956) 896

SLUYTERS, J. M. and KISTEMAKER, J., *Proceedings of the Third International Conference on Ionization Phenomena in Gases*, Venice, 1957

BARNETT, C. F. and REYNOLDS, H. K., *Phys. Rev.*, **109** (1958) 355 (in $H_2$ at high energies)

BOYD, T. J. M. and DALGARNO, A., *Proc. phys. Soc. Lond.*, **72** (1958) 694 (theoretical cross sections for $H^+$ in H, and $H^*$)

YEUNG, T. H. Y., *J. Electron. & Cont.*, **5** (1958) 313 ($I^-$ in $I_2$)

FITE, W. L., BRACKMANN, R. T. and SNOW, W. R., *Phys. Rev.*, **112** (1958) 1161 ($H^+$ in H)

*Photo-ionization, Photon Absorption and Photo-electric Effect*

WEISSLER, G. L., *Proceedings of the Third International Conference on Ionization Phenomena in Gases*, Venice, 1957

WALKER, W. C. and WEISSLER, G. L., *J. chem. Phys.*, **23** (1955) 1962

MAUNSELL, C. D., *Phys. Rev.*, **98** (1955) 1831

WAINFAN, N., WALKER, W. C. and WEISSLER, G. L., *ibid.*, **99** (1955) 542

*Electron Emission from Surfaces*

BARRINGTON, R. E. and ANDERSON, J. M., *Proc. phys. Soc. Lond.*, **72** (1958) 717; see also ANDERSON, J. M., *Nature, Lond.*, **183** (1959) 241 (theory of secondary electron emission)

STREITWOLF, H. W. and BRAUER, W., *Z. Naturf.*, **13a** (1958) 700 (time constant for secondary emission)

RASHKOVSKY, S. F., *Radiotek. i. Electron.*, **3** (1958) 371 ($\delta$ on surfaces of controlled roughness)

OERTEL, G., *Ann. Phys.*, **1** (1958) 305 ($\delta$ on Se)

BERRY, H. W., *J. appl. Phys.*, **29** (1959) 1219 (fast He atoms on W)

WATERS, P. M., *Phys. Rev.*, **111** (1958) 1053 ($Cs^+$ and $Li^+$ on W)

DAVIES, D. K., DUTTON, J. and LLEWELLYN JONES, F., *Proc. phys. Soc. Lond.*, **72** (1958) 1061 ($\gamma$ in high-pressure $H_2$ discharges)

DE BITETTO, D. J. and FISHER, L. H., *Phys. Rev.*, **111** (1958) 390 (large $\gamma$ in high-pressure $O_2$ discharges)

YOUNG, R. D. and MÜLLER, E. W., *ibid.*, **113** (1959) 110, 115 (field emission: energy of electrons at different temperatures)

*Attachment, Detachment and Dissociation*

DUKELSKI, V. M. and FEDORENKO, N. V., *J. exp. theor. Phys.*, **29** (1955) 473

FOGEL, Y. M. and KRUPNIK, L. I., *ibid.*, **29** (1955) 209; **30** (1956) 450

GROTH, W. E. and OLDENBERG, O., *J. chem. Phys.*, **23** (1955) 729

SMITH, S. J. and BRANSCOMBE, L. M., *J. Res. nat. Bur. Stand.*, **55** (1955) 165; *Phys. Rev.*, **98** (1955) 1028

SIDA, D. W., *Proc. phys. Soc. Lond.*, **A68** (1955) 240

HASTED, J. B., *Appl. sci. Res. Hague*, **B5** (1955) 63

BATES, D. R. and MOISEIWITSCH, B. L., *Proc. phys. Soc. Lond.*, **A68** (1955) 540

HASTED, J. B. and SMITH, R. A., *Proc. roy. Soc.*, **A235** (1956) 349, 354

BERG, D. and DAKIN, T. W., *J. chem. Phys.*, **25** (1956) 179

KUPRIANOV, S. E., *J. exp. theor. Phys.*, **30** (1956) 569

GRAY, E. P., HART, R. W. and GUIER, W. H., *Proceedings of the Third International Conference on Ionization Phenomena in Gases*, Venice, 1957

BRANSCOMB, L. M., *Advances in Electronics and Electron Physics*, Vol 9; New York; Academic Press, 1957 (review of negative ions)

JOHNSON, H. R. and ROHRLICH, F., *Nature, Lond.*, **183** (1959) 244 (atomic electron affinities)

HOLØIEN, E., *ibid.*, **183** (1959) 173 (atomic electron affinities)

KLEIN, M. M. and BRUECKNER, M. A., *Phys. Rev.*, **111** (1958) 1115 (formation of $O^-$ and $N^-$)

BUCHELNIKOVA, N. S., *J. exp. theor. Phys.*, **35** (1958) 1119 (formation of $O_2^-$, $H_2O^-$ and halogenated molecules)

TOZER, B. A., THORBURN, R. and CRAGGS, J. D., *Proc. phys. Soc. Lond.*, **72** (1958) 1081 (attachment in $O_2$ and air); see also *Proc. roy. Soc.*, **240** (1957) 473 (attachment in H)

SCHULZ, G. J., *Phys. Rev.*, **113** (1959) 816 (formation of $H^-$)

FOGEL, Y. M., MITIN, R. V. and KOZLOV, V. F., *Z. tech. Phys.*, **28** (1958) 1526 (attachment cross section measurements)

CHANIN, L. M., PHELPS, A. V. and BIONDI, M. A., *Phys. Rev. Lett.*, **2** (1959) 344 (attachment of slow electrons in $O_2$)

BIONDI, M. A. and FOX, R. E., *Phys. Rev.*, **109** (1958) 2005 (several papers on dissociative attachment in $I_2$)

BURCH, D. S., SMITH, S. J. and BRANSCOMB, L. M., *ibid.*, **112** (1958) 171; also with GELTMAN, S., *ibid.*, **111** (1958) 504; see also GELTMAN, S., *ibid.*, **112** (1958) 176 (detachment of electrons)

SMITH, S. J. and BURCH, D. S., *Phys. Rev. Lett.*, **2** (1959) 165 (photo-detachment of $H^-$)

*Drift, Diffusion*

MADAN, M. P., GORDON, E. I., BUCHSBAUM, S. J. and BROWN, S. C., *Phys. Rev.*, **106** (1957) 839

MCAFFEE, K. B., *J. chem. Phys.*, **23** (1955) 1435

COCHET, R., *C.R. Acad. Sci. U.R.S.S.*, **240** (1955) 2387

HALL, B. I. H., *Aust. J. Phys.*, **8** (1955) 468, 551

HUXLEY, L. G. H. and CROMPTON, R. W., *Proc. phys. Soc. Lond.*, **B68** (1955) 381

VARNEY, R. N., *Proceedings of the Third International Conference on Ionization Phenomena in Gases*, Venice, 1957

BALOG, I. I. and DZHERPETOV, K. A., *Ž. tech. Phys.*, **28** (1958) 1263 (drift of negative ions in air)

SODHA, M. S., *Phys. Rev.*, **113** (1959) 1163 (electron drift in atomic H; theoretical)


*Recombination*

SAYERS, J., *J. atmos. terr. Phys.*, Supplt. (1956) 212

BAYET, M. and QUEMADA, D., *J. Phys. Radium*, **16** (1955) 334

HERMAN, L., AKRICHE, J. and HERMAN, R., *Proceedings of the Third International Conference on Ionization Phenomena in Gases*, Venice, 1957

SCHULZ DU BOIS, E., *Ž. angew. Phys.*, **8** (1956) 267

MULLER, A., *Ž. Phys.*, **145** (1956) 469

MCCOUBREY, A. O. and MATLAND, C. G., *Phys. Rev.*, **101** (1956) 603

FAIRE, A. C., FUNDINGSLAND, O. T., ADEN, A. L. and CHAMPION, K. S. W., *J. appl. Phys.*, **29** (1958) 928 (electron—$N_2^+$, low $p$); see also FAIRE, A. C. and CHAMPION, K. S. W., *Phys. Rev.*, **113** (1959) 1 (recombination and ambipolar diffusion)

BIALECKE, E. P. and DOUGAL, A. A., *J. geophys. Res.*, **63** (1958) 539 (electron—$N_2^+$ as $f(p)$ and $f$(temp.))

YEUNG, T. H. Y., *J. Electron. & Cont.*, **5** (1958) 307 ($Cs^+ + I_2^-$)

FOWLER, R. G. and ATKINSON, W. R., *Phys. Rev.*, **113** (1959) 1268 (electron — $H^+$)


*Shock Wave Ionization and Excitation*

FOWLER, R. G., GOLDSTEIN, J. S. and CLOTFELTER, B. E., *Phys. Rev.*, **82** (1951) 879

FOWLER, R. G., ATKINSON, W. R. and MARKS, L. W., *ibid.*, **87** (1952) 966

BOND, J., *ibid.*, **105** (1957) 1683

# INDEX